CERAMIC PROCESSING

Prepared by
THE COMMITTEE ON CERAMIC PROCESSING

MATERIALS ADVISORY BOARD
DIVISION OF ENGINEERING
NATIONAL RESEARCH COUNCIL

PUBLICATION 1576
NATIONAL ACADEMY OF SCIENCES
WASHINGTON, D.C. · 1968

This report is one of a series in a study undertaken by the Materials Advisory Board for the National Academy of Sciences and the National Academy of Engineering in partial execution of work under Contract No. DA-49-083 OSA-3131 with the Department of Defense.

The Materials Advisory Board performs study, evaluation, or advisory functions through groups composed of individuals selected from academic, governmental, and industrial sources for their competence or interest in the subject under consideration. Members of these groups serve as individuals contributing their personal knowledge and judgments and not as representatives of any organization in which they are employed or with which they may be associated.

Available from
Printing and Publishing Office
National Academy of Sciences
2101 Constitution Avenue
Washington, D.C. 20418

Library of Congress Catalog Card Number 68-60017

Preface

Ceramics is one of the oldest arts practiced by man. Unfortunately, tradition and familiarity often conflict with the realistic appraisal of capability, and thus the innovations necessary to fulfill the potentials of the art and its further technological expansion are delayed. In a sense, then, the consideration of ceramics as a possible answer to current exacting performance requirements for engineering materials may have been hindered rather than helped by this long tradition.

In the past, people have tended to think of ceramics in terms of household pottery, objets d'art, furnace bricks, and other useful but not structurally vital applications. Today, difficult demands are being made on materials by the extremely forward-looking and sophisticated designs of equipment and vehicles for underwater, surface, and aerospace applications. These demands have forced materials and ceramic scientists, engineers, and designers to consider many roles for ceramics as structural materials. Their potential virtues are discussed in Chapter 1 of this report. The long and extensive use of ceramics (in its broadest definition) has created a wealth of data, a broad art, and an extensive technology that probably have been adequate and efficient for the purposes served. Current capabilities, however, are sorely deficient in relation to the newer demands. Thus, in recent years materials engineers and designers have asked themselves whether the ceramic art and existing technology can be extended to a higher scientific level that would permit exploitation of its tantalizing potential and, if so, how?

Three major matters of concern for structural ceramics are: the need to provide consistent, reproducible, reliable, high-level structural properties and data; the problem of coping with an inherent brittleness in ceramic materials; and the need for a design philosophy applicable to ceramic materials. Obviously, the first of these is, pragmatically, the principal prerequisite.

Earlier studies by the Materials Advisory Board, in 1961 and 1963, emphasized that a detailed examination of ceramic processing was a necessary step toward obtaining reliable high-integrity ceramic materials with superior properties. In 1964, at the instigation of the Navy Bureau of Weapons, the Department of Defense requested the Materials Advisory Board to initiate such an examination. During the course of this study, the committee making the study provided guidance and stimulation for a relevant research-and-development effort among the military services. This report discusses and summarizes the conclusions and recommendations of the study committee and emphasizes the work yet to be done to produce ceramic materials with the characteristics required for use in structures and, to a degree, electrical and electronic applications.

A study on the design of brittle materials was conducted by the Materials Advisory Board several years ago, and considerable effort is currently being made nationally and internationally to provide guidelines for the successful design and application of ceramic materials—including the preparation of a design manual under the aegis of the North Atlantic Treaty Organization.

Although there is currently no basis for anticipating the elimination of brittleness to any major degree, one can be very optimistic about the development of appropriate processing, good quality control, and an adequate design approach for enhancing and increasing the reliability of ceramic properties. Add to these the designer ingenuity that has already been manifested in other areas, and there is every reason, after these many centuries, to look forward to a new era in ceramics, which may extend the current spectrum of materials. This report is intended to stimulate progress toward this end.

N. E. Promisel

Washington, D.C.
February 1, 1968

<u>Ad</u> <u>Hoc</u> Committee on Ceramic Processing

JOSEPH A. PASK, <u>Chairman</u>
Professor, Ceramic Engineering
Department of Mineral Technology
University of California

Members

GEORGE J. BAIR
Director, Technical Staff Services
Corning Glass Works

STEPHEN C. CARNIGLIA
Section Chief, Materials Section
Atomics International, Division of
  North American Aviation, Inc.

ALEXIS G. PINCUS
Scientific Advisor
Ceramics Research
Illinois Institute of Technology
  Research Institute

KARL SCHWARTZWALDER
Director of Research
AC Spark Plug Division
General Motors Corporation

THOMAS VASILOS
Manager, Material Sciences Department
Avco Space Systems Division

JESSE D. WALTON, JR.
Chief, High Temperature Materials Division
Engineering Experiment Station
Georgia Institute of Technology

LIAISON MEMBER FROM THE MATERIALS ADVISORY BOARD
<u>AD</u> <u>HOC</u> COMMITTEE ON CHARACTERIZATION OF MATERIALS

RUSTUM ROY
Professor, Chemistry, and Director,
  Materials Research Laboratory
The Pennsylvania State University

LIAISON MEMBER FROM THE PANEL ON FINISHING OF THE MATERIALS
ADVISORY BOARD <u>AD</u> <u>HOC</u> COMMITTEE ON CERAMIC PROCESSING

N. M. PARIKH
Director, Metals Research
Illinois Institute of Technology
  Research Institute

LIAISON MEMBER FROM THE PANEL ON EVALUATION OF THE MATERIALS
ADVISORY BOARD <u>AD</u> <u>HOC</u> COMMITTEE ON CERAMIC PROCESSING

FRANK A. HALDEN
Director, Ceramics and Metallurgy Division
Stanford Research Institute

Contents

CERAMIC
PROCESSING

CHAPTER 1

Report of the Materials Advisory Board
Ad Hoc Committee on Ceramic Processing

INTRODUCTION

Ceramics—inorganic nonmetallic materials—may be polycrystals, glasses, combinations thereof, or single crystals.

Ceramics exhibit a wide range of desirable properties. For example, properties of individual ceramics include resistance to heat, oxidation, corrosion, and abrasion; high elastic modulus, high strength, and low density; dimensional stability and rigidity; and several desirable nuclear, optical, magnetic, electronic, and energy-conversion capabilities. Moreover, the nature of these properties makes ceramics useful for a great variety of current and projected Department of Defense hardware requirements (see Table 1).

Since World War II, much knowledge of a significant nature has been accumulated about ceramics, their microstructure, atomic character (composition, structure, and defects), and the theoretical limits of their properties. This knowledge indicates that certain properties can be tailored to meet specific requirements, and that special properties or combinations of properties can be substantially improved over presently achievable levels.

However, the engineering use of ceramics for a variety of needed candidate applications is still limited. Specifically, the uniformity, reproducibility, reliability, and mechanical performance of ceramic hardware are presently below intrinsic capability and are strongly influenced by size.

What are the main reasons for this situation?

In attempting to answer this question, several past Materials Advisory Board (MAB) Committees, notably the 1962-1963 MAB Ad Hoc Committee on the Processing of Ceramic Materials (MAB Report No. 195-M), largely attributed the restrictions on the wider use of ceramics to the inadequate knowledge and control of ceramic processing and finishing operations, reflecting the lack of a science of ceramic processing; and to the inherent brittle nature of ceramics.

THE COMMITTEE, ITS OBJECTIVES, SCOPE, AND RATIONALE

With this background, the Department of Defense in 1964 requested that the National Academy of Sciences initiate an appropriate committee study to explore various solutions to these problems. This assignment was subsequently given to the Materials Advisory Board of the Academy, with the stated over-all objective of recommending research and development studies that would improve our national capability to produce uniform and reproducible ceramics.

2

Table 1. Department of Defense Needs in Oxide Ceramics for Structural Applications[a]

Types of Applications	Primary Function and Critical Properties	Incidental Function and Important Properties	Type of Ceramic Configuration and Internal Structure	Mechanical Deficiencies of Oxides
Infrared, radar, and optical windows; cones	Transmission; electromagnetic transparency	Steady and shock load; high T and ΔT; strength, refractoriness, erosion resistance, oxidation resistance, low density	Large sheet, shell; single- or polycrystal or glass	Strength; thermal shock; erosion resistance
Electronic components	Insulation, electronic or magnetic activity; electronic properties	Steady and shock load; thermal stress; strength	Small sheet, film; single- or polycrystal or glass	Strength; thermal shock
Bearings, turbine parts, gyro parts	Mechanical; strength, hardness, dimensional stability, low density	Thermal or chemical; refractoriness, abrasion resistance, corrosion resistance	Small bulk; single- or polycrystal or composite	Strength, fatigue; strength at high temperature; thermal shock
Nose caps, leading edges	Mechanical and thermal; strength, erosion resistance, refractoriness, low density	Chemical; oxidation resistance, ablative properties	Small shell, bulk; single- or polycrystal or composite	Strength; strength at high temperature; thermal shock; erosion resistance
Vehicular stressed skin, pressure vessels, submersibles	Mechanical; strength and rigidity, low density	Thermal or chemical; oxidation or corrosion resistance, transparency	Small to large shell, single- or polycrystal, glass, or composite	Strength, fatigue; thermal shock; stress corrosion
Structural frame members	Mechanical; strength and rigidity, low density	Thermal or chemical; oxidation or corrosion resistance	Small to large bar, rod, etc.; single- or polycrystal, composite	Strength, fatigue; thermal shock; stress corrosion
Armor, transparent armor	Mechanical, esp. shock; strength, hardness, rigidity, fracture isolation, low density	Transmission; optical transparency	Large sheet, shell; single- or polycrystal, composite	Strength, esp. shock; fracture isolation

Table 1 (continued)

Types of Applications	Primary Function and Critical Properties	Incidental Function and Important Properties	Type of Ceramic Configuration and Internal Structure	Mechanical Deficiencies of Oxides
Structural reinforcement	Mechanical; strength, rigidity, low density	Thermal and chemical; refractoriness, chemical inertness	Fibers, filaments; single crystal, glass, or amorphous	Strength, fatigue; rigidity and refractoriness (of glass)
Matrix for reinforcing	Mechanical; strength, ease of application, bonding to fibers, low density	Thermal and chemical; refractoriness, chemical inertness	Large shell, sheet; polycrystal	Strength, fatigue; bonding to fibers
Protective coatings, thermal-control coatings	Chemical and thermal; very high T; oxidation or corrosion resistance, optical and thermal properties, ablation	Mechanical; strength, hardness, bonding to substrate	Small to large surface areas; polycrystal, glass, or composite	Strength; expansion matching, bonding to substrates; erosion resistance

[a]This table was compiled with the help of the Department of Defense liaison representatives to the Committee and from the following references:

DEPARTMENT OF THE ARMY
   "Army Research Plan for Ceramic Materials, 1966-1970," Technical Working Group, Army Materiel Command, November 1964; and subsequent revisions and additions.

DEPARTMENT OF THE NAVY
   "Navy Research and Development in Ceramics," Ad Hoc Committee on Ceramics, Advisory Council on Materials, September 1962.
   "Navy / Marine Corps Research and Development Problems," Department of the Navy Headquarters, Naval Material Command, July 1967.
   "Bureau of Naval Weapons Research and Engineering Problems," NAVWEPS Report 7682B, Vol. 1, January 1965.

DEPARTMENT OF THE AIR FORCE
   "Technical Objective Document: Materials," Air Force Materials Laboratory, R&T Division, AFSC, November 1965.
   "A Survey of New Aerospace Applications for Ceramics," Battelle Memorial Institute Report to Systems Engineering Group, R&T Division, AFSC, March 1967.

NATIONAL AERONAUTICS AND SPACE ADMINISTRATION
   "Ceramics, a Compilation of NASA R&D Projects," Headquarters, September 1965.
   "Materials Research Contract Program, 1965," Headquarters.

ATOMIC ENERGY COMMISSION
   "Summaries of the USAEC Basic Research Programs in Metallurgy, Solid State Physics and Ceramics" (Fiscal Year 1964), TID-4005 (Part 1, 8th Edition).
   "Summaries of Fuels and Materials Development Programs," TID-6506 (Part 1, 3rd Edition), October 1964.

ADVISORY
   "Federal Materials Research Program: Opportunities, Roadblocks," Coordinating Committee on Materials R&D, Federal Council for Science and Technology, Report TID-22424, November 1965.
   "Report of the Ad Hoc Committee on Processing of Ceramic Materials," National Academy of Sciences - National Research Council, Materials Advisory Board, Report MAB-195-M, October 1963.

By the limiting conditions of this assigned study, it was intended that structural (load-bearing) applications for ceramics receive primary attention and that the study probe the problems of ceramic processing (by both conventional and novel methods) of existing ceramic types, primarily of an oxide nature. Investigations of new basic chemical compositions were not intended, although the development of characteristics presently unattainable or commercially nonreproducible was considered to be within the scope of the study.

With this charter, the MAB Ad Hoc Committee on Ceramic Processing was established in September 1964.

The work of defining the many detailed facets of the over-all problem related to processing, and of establishing the particular charters of the various study panels of the MAB Ad Hoc Committee on Ceramic Processing, was governed by a rationale that the Committee developed; this is outlined in the following pages. Some of the terms employed in this study are listed and defined as follows:

A Ceramic is an inorganic nonmetallic material or article. Ceramics may be polycrystals, glasses, or combinations thereof, or single crystals.

Ceramic Processing is the combination of science and engineering that is directed toward developing and reliably manufacturing a ceramic product with a desired character.

Characterization or character describes those features of the composition and structure (including defects) of a (ceramic) material that are significant for a particular preparation, a study of properties, or use, and suffice for the reproduction of the material.[*]

Description is used in cases where insufficient correlatable character features are known, to include character, properties, and processing history. Both bulk (body) and surface features, as well as size and shape, are included in the description.

Microstructure is generally defined as those elements of character referring to identifiable grains and phases, their geometric features, and their distributions.

Uniformity refers to the control of variations in the character within a piece.

Reproducibility refers to control of variations from piece to piece in repetitive production.

Reliability is a requirement demanded by the consumers of ceramic materials and depends upon both uniformity and reproducibility.

Evaluation includes the correlation of the character with the properties and behavior.

DISCUSSION OF THE COMMITTEE'S WORK

The Committee feels that, basically, the expanded use of ceramics is dependent upon achieving reliability of maximized or compromised properties, which, in turn, is dependent upon maintaining an established character uniformly throughout a given part and reproducibly from part to part. In addition, the use of ceramics will be dependent upon processing capabilities for realizing required shapes, sizes, and surface characteristics. These character and dimensional requirements can be reliably achieved only by controlled processing, which includes a knowledge of the character of the material at every step in the processing sequence.

In the conversion of starting materials to a product, the frequently used practice of relating processing parameters directly to properties and behavior characteristics is basically incorrect. The nature or character of the starting

---

[*]From the Committee on Characterization of Materials, Materials Advisory Board, "Characterization of Materials," Publication MAB-229-M, National Academy of Sciences - National Research Council, National Academy of Engineering, March 1967.

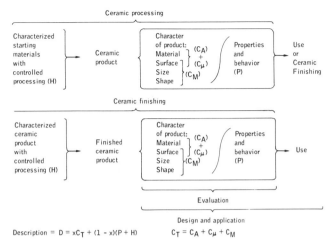

Description = $D = xC_T + (1 - x)(P + H)$ $\qquad C_T = C_A + C_\mu + C_M$

FIGURE 1. Ceramic processing and finishing

materials, and the processing, establish the character of the ceramic, which in turn determines its properties and reaction to environmental conditions. The achievement of a desired character is largely dependent upon understanding the appropriate fundamentals of chemistry and physics and applying them to the procedures of ceramic processing. The maintenance in production of a given character, free of extrinsic flaws,* is, in addition, largely dependent upon good engineering practice and control.

Any additional processing, such as material removal and surface finishing, that the primary ceramic product may receive is referred to as "ceramic finishing." Finishing is subject to the same analysis as the initial processing sequence with regard to the importance of characterization.

It should be evident that the success of any ceramic processing program is dependent upon the ability to correlate processing parameters with selected features of the character of the product. This situation indicates the additional need for the capability of correlating features of the character of the product with its properties and behavior, since the ultimate use of the product is dependent upon the latter. In order to achieve this evaluation, improved means are necessary for determining and expressing the character, properties, and behavior of the product.

Testing methods are critical because they are the means by which properties and behavior are evaluated. Incorrect test methods or practices applied to brittle materials can lead to an unrealistic scatter of data. A critical analysis of testing and the response of the material to testing methods could, in addition, provide information that would contribute to the development of the field of design with brittle materials.

With this background, the sequence in the progressive transformation of starting materials to finished products and their utilization can be assembled and summarized in the schematic chart shown in Figure 1. Technically, only the left-hand linkages associated with the making of a ceramic product with a given character constitute the area of ceramic processing that was of primary concern to this Committee. In actuality, the nature of the succeeding operations (e.g., characterization, property measurements, observations of behavior, testing, and inspection) can influence the final evaluation and utilization of the product and thus were also of concern to the Committee. Therefore, all the couplings indicated in the chart were considered.

*Extrinsic flaws (e.g., large pores and foreign inclusions) are defined here as those that occur due to inadequate processing, and are differentiated from the intrinsic flaws that are inherent in some characters.

Consequently, four Panels were established to review particular areas in greater and more analytical detail.

Panel I, Solids Processing, and Panel II, Fluid Processing, dealt with the coupling labeled Ceramic Processing. Panel I was concerned with processes that are based on the use of particulates that do not form or do not reach a completely liquid state during any stage of processing. Panel II was concerned with processes by which the ceramic is prepared via the liquid or vapor phase.

Panel III, Finishing, reviewed the state of the art in regard to additional treatments the ceramic product may receive—such as material removal, chemical treatments, joining and assembly, and supplementary heat treatment—as well as their effects on the surface character.

Panel IV, Evaluation, dealt with the coupling of character with properties and behavior. It reviewed the areas of characterization, testing, and the character - property and behavior relationship. Preliminary discussions indicated inadequate knowledge and a need for an effort in this direction. This input on features of character that are critical for a desired property was necessary for establishing a perspective on pertinent fundamental knowledge needed in a scientific approach to ceramic processing. Evaluation thus was considered one of the most important of the Committee's activities, in that characterization provides the means of communication between the processor and the designer or user.

A panel was not established for the last coupling, labeled Design and Application, linking properties and behavior with uses, since this function is neither directly nor indirectly a responsibility of the ceramic processor. However, joining and assembly to achieve a component or system, because of its critical nature in terms of the proper and successful use of a ceramic, was undertaken for review by the Panel on Finishing.

General Objectives of Ceramic Processing Based on Character and Description

In present-day technology a material can be described by

$$D = xC_T + (1 - x)(P + H)$$

where D represents description; C_T, total character; P, properties presently not capable of being related to character features; H, the processing history of the material; and x, a factor that lies between 0 and 1. These factors include both bulk and surface of the material.

The term "description" thus includes the measurable significant features of character, property measurements that cannot presently be expressed in terms of distinctive and significant features of character, and processing history, if the first two do not suffice for the reproduction of the material. If a particular property can be expressed in terms of recognized and measurable features of character, then it should not be included as part of the description. From a practical viewpoint, judgment and fundamental knowledge will have to be applied in identifying and using the critical features of character related to a desired property. Ultimately and ideally, it may be possible to express all properties and behavior characteristics in terms of features of character. Then x in the formula will become unity and the need for the term "description" will disappear.

The total character[*] is represented by

$$C_T = C_A + C_\mu + C_M$$

where C_A represents atomic character; C_μ, microcharacter; and C_M, macro-

[*]See MAB Report No. 229-M, "Characterization of Materials."

character, which includes size and shape. C_A and C_μ apply to both the bulk and surface of the material.

The processor is concerned with making a product with a given character of material and surface finish $(C_A + C_\mu)$, and a given size and shape (C_M). Although these two objectives cannot be completely separated, emphasis can be placed on either one. Traditional ceramic processing has generally been concerned with problems of achieving a desired size and shape (C_M). These objectives involve good engineering design of operational techniques and equipment for starting-material treatment, batch preparation, forming, drying, and firing. The scientific input is the fundamental understanding of the response of the material to these processes. Lack of this understanding has resulted in unrealistic limitations on size, shape, and character of the material, as well as lack of uniformity in the product.

However, the processor could place additional emphasis on the achievement and maintenance of a certain specified character of material $(C_A + C_\mu)$. This objective has been receiving attention in recent years because of the desire for new compositions and structures. Studies in progress have indicated the resulting dependence on knowledge of solid-state chemistry and physics, both thermodynamic and kinetic in nature. These situations have led to the realization of the need for a science of ceramic processing.

In addition, a ceramic may be subjected to supplementary processing in order to achieve a final ceramic product. This additional processing involves finishing treatments for purposes of achieving a modified structure and/or desired tolerances of size and shape (C_M). Such processing affects the atomic- and microcharacter $(C_A + C_\mu)$, primarily of the surface, which in turn affects the properties and behavior of the finished product.

With this definition of objectives, it becomes apparent that the activity of ceramic processing can be approached either on the basis of manufacturing production or research involving processing, or both. It should be realized that good production processing is based on the maintenance of a steady-state condition once a pattern has been established. Such control, and good processing practices, will minimize variations in atomic- and microcharacter, and help prevent the appearance of extrinsic types of flaws that are foreign to the desired character of the product. In processing research, fundamental principles of science and engineering are applied to develop and define processing sequences required to achieve a certain, often novel, uniform character of material $(C_A + C_\mu)$, or a certain size or shape (C_M). An engineer with an adequate background of the fundamentals necessary to maintain a defined character of material (i.e., to cope with variations in starting materials and processing steps that may occur at any time) can apply a certain amount of research and development skill to production processing to optimize some feature of character. This capability is particularly valuable in cases where uniformly distributed intrinsic or inherent flaws, known or unknown, are associated with the procedures being currently followed.

SOURCES OF VARIABILITY IN STRENGTH DATA

The character-property relationships were found to be relatively well established for some properties, but inadequately understood for certain other properties, including the strength of brittle materials. This strength is usually controlled by a combination of surface condition and resistance of the bulk to crack propagation. Strength, whether expressed as an average value or a distribution of values, is a numerical measure of a process rather than a measure of a single event and is sensitive to rate of loading, although the degree of rate sensitivity varies greatly. The strength of brittle materials also frequently depends on the environment through chemical and surface-energy effects. The complex nature of the process underlying strength measurements implies that engineering data on strength of brittle materials should be accompanied by specification of loading rate, environment, and surface character, and should be obtained with the use of good mechanical testing procedures on specimens with good bulk characterization (including residual microstresses). The best currently available bulk and surface characterization is generally inadequate to specify the strength of brittle polycrystalline materials.

The use of ceramics in critical Department of Defense (DOD) structural applications has certainly been limited. This is due to a number of factors. Data have been scarce on properties that describe the material's response to dynamic environmental conditions. A more critical factor is that, although average property values (e.g., strength values) are often satisfactory and attractive, the spread in those data normally cited requires designers to use values considerably lower than average to be sure of minimum safety levels. This condition, although generally acceptable for many consumer requirements, is not satisfactory for most DOD applications. This scatter of data has previously been equated to an inherent lack of reliability.

A major objective of the Committee thus was to attempt to determine the reasons for the scatter of data in ceramic materials. Some of the questions that arose with respect to the problem of scatter of data were:

1. To what extent is scatter due to testing methods and techniques?

2. To what extent is it due to the lack of uniformity within a part, or lack of reproducibility from part to part?

3. To what extent is it due to extrinsic flaws that are difficult to identify, in either the bulk or the surface?

4. To what extent is it an inherent behavior of brittle materials, and does it vary as the character of the material is modified?

The Panel on Evaluation was assigned the task of analyzing the relative significance of the various interrelated sources contributing to the scatter of data. It has concluded that much of the data, upon which the reputation of ceramics for variability has been based, were obtained under conditions where neither the test nor the material was adequately described or characterized. Therefore, judgments on the source of variability are presently quite difficult.

A few research programs were found in which sufficient characterization of the material was performed and care in testing was exercised so that confidence could be placed on the property data cited. This was possible only in cases where the test was properly used and the test specimens were properly prepared, machined, and surface-finished. The results of these programs have demonstrated that the ceramic processor tends to overestimate his ability to provide the same product from day to day and batch to batch. This is true for research processors as well as for production processors.

Processors have assumed that they are aware of the parameters that determine the character of their product and that these are under adequate control. However, sophisticated testing has uncovered character features that were not controlled and as a result were directly responsible for variability in property data.

Because there are so many interrelated factors in character, the independent contribution made by each factor (or by the interaction among factors) to the scatter of property data often is not ascertainable. It is this situation that has confounded the work of so many investigators who have attempted to study the effect of a certain character feature on property data but who have failed to control testing conditions, surface character, or other subtle material-character features.

The factors that have been identified as contributing significantly to the scatter of strength data are briefly discussed in the following paragraphs.

Variability as a Characteristic of Brittle Materials

The previous discussions have illustrated the fact that there are numerous factors that contribute to the scatter of data. These may be related to material flaws as well as to the test procedures themselves. Until each of these factors has been systematically studied, with adequate attention given to controlling all the other potential sources of variability, it will not be possible to answer the question, "To what degree may the scatter in data be attributed to the intrinsic nature of brittle materials?" It is possible that the question may never be answered completely. The answer will depend upon the quality of the product of the ceramic processor and the ability of characterization procedures to characterize that product adequately, particularly with respect to surface flaws and other less obvious sources of scatter of data. One case has been reported in which an aluminum oxide body was carefully machined into specimens that were exposed to uniaxial tension with a minimum of parasitic bending. The average tensile strength of eight specimens was 23,680 psi with a 2.6% coefficient of variation. In another case, an aluminum oxide body having a high degree of microstructural anisotropy was tested by four-point loading, using carefully machined and annealed specimens. The average flexural strength of 14 specimens was 39,200 psi with a 3.2% coefficient of variation. It is highly unlikely that these specimens were free of surface microflaws, strains in grains, strains at grain boundaries, or many of the other potential sources of variability. Thus, it appears likely that the great majority of the scatter of data may be related to flaws in the body and surface—flaws that may be eliminated, or at least their effect reduced, through improved ceramic processing and finishing.

GENERAL OBSERVATIONS OF THE STUDY

Awareness of the many factors that contribute to the scatter in the data on strength of ceramics could immediately raise ceramic reliability to a higher level. One example has been reported in which the allowable design strength of a particular ceramic material was doubled simply by the application of a suitable proof test. Therefore, in this case it was not necessary for the designer to wait until the ceramic processor developed some new material, or radically altered his processing, in order to consider these materials for particular structural applications.

From the Panel reviews of current competence in processing, it was concluded that the scatter attributable to processing is associated with the problems of producing a character of material and surface that is uniform on a microscale throughout the piece and reproducible from piece to piece and day to day.

Achievement of a uniform product character demands that the material in process be uniform and characterized at every step in the processing sequence, both independently and in relation to preceding and following steps. Most heterogeneities introduced during earlier steps can be eliminated only if the maturation process permits enough mass transport. Traditional ceramics facilitated such mass transport by the use of additives specifically for this purpose; for example, fluxes to provide a liquid phase at the highest temperature of thermal maturation. Property requirements for modern technical ceramics increasingly reject the use of such fluxing additives because of the undesirable effects introduced by the resulting secondary phases. Yet, only with the aid of a liquid phase can many essential characters and properties be currently attained by solids-processing techniques. Solids processing merits continued research and development support directed toward the achievement of uniformity in character and improved capability for dimensional control, scale-up in size, and more complex shapes.

Current interest in fluid processing includes the achievement of large sizes and the development of phases and microstructures not otherwise attainable. In addition, some of the fluid-processing methods show promise for producing graded characters by progressive variation of composition through a cross section. These processes are also of interest because binders that introduce complications in solids processing are not needed and the physical nature of the starting materials is often not critical.

Finishing serves a variety of important functions. By material removal it corrects dimensional deficiencies remaining in the products of solids and fluid processing, but must do so without introducing flaws into the surface. Conversely, by removing flaws or modifying strain distributions at surfaces, it can minimize the dominant influence of the surface on fracture and strength.

Another approach to increased reliability for a given set of specifications is by enhancement of property values. Higher strengths are being realized by utilization of existing knowledge about the character features to which strength is sensitive and, subsequently, by alterations of the process steps on which these features of character depend. Still higher strengths and reliability being sought by defense requirements demand further advances in understanding character - property relationships.

It became evident during the Committee's discussions that the "physical ceramist," whose objective is to achieve a given character in order to attain a certain property level, is inherently dependent upon research in processing, just as the "process ceramist" is dependent upon the teachings of physical ceramics.

In attempts to learn which are the critical features of character with respect to mechanical behavior, the Committee found the state of knowledge to be inadequate. Although it has been assumed that the two character features in oxide bodies that will lead to enhanced strength are freedom from pores and uniformly submicron grain size, quantitative data to support this assumption unequivocally are scanty and hedged with conditions, because most of the time other features were out of control. In addition, there are phenomenological difficulties because of the relation of the fracture path to the grain boundary instead of the size of the grain. Because these features of theoretical density and submicron grain size are normally difficult to attain, the Committee assessed processing methods, both traditional and novel, in terms of their ability to achieve such characters uniformly and reproducibly.

A large gap in fundamental knowledge was detected in techniques for characterization of surfaces and measurement of internal strains in relation to fracture phenomena and optimization of strength.

The grain boundary is also poorly understood, both in terms of its composition and structure and of its effects on material properties. Closely allied is the general question of the effects of impurities, whether intentional or accidental. Both cationic and anionic impurities may be distributed either in grain boundaries or within the grains. Phase-diagram data are insufficient to provide guidance on solid solution, compound formation, and segregation tendencies.

Knowledge of the all-important link between properties and character is obviously inadequate. Since the science of ceramic processing is based on the capability of correlating process parameters with features of character, it will not be realized completely until the processor knows what features of character to control and how to control them.

SUMMARY OF COMMITTEE RECOMMENDATIONS

Each of the four Panels has prepared its own report, including detailed development of specific recommendations for scientific and engineering research that will improve the over-all capabilities for processing ceramics.

In reviewing the Panel recommendations, and from the deliberations of the Ad Hoc Committee, it became evident that, in order to attain the capability of achieving the desired reliability and the enhancement of certain properties in ceramics, several factors are most important and significant. These factors are included in the following generalizations that are considered essential in the development of a ceramic processing program.

1. Characterization of the starting material, as well as the characterization or description of each step in processing, is essential. Such characterization will lead to the production of uniform and reproducible products by minimizing the variability of the material at succeeding processing steps.

2. New tools and techniques are required to characterize material in process and the final ceramic product (especially particulates, surfaces, and interfaces).

3. The character of the ceramic surface is critical in processing, testing, joining, and in subsequent use.

4. Standardized lots of starting materials, forming batches, and test specimens, and reliable standard test methods should be available in order to realize uniformity in product character and property data, and to promote communication among processors, research laboratories, and users.

5. Further development of the scientific approach to ceramic processing is necessary to overcome size limitations without sacrificing reliability.

6. Improved understanding of character-property relationships is necessary for identification of those features of character that are essential to enhance property values and to extend applications.

7. The essentials propounded in this report should be brought forcefully, through various educational media, to the attention of all those concerned with ceramic processing and application.

8. Interdisciplinary programs should be developed that include consortia among universities, research laboratories, and industries, in order to maintain programmatic approaches and thus reduce to a minimum the time required for the realization of the objectives of improved ceramic processing.

In the context of these observations and the Panel recommendations, the Committee, on an over-all and relative basis, makes the following conclusions and minimum recommendations, generally in the order of importance.

Correlation of Process Parameters with Features of Material Character

Since the character of a ceramic is process sensitive, scientific and engineering control of each of the process steps is essential. Studies are necessary to identify the process steps or parameters (relative to both preceding and following steps) to which certain character features are most sensitive, to determine the response of the material at each process step, and to relate these parameters and responses to features of character in the product.

The following coordinated and programmatic processing studies are urged:

1. Improved understanding of the relationship between particle characteristics, processing steps, and variability in final-product character in solids processing is essential. These researches should be done on several standardized materials of varying levels of impurities and should ultimately be applied to full-scale hardware production.

2. Improved understanding of fluid-processing variables and the corresponding effects on material character, including variability, is necessary.

Programs are needed in each of the following three approaches: bulk melting and crystallization control, molten-particle spraying, and vapor deposition. Fundamental studies are needed on nucleation and crystallization to achieve fine-grain, high-density, flaw-free characters from both bulk and particulate melts and from the vapor phase.

3. Improved understanding is required of all changes in surface and body character during material removal, surface and body after-treatments, and joining and assembly in relation to the initial character.

Standards for Materials and Testing

Because of lack of knowledge about the significant features of character for a particular property, and lack of capability in characterization, standard materials are necessary. These will help establish proper communication and consistency among different producers, producers and researchers, and also among producers and users.

1. Characterized, reproducible lots of particulate material are required as standards, especially for laboratories engaged in programmatic studies, because of: the general concern in regard to chemical standards for compositional analysis for cations, anions, trace impurities, and nonstoichiometry; the need for calibration of physical character features, such as particle-size distribution, shape, density, and integrity; and the need for a standard material for processing studies of such phenomena as densification, grain growth, kinetics, and strength development.

2. Provision of ceramic specimens having known and controlled body and surface characters for strength measurements should enable calibration of testing equipment and elimination of the individual laboratory and operator factors responsible for much of the scatter in data.

It is further recommended that a producer or producers be given the task of preparing the standard starting materials, standard bodies and test specimens, and that their characterization be performed by a number of laboratories having such capabilities.

Finishing and Other Surface Modifications

Finishing, or after-working, has become a nearly universal process in order for a technical ceramic to meet acceptance specifications and be considered a component in a device or a system. Several functions can be served by finishing, such as achievement of precise dimensional tolerances and modification of surfaces for improvement of strength. Because the character of surfaces is sensitive to processes of this type and because the properties are critically dependent on extrinsic defects introduced into the surface during finishing, the following studies are recommended:

1. Technological research should be performed on methods and mechanisms for effective material removal involving mechanical, ultrasonic, and chemical energies, and leaching followed by mechanical machining.

2. Technological and basic research should be performed on processes involving surface and bulk modifications in order to induce controlled compressive layers for purposes of enhancement of strength (e.g., minimum of fatigue and notch or flaw sensitivity).

Physical Ceramics: Character - Property Relationships

The character-property relationships were found to be inadequately understood for certain properties, including strength. This situation is unfortunate, since such evaluations are necessary to establish the critical body and surface character features to serve as goals for the ceramic processor. One area of concern is the measurement of the effect of internal strains and localized stresses on the initiation and propagation of fracture, and hence on the strength of ceramics and the relationship of such factors to character features. Another area is the interrelationship of environmental effects, rate sensitivity, and character features. Until these points are resolved, these and other areas will necessarily remain empirical. The following recommendations are thus made:

1. Fundamental studies should be undertaken to evaluate the relationships of bulk and surface character features to mechanical properties and behavior and to establish the principal limiting features.

2. A study should be made on methods for measuring internal strains in ceramics and correlating such strains with the character of the ceramic.

It is further recommended that character - property relationships be emphasized in the existing programs dealing with ceramic materials.

Testing

Support should be provided for studies on techniques for improved testing of mechanical properties of ceramics, in order to avoid the current problems of test variability and tests of little or no significance. These should include:

1. Attainment of uniform stress distribution in the specimen over a wide range of environmental test conditions and specimen gage volume.

2. Experimental and analytical studies of different test techniques to establish the criticality of the test conditions.

3. Evaluation, development, and organization of stress analysis of mechanical tests.

4. Development of test methods for studying stress and strain in the microstrain region, fracture-surface energy, fatigue behavior, creep behavior, and multiaxial stress - strain behavior.

5. Initiation of studies to relate properties determined by nondestructive testing with properties measured by destructive techniques.

Fundamentals of Agglomeration and Effect on Uniformity of Character in Forming

The Committee study indicates that agglomeration of particulates to form granules, and the nature and behavior of these granules, is critical in the forming step of ceramic processing and warrants specific attention. The character established in the particulate stage affects the character of the final ceramic product in ways that are not well understood, and the relationships between rheological behavior and the character of particulate systems are not known. Thus, basic research is needed on the fundamentals of agglomerate development and characterization, including binder and moisture distribution; of rheological behavior of such systems; and of their behavior during consolidation.

Scale-up Size Capability

Projected applications of ceramics include high reliability figures of revolution from 4 to 10 ft in diameter. Slip-casting, isostatic pressing, and glass-crystallization processes could be scaled-up to requisite size through the design of appropriately large equipment; however, the reliability of parts prepared by these means would be contingent upon the existing state of the science and art of processing. Another approach with very high promise is fluid processing by incremental deposition.

In addition, achievement of means of joining ceramics to themselves and to other materials without loss of strength and reliability in the bond areas will be required for the assembly of such articles, whether a monolithic or mosaic design is used. Thus, support is recommended for feasibility studies to determine potential capabilities of making and assembling very large shapes having a desired character and reliability.

Implementation of Recommendations

A consortium approach involving universities, research laboratories, and industry should be utilized in programmatic studies.

Education in Ceramic Processing

A program of continuing education should be pursued to increase the awareness of the need for characterization and utilization of fundamental sciences in both research processing and production processing.

Paths to such education sould include: lecture series for processors, designers, educators, and contract administrators; stricter requirements by journals and agencies for more thorough characterization of materials, test procedures, and processes; preparation of textbooks and monographs; appropriate symposia and conferences; and introduction of characterization philosophy into university curricula.

ACKNOWLEDGMENTS

It is a great pleasure to express sincere gratitude and warmest thanks to the 45 members and liaison representatives who accepted invitations to participate in this Materials Advisory Board study of ceramic processing. The work was most demanding, and each participant gave of his knowledge and time willingly and unselfishly.

Many professional colleagues of the members and liaison representatives of the Committee and Panels also served unofficially, lending their advice and suggestions to various portions of the work. Their assistance and guidance are greatly appreciated.

Grateful acknowledgment and thanks are given to the following guests of the Committee who contributed tutorial-type presentations at various meetings of the Committee or its four Panels:

F. Robert Barnet, Naval Ordnance Laboratory, Silver Spring, Maryland

Winston H. Duckworth, Battelle Memorial Institute, Columbus, Ohio

David Duke, Corning Glass Works, Corning, New York

H. M. Davis, U.S. Army Research Office, Durham, North Carolina

William Flock, General Motors Corporation, Flint, Michigan

Peter J. Gielisse, General Electric Company, Detroit, Michigan

Michael Humenik, Jr., Ford Motor Company, Dearborn, Michigan

James Hunt, Nuclear Metals Division, Whittaker Corporation, Concord, Massachusetts

J. A. Kies, Naval Research Laboratory, Washington, D.C.

H. W. Leverenz, RCA Laboratories, Princeton, New Jersey

Wilfred Mathewson, General Electric Company, Detroit, Michigan

Louis R. McCreight, General Electric Company, Philadelphia, Pennsylvania

William Wayne Meinke, National Bureau of Standards, Washington, D.C.

John F. Pelton, Union Carbide Corporation, Indianapolis, Indiana

George S. Reichenbach, Norton Company, Worcester, Massachusetts

Alfred Rudnick, Battelle Memorial Institute, Columbus, Ohio

William P. Shulhof, General Motors Corporation, Saginaw, Michigan

Edward R. Stover, University of California, Berkeley, California

Leo P. Tarasov, Norton Company, Worcester, Massachusetts

Thomas J. Whalen, Ford Motor Company, Dearborn, Michigan

Particular thanks are extended to Donald G. Groves, the Materials Advisory Board Staff Engineer for the Committee. His enthusiasm and interest in the study were a continuing inspiration to the Committee members. His assistance and encouragement throughout the study are greatly appreciated.

Joseph A. Pask, Chairman
Materials Advisory Board
Ad Hoc Committee on Ceramic Processing

CHAPTER 2

Report of the Panel on Solids Processing

ABSTRACT

The extensive application of ceramic materials in a variety of systems has been retarded by their general lack of reproducibility, reliability, and uniformity in terms of character, which has evolved from processing limitations.

To enhance the state of art in solids processing it is recommended that selected programs in research and technology, and studies of scale-up in numbers, size, and configuration be supported independently of end-item efforts.

In view of the close interconnection between the various stages of solids processing and developed character, it is appropriate that emphasis be given to the study of character evolution at each processing stage in relation to preceding and following steps in order to develop a general basis for materials-processing control.

Specific research and technology needs have been identified in the areas of:

1. Preconsolidation—particulate-materials preparation and characterization; and agglomerate-materials uniformity and characterization.

2. Consolidation—elimination of density gradients and development of methods to characterize green bodies.

3. Final densification—identification of impurities and their effects; subsolidus phase relations and kinetics; densification mechanisms; and development of preferred orientation.

Size scale-up and production studies are recommended on: instruments and techniques for material characterization and controlled material handling; development of in-process controls; scale-up of shapes to > 10-ft dimensions; continuous hot-forming; and isostatic hot-pressing.

SUMMARY OF RECOMMENDATIONS

The objective of the Panel on Solids Processing has been to examine the state of art of pertinent processing stages in terms of composition as well as process features and to make recommendations for investigations that would lead to improvements in ceramic body preparation from the point of view of character development and reproducibility in a variety of compositions and configurations.

An assessment of the state of art has revealed the close interconnection that exists between the characteristics of particulates and the character that develops in sequential processing steps in solids processing.

The lack of available knowledge that is needed to interconnect the processing steps—preconsolidation, consolidation, and final densification—in a predictable and quantitative fashion leads to the most important recommendation that broad research programs are needed to develop an understanding of interrelations in the essential processing steps and mechanisms with respect to starting raw-material particle characteristics. Emphasis must be given to the study of character evolution at each processing stage in relation to preceding and following steps to develop a general basis for materials-processing control.

Investigations should include emphasis on particulate characterization for specific types of available minimum 99.9% pure oxides, with an extension to higher purity materials when available.

Other significant recommendations in areas of science and technology specifically separated in terms of preconsolidation, consolidation, and final densification are as follows:

Preconsolidation

The state of art in ceramic particle technology requires further advancement, and areas of prime significance include:

SYNTHESIS OF ULTRAHIGH-PURITY MATERIALS

Ultrahigh-purity (>99.99% pure) oxides in controlled submicron particulate form are currently unavailable, and these materials are essential for use as chemical standards and for fundamental processing and physical-ceramics research activities.

IMPROVED CHARACTERIZATION OF PARTICULATES

Investigations in particulate characterization are required to improve the ability to evaluate quantitatively those variations in particulate chemistry and physics that contribute significantly to character development and variability in a finished body.

IMPROVED UNDERSTANDING OF FLOW AND AGGLOMERATION IN PARTICULATE SYSTEMS

Agglomerate character strongly influences the pore and grain-structure development during the consolidation and final-densification steps. Uniformity in agglomerate size, density, and additive distribution is necessary for effective control of final character.

The development of methods is required, therefore, to prepare and characterize uniform agglomerates and to handle them to avoid segregation.

Consolidation

Consolidation processes present particular problems in character uniformity and reproducibility that are primarily associated with density inhomogeneities resulting from cold-forming operations.

Specific recommendations include:

1. Relationships between rheological behavior during consolidation and the fundamental structural and compositional characteristics of particulate systems.

2. Methods of characterizing agglomerates and green bodies.

3. Fundamental research into the response of particulate systems to applied pressure and to development of methods to eliminate density gradients during consolidation.

Final Densification

Several areas require extensive investigation:

1. Identification is needed of impurities and their effects on resulting character, especially in very-high-purity compositions.

2. Determination of subsolidus phase relations and kinetics of phase interactions that are important to ceramic processing are needed. These include the

determination of solid solubility as a function of composition and temperature and the study of nonstoichiometric systems.

3. Systematic studies involving a complete description of character evolution during the various processing stages are required to enhance the understanding of densification mechanisms (for both sintering and hot-forming) and to enhance the prospects of predicting and controlling character development.

4. Development of preferred orientation in terms of phase, grain, and/or pore structure deserves special attention. Effort is needed to explore the methods and mechanisms for accomplishing orientation.

Scale-up and Quantity Production

In addition to the science and technology aspects cited above, there are special needs for programs to enhance the capability for size scale-up and quantity production.

The goal is the capability for producing in quantity large or small pieces with desired character and properties, shapes, and dimensions.

Preconsolidation

Raw material variability and lack of control and characterization of particles and agglomerates become more important with increasing size and/or numbers of products because such variability can manifest itself in terms of nonuniform shrinkage, undesired density, and phase-chemistry gradients, with resulting loss in uniform properties.

Recommendations include, therefore, the development of monitoring instrumentation for effective particulate and agglomerate materials control and handling.

Consolidation

Discussions have indicated that present forming or consolidation techniques are restricted essentially to 4 to 6 ft-size ware. It was considered worthwhile to recommend the scale-up of shapes to several feet (>10 ft) dimension hardware in the <99% and >99% pure oxide categories. The availability of such forms would enhance the prospects of their use, e.g., for radomes and deep submergence vehicles.

The yield and product quality-character from current cold-forming production processes can be improved by developing and employing in-process (nondestructive test methods) control measures to predetermine phase and density gradients and flaws in green microstructure.

Final Densification

In this area, effort is recommended in terms of process improvements that include:

1. The development of large-scale furnaces and methods leading to the successful firing of ware >10 ft dimensions.

2. Minimization of contamination by furnace refractories.

3. Better control of temperature and its distribution in furnaces.

4. For hot-forming processes, specific mold development and mold-compact interaction studies to extend mold life.

5. Development of continuous hot-forming methods and evaluation of process in terms of composition, size, shape, and tolerance capabilities.

6. Further development of high-pressure isostatic hot-pressing.

INTRODUCTION

Solids processing, which comprises the group of process operations assigned to this panel, is defined as: those means of preparing ceramic materials in which solid particulate matter is employed as the immediate precursor of consolidated product material.

The objectives of the Solids-Processing Panel are concerned with:

1. An evaluation of the capabilities and limitations of present solid-forming processes in terms of the scientific and engineering knowledge that is required for the preparation of ceramics with uniform and controllable character on a consistent basis. (The character of a ceramic is the sum of the compositional and structural descriptions that identify a specimen uniquely and may be correlated with its properties.)

2. An assessment of significant characterization parameters.

3. A recommendation of activity needed to fill existing gaps in current scientific knowledge and technology in order to enhance the realization of ceramics with uniform and controllable character.

It was recognized that the realization of these objectives would be of considerable importance in the ultimate production of ceramics with increased reliability, or a reduction in scatter of properties, and in improved properties, e.g., strength at low and elevated temperatures.

Such improvements would enhance the use of ceramics as engineering materials in such interest areas as deep submergence, lightweight armor, radomes, and advanced-flight-vehicle hardware.

In the course of discussion, the Panel agreed that the realization of such improvements would depend on the ability to control the character of ceramics, having first recognized what the significant characterization parameters are. In this connection, it was decided on the basis of background experience that the significant characterization parameters for a given processed body would include chemical and physical composition.

Typical Characterization Parameters for Solids Processing

Chemical	Physical
Composition—existence of additional chemical phases, cations, or anions and their distribution, e.g., in grains and/or grain and phase boundaries	Grains—size, shape, distribution, orientation, substructure; porosity—amount, size, shape, distribution; structures of phases present, strain, cracks

(A more comprehensive treatment is given in the body of the report by the Panel on Evaluation).

It was recognized, however, that in order to achieve such control in the processed material, it was essential that control and characterization of processes and composition be exercised during the sequence of operations employed to produce it.

In addition, in view of the problems that developed in connection with attempting to characterize a wide range of chemical compositions at the same time with physical parameters, it was arbitrarily decided to delineate three particular composition purity ranges for bodies, i.e., minimum 99.9% pure, or very high purity (current availability limited to research-lab operation); 99 to 99.9% pure, or high purity (current limited production and sizes); and less than 99% pure, or multiphase (large commercial production). (It is recognized that even in the 99 to 99.9% purity range, a significant amount of second- and tertiary-phase material may be present and even intentional in some cases; however, the processing steps and resulting microstructure are sufficiently different to be considered in a separate discussion.) Furthermore, the Panel agreed to concentrate primarily on aluminum oxide (Al_2O_3) for practical and model purposes.

A consideration of the minimum 99.9% purity range indicates that there has been very limited effort expended and therefore little progress to report, particularly in terms of polycrystalline oxides such as alumina and magnesia for mechanical-strength applications. Two problems confronting further progress in this area are reviewed below.

Analytical Limitations

A considerable number of techniques are currently available that make it possible to perform cation and elemental analyses on materials down to the parts-per-million and parts-per-billion ranges. The lack of suitable reference standards for refractory inorganic nonmetallic materials, however, makes it impossible to determine impurity levels precisely. Irregular impurity distribution and locational segregation such as is found at the grain boundaries of refractory oxides often cannot be determined by methods appropriate for gross-impurity-level analysis. Anion impurities are generally not measured or known and methods for their determination are inadequate. Appended to this report is a discussion of analytical techniques for refractory materials, with examples of specific analytical problems and the potential of the newer instrumental and chemical methods for giving satisfactory results. A more generalized discussion of analytical methods, which places them in larger perspective as a key to improved characterization of materials needed to develop materials science and technology, is contained in the report of the Committee on Characterization of Materials (MAB-229-M, March 1967).

Processing Limitations

Current process controls for very-high-purity preparations are probably not adequate. Powder handling, pressing, and heat-treating processes limit impurity control. Analysis of impurity pick-up during processing is commercially restricted to major cations with limited batch-to-batch control and scant attention to anion analysis. Contamination in high-temperature heat treatments is a major problem, and inert atmospheres and inert furnace liners are seldom inert.

If achievable, the availability of ultrahigh-purity material, minimum 99.99% total purity including anion concentration, would make it possible to study grain growth and densification kinetics on an intrinsic basis. It would also make possible an understanding of the role of "quenched-in" vacancy defects, specific anion or cation impurities in dislocation development and interactions, and strength levels for twinning, creep, and fracture. At low impurity levels, non-stoichiometric effects may also become discernible.

PERTINENT OPERATIONS AND PROCESSES

The panel adopted three subclasses of solid processes for the organization of its activities: Preconsolidation, Consolidation, and Final Densification.

The particular operations and processes under these headings, which have been considered by the Panel to be appropriate, are given in terms of a flow sheet (p. 24) which includes the sequence of operations from raw material to fired body, with a listing of commonly employed characterization parameters for particular steps in the sequence.

STATE OF THE ART

Preconsolidation

RAW MATERIALS

Prior to consolidation, particulate processing must fulfill two distinct functions:
(a) achieve optimum chemistry (purity, stoichiometry, amount and distribution
of additions), and (b) achieve optimum physical structure for compactibility,
such as size - shape distribution, surface coatings of lubricants, and agglomeration for optimum rheology. The first of these is necessary to control structure
and properties during heat treatment and in the finished product. The second is
required to control structure and resulting rheological properties of the particulate mass during consolidation by mechanical means.

Currently, numerous sources of powdered raw materials are available, particularly for multiphase (85-99%) and high-purity (minimum 99% pure) ceramics.

In the case of alumina, raw-material powders for <99% pure ceramics are
available in large quantities. Lot sizes above 300 tons are common for continuous kiln operation. Particle sizes are generally in the 1- to 15-μ range, with
approximately 2,000 parts-per-million total cation impurities. These materials
are generally classed as calcined, tabular, or fused aluminas and are available
from alumina suppliers. Raw materials for minimum 99% pure alimina are
available in 100,000-lb lots and in the 0.3- to 4-μ particle-size range. Materials
for minimum 99.9% pure ceramics are only marginally available in small lots
(1#-300#), with particle sizes generally well below 1 μ. Full chemical analyses
are generally not run.

The situation for nonoxide compounds such as borides, carbides, nitrides,
and silicides in particulate form is not nearly as well developed. In general,
even in small lots, materials are unavailable commercially in high-purity form;
e.g., significant amounts of additional phase(s) are always present. Furthermore,
a significant amount of major-element constituents in uncombined form, as well
as uncontrolled stoichiometry, is generally found in such materials.

Another important limitation in such materials is their relative unavailability
in fine-particle sizes, i.e., much below 1 μ in particle diameter. Such availability would have considerable value in improving the state of sintering technology associated with these materials.

In commercial usage, various methods are employed to maintain control
over incoming raw material used in product fabrication. (In such practice, the
selection of a particular source results from a natural trade-off between cost,
availability, reproducibility, and properties.) As a result of significant background experience in assessing raw-material inhomogeneity, ceramic-product
manufacturers are often able to indicate to raw-material suppliers the qualitative if not quantitative inconsistencies of lot materials in terms of chemical and/
or physical content. In fact, with enough background, the cause of ceramic-product difficulty can frequently be traced to a particular and identifiable variant in
the raw-material supply. On this basis, an alumina spark-plug manufacturer,
for example, specifies all alpha alumina, but is able to institute satisfactory
in-process control when some nonalpha alumina is also present in supplied
batches in order to maintain resulting product uniformity. In general, product
manufacturers employ similar techniques in characterizing incoming raw material, with perhaps some difference in emphasis for particular methods.
Emission spectroscopy, x-ray diffraction, x-ray fluorescence, wet-chemical
analysis, and petrography are frequently used to determine chemical (major
phases and impurity) content. Microscopy and other particle-size measuring
and surface-area measurements are often employed to determine particle physical characteristics. The degree to which variations in character can be tolerated
often results from these methods, with questionable satisfaction for a product
manufacturer even after a certain amount of background familiarity has been

SOLIDS PROCESSING

Flow of Materials (by operations and processes)	Characterization Parameters in Processing	

I. PRECONSOLIDATION

Flow of Materials	CHEMICAL	PHYSICAL
A. Raw material(s)	**Bulk**	**Bulk**
Particle preparation (usually with some purification): Precipitation, solid-phase reactions, oxidation (e.g., of pure metals); vapor-solid; electrolytic, decomposition by heat, cryo-preparation; mining and benefication, melting, vaporization, atomization	Elemental, assay, impurities; mineral phase, stoichiometry	Particle size (avg. and range); particle shape, density (porosity), substructures; flaws, stored strain/energy; crystal system; system of particles; particle-size distribution; agglomeration; flow properties; pertinent physical properties
B. Particulate material	**Surface**	**Surface**
Particle-modification process (chemical change): calcining →H_2O, CO_2, etc.; prereaction → new compounds (partial or complete); melting	Adsorbed ions and molecules; chemically reacted layer	Area properties
C. Modified-particulate material		
Operations on modified particles, comminution, encapsulation	Solubility in solvents, composition and chemical behavior of milling aids	Hardness and brittleness
D. Modified-particulate material		
Modifications of particle systems; add forming aids and liquid (usually water); mixing—different phases, single phase, different sizes; de-airing; drying size separation; size blending pelletization, granulation or prepressing } Undesirable sizes, H_2O	% liquid (solids content); % additive; pH, zeta potential; response of particles to mixing medium	Sizes blended, bulk density; rheology—viscosity, thixotropy, yield stress, mobility, negative shear-rate intercept, microstructure, preferred orientation of granules, paste, or suspension

II. CONSOLIDATION

Flow of Materials	CHEMICAL	PHYSICAL
A. Modified-particulate system		
Cold-forming operations Die filling Assists to die filling; vibration, ultrasonics, vacuum pressure		
Forming by: 1. Pressure compaction: a. Rigid die b. Isostatic 2. Plastic a. Extrusion b. Jiggering, etc. 3. Slip casting a. Normal b. Vacuum c. Pressure 4. Injection molding 5. Vibratory packing 6. High-energy impact 7. Film-forming 8. Other	Ion exchange with die material; lubricants; homogeneity of phases, of ion distribution; air (gas) release	Flow; applied pressure—absolute, pressure/density relationships; microstructure as formed. Homogeneity: density, orientations, microstresses; strength for mold release, elastic behavior (spring back), stresses imposed, cracks, contact area between grain surfaces

SOLIDS PROCESSING (continued)

Flow of Materials (by operations and processes)	Characterization Parameters in Processing	
	CHEMICAL	PHYSICAL
B. Green body		
Green-body modification Drying (100°C) Expulsion of organics (200-800°C) Presintering (1000-1400°C) Development of porous body Sometimes shaping, turning, fettling } H_2O CO_2, CO, $(CH)_x$ Sulfur gases, etc.	Changes introduced (desired, undesired)	Dimensional changes, density-porosity, strength, flaws, microstructure
III. FINAL DENSIFICATION		
A. Porous body		
Sometimes additional shaping; final-densification operation; heat treatment—sintering; gas evaluation; reactions—solid-solid, solid-vapor, stoichiometric; shrinkage, pore discharge, grain growth, grain bonding, diffusion (plastic flow), melting, vaporization and condensation	Changes introduced, H_2O, air, binders, degradation, pyrolysis, oxidation, new phases, grain boundary, impurity effects	Dimensional changes, density-porosity, strength, flaws, microstructure, grain boundary
B. Fired body		
1. Sintering Gas evolution, chemical reactions, solid-solid, solid-liquid, gas-solid; stoichiometric effects; shrinkage, pore discharge, grain-bonding; diffusion, vaporization, and condensation; melting and recrystallization	Elemental composition, phase composition, stoichiometry, impurities, proportions; homogeneity of distribution, in bulk or at surfaces of grains or in grain boundaries, at surfaces	Dimensional uniformity, flaws-warping, etc.; density—gross, homogeneity of flaws—cracks, blisters, blebs, holes, microstresses, pertinent physical properties; microstructure—grain size, average and range distribution, grain shape (equiangular, platey, elongated) grain orientation (crystallographic)—carried over from forming, none developed completely; second phases—distribution/continuity, crystallinity, size; pore phase—proportion, uniformity of distribution, location, size (uniformity)
2. Hot-forming Gas evolution, chemical reactions, solid-solid, liquid-gas; shrinkage, pore discharge, grain-bonding, diffusion (plastic flow), melting and recrystallization, vaporization and condensation	Same as above	Same as above

obtained in dealing with a particular raw-material supplier. There is difficulty in specifying the degree to which variations in raw-material character can be tolerated and in determining the relative importance of particular variations: e.g., is a particular variability in particle size more significant for a manufacturer than a particular variability in chemical content?

A qualitative solution to certain of these problems is sometimes obtained through exhaustive, empirical, follow-through processing steps in order to relate final-product properties to starting-material characteristics. In general, however, in the <99% pure composition field, because of the compensating effects of purposeful additives, acceptable commercial-product properties are obtained despite rather significant character variations in raw-material supplies.

In the high-purity or principally single-phase composition field, the accept-able tolerance in raw-material variability is known to be more stringent, yet the relative importance of one character parameter (e.g., particle size over another, e.g., cation-impurity content) is generally unknown. Again, control over incoming source material is often exercized by follow-through processing to check final-product variation against starting-material character. Through such systematic experimentation, the effects of particular raw-material characteristics on final character can be delineated and raw-material specifications introduced. While the degree to which raw material is routinely characterized is often inadequate, it is most important to reflect the characterization in a predictable fashion, with the whole sequence of solids-processing operations that produce the final body. At present the understanding of the influence of particular raw-material variations on the sequence of processing operations is minimal. In addition, although significant characterization can be performed with current instrumentation, methods are yet to be developed that will allow for reasonably rapid batch quantity characterization and composition control.

MODIFIED PARTICULATE MATERIAL

There are a number of preconsolidation particle-system-modification operations that are conducted to supply appropriate feed material for given consolidation processes. Several of the more common operations are discussed below.

Extrusion

The principal work in extrusion is accomplished with <99% pure and >99% pure systems. Very little work has been performed on very-high-purity alumina systems. A notable example of high-purity-extrusion effort has been that of the 99.9+% pure beryllia field.

In batch preparation, standard methods of composition formulation and mixing are used. Ball-milling of the rotating or vibrating type, usually on a wet basis; dry-milling with comminution; or dry-mixing of powders without comminution are used. There are few effective ways of consistently producing extrusion-preconsolidated masses that have known and reliable extrusion characteristics. The process of extrusion itself can be divided somewhat arbitrarily into two classes: low-pressure plastic extrusion (<5,000 psi), and high-pressure nonplastic extrusion (>5,000 psi). The input material for low-pressure extru--sion is a plastic mass that is thoroughly wet by either water or a nonaqueous medium ~20% moisture. This plastic mass is produced by combining virtually nonplastic refractory particles with organics such as methocellulose or polyvinyl alcohol, which are soluble or emulsifiable in the particular solvent being used. A plastic mass is formed by employing various mixing and kneading devices. De-airing of the plastic mass is accomplished prior to creating a solid compact of material that is later extruded.

High-pressure-extrusion input materials are generally granular. Moisture contents are frequently less than 10%, and high-pressure consolidation of the granules under vacuum in the extrusion device is practiced.

The basic problems in both systems are uniform distribution of binders, and uniform distribution of moisture on both macro- and microscale. The green microstructure of the input materials is reflected in the fired product as modified by the extrusion processes. Generally, the preconsolidation stage in extrusion-body preparation is a randomizing process for particle orientation.

The preparation of homogeneous distribution of binders and moisture is attempted but not achieved. Green-microstructure examination methods for both plastic and granular systems, as well as improved mixing methods and equipment require development.

Isostatic-Pressing

The bulk of isostatic-pressing work is done using <99% pure and minimum 99% pure systems. Preconsolidation processing for the largest segment of the industry is accomplished using wet-ball-milling and spray-drying. In some organizations dry- and wet-milling are combined. Granulation techniques are used as secondary source methods for preconsolidation. Some preconsolidation is accomplished by making prepressed slugs of materials in the moist (up to ~6% water) or dry state. These slugs are later crushed, and the resulting pellets are tumbled and classified by standard screening methods to produce pellet-size distributions that approach maximum packing for the consolidation process.

Pressed slugs, when fractured, produce granules of high green density, which subsequently produce high-green-density feed material for consolidation processes. Granulation by tumbling is also practiced, and granules produced by this method are generally of lower green density than the pressed-slug-derived or spray-dried types.

Binder-lubricant systems range from soft to hard for both hollow- and solid-pellet technology. Examples of soft binders are paraffin waxes, and hard-binder systems are typified by polyvinyl alcohol-containing compositions. Binder-lubricant systems cover the range from soft to hard, as an infinite number of systems exist.

Recent improvements on dry-ball-milling systems that can produce materials capable of being processed to higher green densities (up to 3.0 g/cc) are causing a reorientation in thinking with regard to preconsolidation processing. Prolonged dry-milling also introduces a factor of grain rounding and polishing not usually found in wet-milling practices. The resulting high-green-density compacts offer promise of fired-shrinkage reduction, microstructural uniformity, and lower firing temperatures.

In most instances, standard methods of wet- and dry-ball-milling combined with spray drying produce hollow pellets. These pellets, if not morphologically destroyed in subsequent pressing or consolidation operations, can create characteristic pellet-based green and fired microstructures. Solid-pellet technology can produce similar microstructure, but without the characteristic void of the single-pellet structure. Both these systems produce green and fired microstructures that are considered uniform in their microdefects. The desired system is one in which the pellet morphology, either hollow or solid, is disintegrated during the consolidation process. The existing state of the art ranges from complete pellet or granule disintegration to nearly complete morphological retention. As such, it provides a way to control final microstructure and surface structure.

For <99% pure and min 99% pure systems, final properties are known to be processing sensitive. In general, both hollow-pellet and solid-pellet technologies leave their imprints on the microstructure. The basic unit of hollow-pellet technology is the hollow pellet itself. These repeatable units can be responsible for a possible characteristic final microstructure.

Solid-pellet technology attempts to overcome the difficulties of the hollow pellet but introduces other problems. The basic problem of the solid pellet is that it tends to be relatively nonuniform with respect to shape except when it is produced by spray drying. Shape irregularities are thought to produce areas of nonuniform and/or incomplete packing, which can result in a void or low-density area after pressing.

Pellet or granule-size distribution is an important factor, influencing green and fired microstructure. In most ceramic preconsolidation and consolidation processing, materials must flow from one point to another. Pellet or granule segregation occurs because of a differential flow between large and small pellets, which causes materials segregation in the form of a nonuniform fill of consolidation cavities. Microstructural differences often result.

In summary, pellet morphology, microstructure, and size distribution in the green state play a significant role in determining the nature of consolidated structure, and effort is required to develop an understanding of the essential interactions.

Dry-Pressing

Dry-pressing is treated separately from isopressing preconsolidation because differences result from restriction, generally, to "thin" ware. Both solid-pellet and hollow-pellet technologies are presently used for the preparation of dry-press-consolidation feed materials. Standard methods of ceramic processing are used to develop input material for dry-pressing, e.g., ball-milling and spray-drying resulting in flowable dry powders, granulating and/or tumbling and screening to produce desired granule distributions yielding good flow and packing characteristics. Moisture in the form of residual or added water is often used as a pressing aid. It can remain or be added to dry-pressing compositions in a uniform dispersion or be mixed nonuniformly by means of high-moisture granules that are mixed with their drier counterparts.

Two basic technologies exist in preparing feed material for dry-pressing of <99% pure materials. They are the soft- and hard-binder approaches. It is not possible to separate these two methods completely, but in employing the soft binders, pressures required for subsequent consolidation are low, generally less than 20,000 psi. In effect, reasonably high green-density bodies can be produced at relatively low pressures. A principal problem with this method is that production rates are generally decreased because of ceramic materials adhering to die faces. The hard-binder system generally uses higher pressures, in some cases up to 80,000 psi or greater. Equivalent green densities are produced, but often it is not possible to produce the uniform fired microstructures that are possible with the soft-binder techniques. An inherent advantage in the hard-binder system is that there is little die-sticking and high production rates result. In minimum 99% pure systems, production work is limited to shapes up to 6 in. in diameter, perhaps, with limited quantities being produced. No state of the art exists in very-high-purity systems.

Processing of feed material before pressing is very important with respect to production of green- and fired-microstructure differences. Fired microstructure is also directly influenced by binder type, amount, introduction method, and pellet-forming methods. Hard, noncrushable pellets may form either porous or multiclosed pore-fired structures. The "soft" systems can produce materials of high-fired density and lower pore concentration.

Research in binder, lubricant, and grinding contributes to effectiveness, and the development of improved methods of incorporating this research into ceramic compositions is needed. There is a need for studies of actual binder behavior and how binders operate to produce pressure transfer and lubrication during pressing. The potential of employing particulates without binder addition requires evaluation. As the ceramic industry moves into very-high-purity systems, new methods of binder additions and contamination control will be needed.

Slip Casting

Preconsolidation for slip casting of alumina consists primarily of ball- or vibratory-milling of the raw materials in the presence of proper electrolytes in order to create a highly dispersed system. Generally, high-slip specific gravities are desirable (>2.0 g/cc). Dispersion of the particulate materials is essential to preparation of casting slips that do not settle upon standing. If settling of the suspended particulate material should occur, the settled material should be capable of being easily dispersed with a minimum of mixing. When settling produces a hard dense compact, casting cannot be controlled with respect to dimensions of walls of the objects being cast. Less than 99% pure and minimum 99% pure casting slips are currently prepared. Very-high-purity systems do not exist.

For the <99% pure and minimum 99% pure alumina materials, two general dispersion systems are in common use. When highly calcined (1,750°C) or fused raw materials are used, acid (HCl) dispersed systems are most common. The acid-dispersed system could be considered classical. In early alumina casting-slip preparation (about 1920), fused alumina was ground by using steel balls in steel-lined mills, and iron contamination from grinding was removed by acid leaching. An acidic aqueous slip was produced having excellent dispersion, specific gravity, and casting characteristics. For fused or highly calcined materials, the acid system is still in use, although milling is generally carried out in ceramic-lined mills with ceramic grinding media.

For alumina raw materials classified as calcined (~1,450°C) the acid-dispersion system is less effective. Alkaline- and organic-based dispersion systems are frequently used for these systems. Alginates derived from sea kelp, and certain animal-based protein materials, are effective as suspension agents.

The preconsolidation preparation of magnesium oxide casting slips presents problems not associated with alumina slips. Magnesia hydrates readily in water, and milling must be done at a low temperature (~2°C) in order to prevent extensive hydration. Controlled hydration results in the development of casting slips of the proper viscosity, degree of suspension, and specific gravity for casting. Magnesium oxide systems are generally in the <99% pure or minimum 99% pure purity range. Nonaqueous suspensions are also effective for magnesia.

Preconsolidation processes for thixotropic casting techniques consist of introducing moisture such that thixotropic properties are produced in the casting slip. This is accomplished using ball- or rotary-mixing devices.

Additional effort is required to learn more about the fundamentals of particles as they relate to casting-slip preparation and properties. The remarkably dense properties of fused-silica casting slips should be evaluated and exploited for other systems. Studies are needed relating bulk and surface characteristics of fine particles with casting-slip properties and subsequent ceramic ware produced by slip casting.

Plastic Molding

The principal preconsolidation effort for the plastic-molding processes of injection molding, compression molding, and transfer molding is the mixing of organic or other materials with preselected ceramic compositions to produce plastic masses. Since these processes are flow processes, it is necessary to develop ceramic-plastic mixtures with good flow properties, and, in general, thermoplastic organics are used as flow-promoting plastic binders. There is considerable similarity between the problems in the preconsolidation material preparation for extrusion and for plastic-molding processes.

While extrusion is principally a process for long-dimensioned shapes, plastic-molding processes produce complex ones. Maximum flow with minimum pressure drop is required, and the basic problem is coating fine particles with thermoplastic materials. Intense mixing at high temperatures (100-400°C) is often required. Water emulsions of the organic-plastic agents facilitate the initial mixing of the organic with the ceramic particulates, and the initial contact can be made by using an aqueous or nonaqueous slurry and solutions. Removal of the volatile constituents provides an intimate mixture of the organic and ceramic. One important preconsolidation treatment is the production of granules of plasticized ceramic as feed stock for injection-molding presses. Two common processes are granulation by screening and extrusion of rods that are cut to relatively uniform length. Plastic-molding preconsolidation processes are restricted to both <99% pure and minimum 99% pure systems.

Improved methods of binder and lubricant introduction in plastic molding are needed. In general, binder contents of plastic-molded parts are very high, necessitating long and careful binder-removal cycles before sintering. Binder systems that would produce high-temperature plasticity of plastic-molding mixes at low binder content would enhance the ability of the processes to produce large shapes.

Consolidation
SLIP CASTING

Standard plaster-of-paris and bisque-mold techniques are utilized at present. Casting is generally conducted using various methods. The conventional method employs plaster molds, which have the ability to withdraw liquid from a slip or slurry. Pressure casting, another technique that is used, generally employs a feed material of much higher viscosity than that used in standard slip casting. Vacuum-assisted casting is also used to aid in water removal.

Thixotropic slips can be used to produce bodies having relatively thick-walled large shapes, and various alumina refractories are currently being fabricated by using this technique. Medium-sized alumina radomes have been formed by thixotropic casting, and large beryllia crucibles are also produced by this method.

Principal efforts are with <99% pure systems, although limited work is being done with minimum 99% pure systems. It is believed that the casting method could be adapted to economical production of armor, radomes, and deep submersible vehicles and devices. A notable contribution is the development of fused-silica radome configurations with close tolerance control. Further effort is required in developing more advanced and controlled production methods for other materials, including minimum 99% purity in large size form. A study of the application of pressure and atmospheric methods to realize uniform density distribution is needed. Casting methods as applied to minimum 99.9% pure systems may also be practical. Attempts are currently in progress to determine green-density variation by nondestructive x-ray radiography methods and to correlate this with fired-character differences.

Size and Shape Limitations

In general, slip casting represents the one cold-forming process where very large complex ware can be realistically produced with a high degree of success potential.

A wide variety of alumina forms in both <99% and minimum 99% pure categories have been prepared, e.g.,

Radomes 2-ft in diameter x 4-ft high and 3/8-in. to 1/2-in. wall thickness have been prepared with dimension-tolerance control ±2% of fired shape.

Slabs or plates 2 ft x 2 ft up to 1-in. thick have been prepared with dimension-tolerance control ±2% of fired shape.

Tubes 9-in. in diameter x 9-ft long x 1/2-in. thick have been prepared with tolerance control as above.

Solid thicknesses of greater than 1 in. are generally not practical.
A general characteristic is that green microstructure exhibits finer particle or grain size at the casting wall than away from it, with resultant fired differences across the wall. Surface features are dependent on mold-surface properties as replication occurs.

EXTRUSION

Extrusion of preconsolidated masses, either plastic or granular, is generally done by two basic methods—ram-extrusion and screw-extrusion. For the abrasive alumina systems (and BeO), ram-extrusions are generally used. High wear rates, with attendant equipment breakdown and contamination, preclude the use of screw-type machines. In both plastic and granular mass-extrusion, similar die configurations are used. Generally, the material will be forced through a perforated plate, to be broken up and cause disoriented flow, before moving through the extrusion nozzle. Both plastic and granular systems (low pressure and high pressure, respectively) ultimately flow plastically in the extrusion operation.

Tooling for extrusion processes can be made of steel, tungsten carbide, or the ceramic composition being extruded, depending on the level of contamination acceptable.

Grain orientation is a principal effect of the extrusion process and both grain and flaw, or void orientation, occur.

Ultrasonic high-pressure extrusion has been used in a very limited fashion. The extrusion of BeO in the very-high-purity state has been worked on extensively in some classified applications. Results have been outstanding in production of very-high-density material. No >99.9% pure alumina art exists at this point.

Present extrusion methods are generally considered to produce acceptable <99% pure commercial ware. Poor fired-product quality is considered a reflection of poor mixing technique in the preconsolidation stage. Improvements require die-design modifications. Warm extrusion (up to 500°C) might also be considered for improvement purposes. Binder systems producing high green density at minimum extrusion pressure would be helpful. However, a significant and unresolved difficulty is the inherent density gradient developed from die wall to specimen center, which manifests itself in terms of ware distortion and character inhomogeneity.

ISOSTATIC-PRESSING

Isostatic-pressing is presently employed in <99% and minimum 99% pure alumina systems. Basically, pressure is applied to ceramic compacts by first sealing the preconsolidated material to be pressed in a flexible container. The compacts are sometimes evacuated. Container pressures can be between 0.1 and 0.01 atm in commercial practice. The container to be pressed is placed in a pressure vessel and, by use of an essentially noncompressible fluid, is pressurized to a predetermined pressure to create a green or unfired ceramic compact. Pressures used range to 30,000 psi commercially and up to 100,000 psi or greater experimentally. Rods, plates, and cylinders, both hollow and solid, are feasible.

A significant problem in isostatic-pressing is that of pressure transfer through the material being pressed. Generally, the pressure experienced by a compact diminishes with distance away from a pressing surface and into the pressed material. Green-density variations exist in pressed blocks because of a different pressure-transfer experience. These green-density differences result in areas of different fired shrinkage, which could possibly cause residual stresses in parts upon firing. When machining parts from isostatically pressed blocks, care is taken that the machined part is symmetrical about the pressing axis of the part and that the green-density variations are at least uniform ones. In cases where they are uniform and controlled, shrinkage occurs in a uniform and symmetrical manner. Isostatic-pressing is generally applied as a bulk-material pressing process. Some very complex shapes, such as cathode-ray tube containers, are isopressed by use of carefully formed flexible bags and steel mandrels. The general purpose of isopressing is to produce a compact of uniform green density and to produce bulk materials that can be further machined into simple or intricate shapes. Green-density differences owing to pressure-transfer diminution through the body exist in most cases, and these manifest themselves in terms of character inhomogeneity.

The problems of particle segregation and of nonuniformity of the ceramic powder used as feed material for isostatic-pressing have been discussed, and such nonuniformity contributes to the development of green-density variations, which are major problems in isostatic-pressing and cold-forming in general.

Size, Shape, and Surface Limitations

The principal efforts in isopressing have been applied to <99% pure alumina systems, with increasing but minor activity in the minimum 99% pure field.

Radomes are an example of <99% pure alumina ware currently produced by this technique.

Size. The size of radomes is limited to the availability of equipment for pressing, machining, firing, and grinding. Nose cones 2 ft in diameter × 4-ft long have been produced. Cylinders 2 ft in diameter and 7-ft long, with a 2-in. wall, have been produced by isostatic-pressing for the Princeton C Stellerator.

Wall thickness. Fired-wall thickness is limited to 1/2-in. minimum for large-size radomes. Wall thickness in fired state is limited by the rigidity of the system at high firing temperatures. Basically, for large radomes, 2 ft × 4 ft, the 1/2-in. wall would be minimum. Radomes larger and smaller than this would have thicker and thinner wall requirements, respectively. Grinding subsequent to firing could produce wall thicknesses of any dimensions consistent with the stiffness of a particular configuration.

Tolerances—generally pressed as ±1% of any given fired dimension. Very close tolerances, i.e., ± 0.002 in., can be held by grinding.

Uniformity of character. On a comparative basis, product quality is realized in parts made by isostatic methods. However, in terms of character, quantitative assessments of uniformity are not documented and are rather unknown.

Thin Slabs or Plates

Size is generally limited by the size of the pressing, machining, and firing equipment available. Fired diameters of up to 2-1/2 ft are possible.

Thickness. For the size mentioned above, a fired thickness of 3/4 in. would be necessary. 2 ft × 2 ft × 1 in. plates have been produced for electronic applications. Thinner plates can be obtained by grinding.

Tolerances—±1% of fired dimensions.

Character uniformity has not been assessed.

Solid Blocks

Size. The size of the largest solid block is unknown. 30-in. diam × 30-in. lengths have been produced in 85% alumina.

Tubes

Size—2 ft in diameter × 4-ft long.

Thickness—2-in. wall (not necessarily a maximum).

Tolerances—±1% of fired dimensions.

Uniformity of character—unknown.

Surface texture. In practice, two varieties of surfaces have been developed for commercially processed isostatic-pressed alumina: They are as-fired and ground and/or polished. As-fired surfaces are directly related to the prefiring treatment they have received, and it is not realistic to generalize about their development. For example, a surface that has been pressed against a polished steel or other mandrel will retain the imprint of that polished surface after firing. Some surface roughening will occur due to thermal etching at the surface. A surface pressed against a polished-steel surface, having perhaps a 10-

20 rms finish, will likely have a fired-surface roughness in the 20-80 rms range. Surfaces that have been roughened in the machining process will generally retain their rough characteristic through the firing stage.

Ground surfaces will have surface roughnesses that are related to the grit-of-wheel used in diamond grinding. The ultimate finish possible on polishing is dependent on the microstructure of the fired material. There is a direct relationship between ultimate possible finish and preconsolidation processing. Ultimate finishes of 2-4 rms can only be produced on materials having few or no processing microvoids.

DRY-PRESSING

Consolidation processing for dry-pressing consists of compacting powders between die faces in an enclosed cavity. Pressures can range from low (~5,000 psi) to high (greater than 80,000 psi) in normal practice. Dry-pressing is generally used for high production rates of small parts, but can be used for any size part for which equipment is available. Complex shapes are often pressed, but simple flat shapes having parallel faces have the best geometry for pressing. Shapes having varying cross-section thicknesses present problems of obtaining uniform compaction. Pressure transfer of a uniform nature is difficult to accomplish in sections of varying thickness. Green-density variations usually cause size differences during the final densification. A uniform precompacted green density is a prerequisite starting point for minimizing compacted green-density gradients in the cold-pressed part.

Dry-pressing is done using tungsten carbide-lined dies when abrasive materials are being processed, and alloy steel dies are used for short runs and for pressing materials of low abrasiveness.

Force transfer through die walls because of frictional effects between the wall and the material being pressed is often responsible for shape distortions during firing. This frictional effect can be overcome to some extent by using the floating-die-body principle. This method requires that only a small fraction of the total force applied be transmitted into the die body and therefore become unavailable for densification work.

Multiple-punch dies are frequently used to produce parts having irregular cross sections. Generally, these punches are activated separately in order that pressures will remain constant across a part. Irregular-part outlines are produced by contouring the pressing dies to the required shape. A wide variety of shapes and sizes can be made by dry-pressing in this fashion. Size limitations are related to the availability of the equipment. One-hundred-ton ceramic presses are common at present. Presses having capacities of several thousand tons are used in the refractories industry. Dry-pressing is considered a likely process for the production of large flat shapes.

VIBRATIONAL COMPACTION

This is a process by which ceramic particles are compacted by low-frequency high-energy vibrations. Particle inertia is overcome by application of vibrational energy, causing the particles to pack to a density consistent with the geometric and material characteristics of the system and with the conditions of vibration imposed.

The vibration-compaction process has been used extensively in the nuclear-fuels industry to clad and compact ceramic fuels simultaneously, usually in the form of long thin rods. The method provides a means for fabricating clad components having core materials and cladding geometries not amenable to more conventional techniques. Packed densities as high as 95% of theoretical have been obtained, although densities of 90% of theoretical are more common.

Particle-packing theory has been successfully correlated with particle-size distribution and resultant density.

Limitations

1. Since the densification that occurs during vibrational compaction is of a mechanical nature only, it is necessary to clad permanently the material being compacted.

2. The degree of densification is strongly dependent upon the physical characteristics of the particles, including particle size, density, distribution, and shape.

3. Particle-size distributions are extremely critical, necessitating the use of only particles of a certain size (coarse and medium fine) and definite quantities of each. As a result, processing is more costly and time-consuming than for most conventional techniques. Another result is definite inhomogeneity in grain and pore sizes, which is characteristic of process.

4. A continuously variable frequency and amplitude is required to orient particles of various shapes and sizes into the most favorable configuration. In turn, this frequency and amplitude is dependent upon the material being compacted, and on the cladding material and geometry.

5. In vibrationally compacted rods, densification is a function of the length-to-diameter ratio. Uniformity of the density along the length of the rods can vary.

6. Cladding and closures can be damaged by extended vibration at high accelerations and energies.

7. Although considerable work has been done on vibrationally compacted rods and tubes, other geometries have not been completely established.

HIGH-ENERGY-RATE FORMING METHODS

Process

In both the explosive and pneumatic - mechanical impaction processes, the material to be impacted is placed in a metallic container, the container sealed, and high-pressure pulses generated in the material, as follows:

1. Explosive compaction—detonation of a high-explosive charge immediately adjacent to the container.

2. Pneumatic - mechanical impaction—sudden deceleration of a ram propelled by a rapidly expanding gas.

After either type of impaction, the metallic sheathing can be removed by mechanical acid leaching, or left intact to serve as cladding for the densified powder core.

Both processes have been applied to a wide variety of ceramic materials, although work is generally still in the exploratory stage. In the explosive compaction process, pressures of 8×10^6 to 12×10^6 psi are known to be applied to materials at ambient temperature, producing compacts of 94-98% of theoretical in most cases. Geometries such as rods, tubes, and rocket nozzles have been directly formed by this process. In the pneumatic - mechanical impaction process, pressures up to 10^6 psi have been generated in materials preheated at temperatures approaching 2,000°C. Typical densities of 99+% theoretical density are being achieved in some cases, with attendant fine-grain microstructure ($<2\mu$). Direct forming of simple geometries is still in the exploratory stage.

It presently appears that both techniques are most useful in producing high-density agglomerates from ultrafine powders. It has been shown that for explosive compaction, composition or powder reactivity is virtually unaffected by this type of agglomeration. In some instances, sinterability has been enhanced, with subsequently lower firing shrinkages. Pneumatic - mechanical impaction, while employing somewhat lower pressures at elevated temperatures, might be expected to yield similar characteristics.

Limitations of the Process

The response of a ceramic to high-energy-rate processes is highly dependent on characteristics of the material, including crystallite size, shape, orientation, and structure. Mechanical characteristics are also extremely important because insufficient plastic flow of the material will cause it to fracture. In addition, fractures can occur as a result of tensile reflection of shock waves and/or springback of the material after impaction.

The necessity of containing the material to be impacted with a metallic cladding also introduces an additional cost and process step.

It is presently difficult to set size and geometry limitations for either process. In the pneumatic-mechanical impaction process, maximum diameter is currently limited to a few inches, largely due to tooling requirements and insufficient state of the art. In explosive compaction, quite long pieces can conceivably be made, but the difficulty of transmitting the energy through and to the center of a large cross section is still a problem. The cross-section limitation also depends on the specific gravity of the material and its shock-absorbing characteristics.

Other Remarks

1. Neither process requires a binder, thus simplifying the procedure and eliminating the source of contamination.

2. For explosive compaction, the simplicity of the operation and facilities required offers an economic advantage of requiring a minimum amount of capital outlay. Conversely, pneumatic-mechanical impaction requires a considerable investment in equipment and tooling.

Final Densification

SINTERING AND LIQUID-PHASE SINTERING

Process Features

The bulk of ceramic ware produced today is densified by reasonably conventional sintering procedures and this is particularly true of the <99% and >99% pure composition fields.

The rather large firing shrinkage of conventional cold-compacted powders, which in the technical-ceramic field is in the range of 15 to 65% by volume, becomes an increasing detriment to the ability to produce large shapes effectively and efficiently. Another difficulty is the lack of uniformity in shrinkage with location in an object, which is associated with dimensional variations and flaws in fired ceramics. Variations in porosity and pore anisotropy resulting from inadequate control in preconsolidation and consolidation account for many of the difficulties, but some result from difficulties in getting heat energy into the body uniformly and are aggravated by size, low initial density, and chemical reactions.

The characterization of the changes in microstructure that occur during sintering or liquid-phase sintering would require the independent description, during density change, of the pore-shape, pore-size, and grain-size changes that accompany it. There is no material for which a complete description of the microstructure evolution has been made (from the as-fabricated bulk compact to the final-density limit achieved after high-temperature firing). The analyses of the mechanisms of material transport, which have been conducted in many systems, have been based on observations of neck growth between spheres, shrinkage in powder compacts, or densification with observed grain growth during the later stages of the process. From those studies it has become clear that the sintering process should, in general, be interpreted as being a complex mixture of various mechanisms of material transport that can be operative. The relative importance of the given mechanisms in a specific material will vary with temperature, time, heating rate, and other experimental variables such as atmosphere, impurity content, and particle size. Because of the lack of a complete description of the microstructure evolution for any material, and the complexity of the process with multiple mechanisms of operative material transport, it is obvious that our understanding of the microstructure evolution for technological production is predominantly empirically based. However, based on the mechanistic studies that have been conducted, the relative importance of the various variables and the interrelationships among them can be semiquantitatively evaluated.

The experimental variables that have been shown to control or to affect the densification rate, density limit, grain growth, and secondary grain growth, are listed below in order of considered importance.

1. Material composition
   a. Single phase
      i. Covalent bonded-ceramic materials: SiC, B_4C, TiB_2, generally do not shrink.
      ii. Metallic materials: generally exhibit sintering shrinkage.
      iii. Ionic materials: generally exhibit sintering shrinkage.
      iv. Pure doped single phase: The composition effect in this range governs densification rate, grain-growth rate, and density limit through secondary grain growth.
   b. Second solid phase—same effects.
   c. Liquid phase and its viscosity (both affect densification and grain-growth rates).
2. The temperature: together with heating rate, which affects densification and grain-growth rates and density limit.
3. Time at temperature: including maximum and heating rate, which affect density limit and grain growth.
4. Particle size: affects densification and grain-growth rates.
5. Bulk density: affects density limit and maximum shrinkage.
6. Atmosphere: affects densification rate and density limit.
7. Particle-size distribution: affects densification rate, density limit, and secondary grain growth.
8. Bulk density distribution: affects distortion and density limit.

With this range of variables and the complex interactions among them affecting the different possible mechanisms of material transport, it is obvious why the empirical controls developed by technologists frequently break down. The impurity effects alone, variable impurity contents from batch to batch, and particle-size changes, make careful control over the final density, distortion, and general reproducibility of the microstructure exceedingly difficult to guarantee.

Compositional Features

Composition plays an important role in sintering behavior, and the effect of impurities or additions has been demonstrated to be most significant.

The three purity classifications follow:

1. Very high purity, >99.9% pure. No information is currently available for this composition category, and it should be investigated.

2. High-purity or minimum 99% pure single phase. Very-high-density alumina, beryllia, magnesia, yttria, ferrites, and zirconia are state of art. The

achievement of very high density in these materials has required control of discontinuous grain growth, atmosphere, particulate size and size distribution, and bulk density.

Impurity, particle-size, and agglomerate-size variation from batch to batch are apparent sources of difficulty in achieving consistently reproducible behavior. For production of theoretical density, as has been achieved with Al_2O_3 + MgO, Y_2O_3 + ThO_2, ZrO_2 + Y_2O_3, MgO + LiF, and some ferrites, critical control of the preceding variables has been shown to be necessary. From those successes it may be anticipated that many more materials will be made to theoretical density in the near future, using the techniques that have been demonstrated for evaluation of a dopant's effect on discontinuous grain growth.

The principal areas for which the necessary basic information is lacking are on subsolidus equilibria for gases and solids, their effects on transport in crystal lattices, their segregation at grain boundaries, and their consequent effect on grain-boundary diffusivities and mobilities.

Increased low-temperature strength with decreased grain size has been observed in many materials and provides the basis for the need for controlling grain growth during sintering. (Grain enlargements of 100x are typical for sintering when grain-growth control by doping is exercised. They may be greater than 1,000x when not exercised, and may be restricted up to 2x by hot-pressing.) The grain-size effect on strength is illustrated by typical data for alumina tabulated below:

High-Density HP Alumina

Grain Size	Strengths (in bending)
1-2 μ	~100,000 psi
5 μ	~ 80,000 psi
100 μ	~ 30,000 psi

Greater control, by doping grain growth during sintering, is needed to make higher strength nonalumina bodies available.

Commercial Bodies < 99% Pure

The processing of oxides containing an 85-99% crystal phase is under better empirical control than for 99+ bodies; the (generally) siliceous liquids, by smothering the variable impurity effects, provide more reproducible behavior in controlling densification and grain growth. The bodies are generally not of theoretical density. The main problem in density control probably arises from gas trapped from air-firing, the use of inexpensive materials, and grinding for blending. This processing provides commercial ware with adequate properties. It is not known how much greater potential would be available if better character were developed. The grain sizes are held to 5 μ in the strongest bodies, which show bend strengths of 50K psi. In contrast to the higher-purity materials, the strength is less sensitive to grain size after firing and is probably more dependent on the nature of the second- and/or tertiary-phase-boundary composition as well as variable pore structure and its distribution.

The strength at high temperatures is probably less dependent on grain size than on type and content of impurities. The tensile strengths of ceramics at high temperatures are generally so low that use is restricted to low stresses or compressive loading, causing creep rate rather than fracture to be more pertinent for design purposes. The creep rate in many materials increases with decreasing grain size, i.e., in opposite sense than low-temperature strength for optimizing properties. For potentially improved high-temperature strength, development of controlled - preferred orientation polycrystalline bodies is needed (based on the observed structure - property relations in metals).

HOT-FORMING

Low Pressure (uniaxial < 50,000 psi)

This technique has been successfully employed in the fabrication of ceramic materials for achievement of microstructure control, enhanced densification, composite fabrication, and pressure-bonding, which are not normally attained by conventional sintering techniques; e.g., full densification has been realized for MgO and very dense Al_2O_3, MgO, BeO, and ZrO_2 oxides. Y_2O_3 with grain sizes of $1\,\mu$ or less has been prepared.

Final-stage densification mechanisms at the lower end of this pressure range are similar to sintering. Initial-stage densification is not as clearly established, since several mechanisms may be occurring simultaneously. The over-all densification mechanisms at the higher end of this pressure range are not clearly established either, although it is generally conceded that the plastic-deformation characteristics of the higher-symmetry materials are important. Further work is needed to describe the densification kinetics in each of these areas.

For oxides, most of the effort has been concerned with Al_2O_3, MgO, and BeO in the 99+% pure state, although some industrial compositions featuring lower-purity levels, e.g., cutting-tool-grade alumina, have also been produced. This forming technique has been generally useful in the fabrication of materials that are very difficult, if not impossible, to densify by conventional sintering procedures, e.g., certain nitrides, carbides, borides, and beryllides.

The equipment and methods used in uniaxial hot-pressing show considerable variation and are most often manually controlled batch operations, although semicontinuous methods of producing alumina and ferrite rods, for example, have recently been described.

In the simplest uniaxial hot-pressing system, the material to be hot-pressed is placed in the center of a cylindrical graphite die. Cylindrical graphite plungers are inserted, and the die assembly is placed between platens of a press, with suitable refractory insulators between the graphite plungers and the platens. Carbon black, carbon wool, or other suitable insulation is packed around the die assembly and retained in place by a nonconducting shell of fused silica or cement-bonded asbestos. An induction coil around the outer shell is used to heat the die assembly. Argon or other inert atmosphere may be circulated over and through the thermal insulation to prevent oxidation. Pressure is applied to the material by a hydraulic jack acting on the graphite plungers. Sometimes the die and material to be pressed are heated to the desired temperature and then pressure is applied, although it is often applied continuously during a run. Maximum temperature and pressure attainable depend on the particular installation and design.

The major variables encountered in hot-pressing equipment are the die material and design, method of heating, atmosphere control, and the pressing aids employed.

Graphite is the most common die material used for uniaxial hot-pressing systems. However, other die materials are being used on a limited scale. Table 1 lists the materials being used or considered for use and limits of temperature and pressure at forming temperature considered to be attainable at the present time.

Graphite, as the most universally used material for hot-pressing dies, is available in many grades with differing densities, strengths, and thermal and electrical properties. Its increase in strength with temperature, low thermal expansion, ease of machining, and low cost make it a nearly ideal die material. Experience with many grades of graphite has not suggested any criteria for selecting one grade for hot-pressing dies. Generally, the 1.6 to 1.8 g/cc density-

Table 1. Uniaxial Hot-Pressing Die Materials

Material	Maximum Use Temperature (°C)	Maximum Pressure (psi)	Remarks
Graphite	2,500	10,000	Inert atmosphere required
SiC	1,500	25,000	Reactive with many materials, difficult to machine
TaC	1,700	8,000	Expensive, difficult to machine
Wc and TiC	1,400	10,000	
W	1,500	3,500	Easily oxidized
Mo	1,100	3,000	
Al_2O_3	1,200	20,000	Difficult to machine, needs
ZrO_2	1,180	5,000	extreme care in loading,
BeO	1,500	10,000	low thermal resistance
TiB_2	1,500	15,000	Expensive, difficult to machine
Inconel X, Hastelloy, and stainless steels	1,100	10,000	

extruded graphites are used. Molded graphites rather than extruded grades are considered best when the die is heated by electrical resistance. Recently developed materials, such as the dense reprocessed grades of graphite and pyrolytic graphite, are being appraised as possible hot-pressing dies and plungers. Because of the enhanced anisotropic properties of these materials, their applicability to hot-pressing dies appears to pose serious problems in die design.

On a very limited scale, the refractory carbides have been tried as hot-pressing die materials. The expense of machining is a chief limiting factor. The refractory metals tungsten and molybdenum have also been used, but creep of the metals at high temperature limits their usefulness. Certain refractory diborides, although showing excellent high-temperature strength (~60,000 psi at 1,800°C), are limited because of the cost in machining.

The alloys based on iron-nickel-chromium or nickel-chromium have been used extensively in hot-pressing the alkali and alkaline earth halides. Their maximum temperature limitation is due to metallic creep.

Interest in oxide die materials for hot-pressing in oxidizing atmospheres has increased significantly, particularly in respect to electrical and magnetic ceramics. High-density alumina has shown promise in this area and can be operated up to 40 hot-pressing cycles, provided extreme care is used in the operation of the equipment. Both alumina and stabilized zirconia are limited by low thermal shock resistance and creep at elevated temperatures; however, the lack of chemical reactivity with some materials, as well as oxidation stability, compensate for these limitations.

Design of hot-pressing dies is generally based on the standard formulas for thick-walled cylinders with internal pressure. For small diameters, these are generally successful in predicting maximum pressures attainable at any temperature, provided the tensile strength-temperature relationships are known for the die material. As the internal diameter of the die increases, imperfections in the die material make the behavior more erratic. This is especially true for large graphite dies, where there has been considerable experience with hot-pressing in both the metallurgical and ceramic fields.

Die washes, liners, or sleeves have been investigated and are known to have been employed in the industry with incomplete assessment of their potential.

Metallic foils of platinum, molybdenum, and tantalum have been used with limited success in graphite dies to prevent reaction between the material being pressed and carbon. Some success has also been attained in using a mold wash such as boron nitride, Al_2O_3, and pyrolytic graphite on graphite. Molybdenum dies have been chromium plated and used successfully to 1,100° C with materials that react with molybdenum. Complex designs such as alumina sleeves in stainless steel have been attempted for low-temperature hot-pressing (under 1,100°C).

Graphite hot-pressing dies are often heated by induction, which is considered a simple and economical method. This method, however, is more difficult to adapt to controlled rates of heating and cooling and to assured temperature uniformity in the specimen. Resistance heating of graphite dies by direct passage of electric current has also been successfully applied. For oxide dies and, in some cases, graphite die assemblies, heating from resistance heating elements has allowed closer control of temperatures. Temperatures attainable by this method are usually under 1,800° C. In many instances, the type of heating employed is coupled to the type of material being hot-pressed and the specific hot-press design.

Atmosphere control in hot-pressing is often necessary. Graphite below 2,200°C must be operated in an inert atmosphere or vacuum. Above 2,200°C, an inert atmosphere must be used because of the vapor pressure of the graphite. In many assemblies the graphite is heated and residual oxygen reacts with the carbon-black thermal insulation or die material to form carbon monoxide as the gaseous atmosphere. The low rate of oxygen permeation through the carbon black prevents serious oxidation. Other systems flood and continuously flush with an inert gas such as argon. In either case, the atmosphere at the sample position is unknown, but is probably reducing in the first stages of hot-pressing.

Vacuum hot-pressing has been attempted successfully in a number of laboratories. In pressing oxides, one would suspect that an applied vacuum would facilitate attaining very high densities. There is some direct experimental evidence to confirm this in MgO and Al_2O_3. When pressing two-phase systems, such as glass-crystal combinations, there is definite experimental evidence that vacuum hot-pressing reduces entrapped gas and leads to more-uniform microstructures.

Pressure distributions similar to those encountered in cold-pressing are known to occur in hot-pressing, although detailed studies on density variations have not been performed.

Hot-pressed shapes, size, and uniformity are important considerations. Cylindrical, square, and rectangular cross sections have been fabricated. By use of collapsible graphite tubes to form the inner diameter, oxide tubes have been formed by hot-pressing. As a "rule of thumb," the length-to-diameter ratio for hot-pressed specimens should not be greater than 4 to 1. Although specimens with ratios as high as 9 to 1 have been formed, density variations along the length become increasingly severe above the 4 to 1 ratio. A unique method, by which the hot-pressed material itself forms the bottom plunger, has allowed alumina rods 4 in. in diameter and up to 6 ft long to be formed on a semicontinuous basis. The density of the product in this case has varied between 90 and 95% of the theoretical density.

Examples of maximum sizes that have been hot-pressed to this time are given in Table 2. It is by no means implied that the sizes in Table 2 are the maximum possible sizes attainable. The general opinion exists that if a large shape were desired, it could be made by hot-pressing if suitable equipment were available.

The smallest size that can conveniently be attained by hot-pressing an individual shape is throught to be approximately 1/4 in. in diameter by 1/4 in. high. No clear-cut limit is apparent, however.

Uniformity of hot-pressed pieces either piece to piece or within one piece has not been subjected to thorough study. Density variations of ±0.2% in one piece and ±0.5% in repeated specimens have been reported with beryllia.

Table 2. Maximum Sizes of Hot-Pressed Shapes

Material	Diameter (in.)	Length (in.)
BN	14	14
BeO	10	10
	12	2
Al_2O_3	12	4
MgO	12	2
TiB_2	6	18
SiO_2	20	8
B_4C	24	2

Alumina tool bits are quoted as having better uniformity from hot-pressing than from cold-pressing and sintering. Grain-size variations in one 12-in. beryllia sample varied from 10 μ at the center to nearly 100 μ at the edge. Grain-size variations in a group of approximately twenty 12 in. × 12 in. × 1.2 in. thick hot-pressed dense pure-alumina tiles were generally from 1 to 2 μ, with scattered concentrations of much larger grains in some tiles. Resulting variations could not be traced either to raw-material variation or process difficulty, although both were suspected.

The number of pieces repetitively produced by hot-pressing has not yet been sufficient to evaluate adequately the uniformity of grain size, density, and other character-properties that can be achieved. Reasonable uniformity has been achieved on a laboratory scale.

Various schemes have been proposed to make hot-pressing more economical by a continuous or volume process. Die assemblies maintained hot with a heated feed and hot ejection have been suggested, but there is no evidence such a system has been tried. The use of many die assemblies that are preheated, passed under a press, and then cooled has been proposed, but die costs are a prohibitive factor. Stacked-pressing of a number of pieces in one die, and gang-pressing of a number of die assemblies, have both been used successfully on a semicontinuous process.

The pressing of large shapes and cutting of the desired specimens from them is practiced by the producers of boron nitride and ferroelectric ceramics. This method has been limited to those materials for which cutting costs are not prohibitive.

Continual production by hot-pressing does not appear to be impossible, but superficial examination of the problem indicates unit costs would probably be high.

Low Pressure (isostatic < 30,000 psi)

Interest in isostatic hot-pressing has significantly increased during the past several years. Several laboratories are actively pursuing this forming method, primarily on an R&D basis. Current interest is in using a gas for the transmission of pressure, and the equipment employed in isostatic hot-pressing consists of a pressure vessel containing a furnace. The material to be pressed is sealed into a metallic container, inserted into the furnace, and heated to the desired temperature. The pressure of an inert gas in the vessel is then raised to the desired level. At pressures of about 40,000 psi, the size limitation is approximately 1-1/2 in. in diameter and 3 in. long for a temperature up to 2,200°C. Large installations have been constructed, which are capable of forming samples 13 in. in diameter and 3 to 4 ft long, and which operate temperatures up to 1,550°C and pressures up to 15,000 psi.

Isostatic hot-pressing has been applied to ceramics, cermets, and other composite materials containing ceramic phases. The technique has produced nearly theoretical dense specimens of up to 99.9% pure alumina with a grain-size range of 2-4 μ. Uniform density and microstructure have been reported for material processed by this technique. Gas entrapment, sheath interaction, and temperature gradients are inherent process limitations, as are size, tolerance, and quantity-production problems.

High Pressure (50,000 psi to 10^6 psi)

Work in this area has primarily been concerned with 99+% pure material, e.g., ZrO_2, Al_2O_3, and MgO, although recent work has included less-pure refractory carbides and borides. Only small (~1 in. diam) specimens have been prepared, with limited evaluation. Except for diamond synthesis the process is primarily of an exploratory interest at present.

Problems of gas entrapment, nonuniform pressure and temperature distribution, and die stability exist. Currently, simple cylindrical geometries are state-of-art shapes that are being studied in connection with several R&D-sponsored efforts. Also, fully dense 0.1-μ grain-size MgO and relatively fine grain size high-density refractory borides and carbides have been prepared.

Hot-Working

Effort in this area has primarily been carried out in an exploratory fashion, in order either to facilitate production of certain compositions in specific forms or to prepare materials with preferred orientation in microstructure.

Hot-rolling of crystalline ceramics for the production of plates or sheets has been investigated in a number of laboratories. The equipment used was essentially metal-working rolls with alumina-ceramic sleeves. Internally heated rolls have not been used; rather, the material has been precompacted and heated, then passed through rolls that were at a lower temperature than the compact. This results in undesirable heat transfer from the material to the roll. Work with barium titanate, forsterite, and synthetic mica under these conditions has indicated that a glass phase was required to hot-roll ceramics successfully. A porcelain body has been successfully rolled by preheating an isostatically preformed body to 1,520°C and passing it between alumina-ceramic rolls. A 25% reduction in thickness per pass was achieved. The glass viscosity and proportional content appeared to be important parameters in hot-rolling. A proportional content of 20 to 40% glass was necessary, with approximately 30% optimum. There was no indication of preferred crystallite orientation.

Hot-extrusion of canned and unrestrained ceramic powders (UO_2, Al_2O_3, and BeO) has been investigated in a number of laboratories. Lithium fluoride powder has been hot-extruded in vacuum to give translucent rods approximately 1/8 in. in diameter. Fine grain sizes were not attained. The extrusion of a single crystal of lithium fluoride has given a glass-clear polycrystalline rod of fairly large grain size. The more refractory materials, such as oxides, have generally been restrained and coextruded with a metal can. Magnesium oxide, for example, has been hot-extruded in a heavy molybdenum can. Success has been realized in obtaining polycrystalline MgO in several-inch sample-size lengths with some preferred crystallographic orientation. Physical properties of such prepared material are currently under evaluation.

Hot-extrusion has posed serious problems on extrusion die materials. The high pressures required have usually necessitated the material to be extruded to be preheated and rapidly placed in a relatively cold extrusion chamber and extruded through relatively cold dies. What effect this has on the material response is generally unknown and may be a limiting factor in character uniformity. Major problems with hot-extrusion are associated with the lack of high-temperature extrusion dies and the inability to characterize the material response.

Hot-forging of cermet materials to both densify and shape has been rather successfully applied. Uranium dioxide - molybdenum and friction materials in which ceramics are dispersed in metallic matrices are two examples. Hot-forging has been used to improve the density of fused silica. In recent work, press-forging has demonstrated some feasibility in producing preferred orientation in the microstructure for 99.9% pure alumina and magnesia. Conditions vary from high temperature (~1,800°C) and moderately low pressures (~6,000 psi) to low temperature (1,200°C) and 100,000 psi. Mechanical properties of materials containing such microstructures are currently under evaluation.

The full potential of hot-forming methods has not been exploited, mainly because of the economic disadvantage relative to other forming processes. Again, the primary commercial usage of the process has been concerned with the preparation of refractory materials that are too difficult to densify by normal sintering procedures, e.g., some refractory borides, boron carbide, and refractory nitrides.

CONTRIBUTIONS TO SCATTER OF DATA

The scatter of data observed in ceramic materials, besides resulting in part from the nature of the text method employed, undoubtedly also results from the presence of critical flaws and/or significant variability in character, wherein the distinction between flaws and character variability is doubtless an arbitrary one. At any rate, the observation has been made in connection with high-purity, hot-pressed, dense-alumina ceramics, that as bend strengths reach maximum values, e.g., ~100,000 psi, the scatter range can be quite significant, with values lower than 40,000 psi being observed for nominally "identical" character material. This variability may result from identifiable or unidentified character nonuniformity, unlocated critical flaw, or, as mentioned before, the character of the test method employed. It is significant, however, that observed variations in character, e.g., grain size and porosity, do register as significant changes in observed-strength properties for such dense high-purity compositions. Scattered concentrations of $>5\text{-}\mu$ grains in a 1 to $2\text{-}\mu$ matrix, or a measurable increase in porosity (0.2%), can alter strength significantly. The character variability observed, e.g., grain size and porosity, is attributed to some extent to inadequate process control, e.g., temperature, pressure distribution, and contamination, as well as to raw-material variability within a sample as well as from piece to piece. Increased character variability results as different lots of raw material are employed to fabricate the same sample type, thus confirming the importance of raw-material variability. However, even within a given lot nonuniformity in impurity distribution or the presence of impurities themselves will be found, in certain instances, concentrated as scattered second-phase material after processing, often observable only by high-resolution electron-microscopy techniques. The significance of such scattered concentrations has not been resolved quantitatively.

In commercial cold-formed and sintered-alumina compositions, e.g., of ceramic-armor variety, the situation is more ill-defined. Such compositions are generally characterized by a distribution in primary-phase grain size and by the secondary phase and its grain size and porosity; the terminology "uniform character" has different meaning. Criteria are generally the percent of content and density of alumina. In view of the wide variations in phase-chemistry grain size and other significant character features inherent in such compositions, it is indeed difficult to reconcile observed scatter in properties to specific character parameters. One opinion is that for a given chemistry the final density is perhaps the most significant parameter to which the observation of other properties should be related.

Table 3. Summary of Solids-Process Characteristics[a]

	Slip Casting and Sintering	Extrusion and Sintering	Isostatic-Pressing and Sintering	Dry-Pressing and Sintering	Vibrational Compaction and Sintering	High-Energy-Rate Forming and Sintering	Hot-Forming Low Pressure (Uniaxial)	Hot-Forming Low Pressure (Isostatic)	High Pressure	Hot-Working
Compositions for which suitable										
Oxides	II(I)	II(I)	I	I	II	III	I	II	II	II
Carbides, nitrides	III(II)	III	II	II	III	III	II	II	II	N
Borides, beryllides	III(II)	III	II	II	III	N	N	II	II	N
Elements (C, B)	N	N	N	N	N	N	N	N	N	N
Composition control	II	II	I	I	I	N	II	I	I	II
Uniformity control	III(II)	III(II)	II	II	II	N	II	I	I	I
High-Purity capability	III(II)	III(II)	I	I	I	I	II(I)	I	I	I
EVALUATION FOR OXIDE MATERIALS										
Configurations										
Shell, sheet, tube	II	II(Tube)	II	I	Tubes II	III	III(II)	II	N	N
Block, bar	III	III	II	II	Rods II	III	II	III(II)	III	N
Max. lateral dim. (in.)	60	100	60 in.	6-8	12	N	24	24	3	N
Max. thickness (in.)	1	10	60 in.	3	1	N	5	8	1	N
Dimensional control	III(II)	III	II	II	II	N	I	I	II	N(I)
Internal structures										
Polycrystal (1 phase)	III	III	II	II	II	II(I)	II(I)	I	I	N
Multiphase crystal	II	II	II	II	II	II	II	II	I	N(I)
Phase-distribution control	III(I)	III	II	II	II	I	I	I	I	N(I)
Polycrystal structures										
Min. grain size (μ)	>5 μ	>5 μ	>5 μ	>5 μ	N	<2 μ	<1 μ	<1 μ	0.1 μ	<1 μ
Size control	III	III(II)	II	II	N	I	I	I	I	II(I)
Uniformity control	III(I)	III(II)	II(I)	II	N	I	I	I	I	II(I)
Grain shape, typical	P, E, F	E, C	E	E, P	E	E	E, P	E	E	P, F
Orientation, typical	R, O	O, R	R	R, O	R, P	R	R, O	R	R, O	O, R
Orientation control	III(II)	II	II	II	III	II	I	I	I	I
**										
Min. porosity, %	1.0	1.0	0	0	N	<1	0	0	0	0
Uniformity	III(II)	III(II)	II(I)	II(I)	N	N	II(I)	II(I)	II(I)	II(I)
Reproducibility	III(II)	II	II(I)	II(I)	N	N	II(I)	II(I)	II(I)	N

[a] Regular entries, present capability. Bracketed entries, future potential. Evaluation: I, superior; II, average; III, inferior, N, not applicable. Numerical Values: Units in left column. Grain size: E, equiaxial; C, columnar; F, fibrous, filamentary; P, platelet. Grain Orientation: R, random; O, oriented; *, over-all assessment.

CAPABILITY OF PRODUCING AND CONTROLLING A SPECIFIED CHARACTER, SIZE, AND SHAPE

At present, the capability to produce a uniform character in respect to size and shape is limited in solids processing to a very few compositions in either a laboratory or limited-production stage. Besides various ferrites and ferroelectrics, examples include high-density high-purity aluminas of the Lucalox variety; zyttrite - zirconia; hot-pressed high-purity magnesia and alumina; yttralox; and, in a marginal fashion, cutting-tool-grade aluminas.

Impurity, particle-size, and agglomerate-size variation from batch to batch are apparent sources of difficulty in achieving consistently uniform character. For development of controlled character in the compositions mentioned above, critical control of process variables, agglomeration, cold compaction, hot-forming, and sintering is necessary, in addition to strict chemistry control and/or use of purposeful additives to minimize discontinuous grain growth.

At present, the limits in size and shape, in which controlled character can be maintained even for the compositions described above, are ill-defined. Thickness limitations are known to exist and it is not clear that these can be surmounted through improvements in processing control.

In the area of commercial compositions, <99% pure, which are normally prepared by cold-forming followed by sintering, it is apparent that the control of character will require considerable processing innovation, which may not be economical if there is no corresponding enhancement in yield and/or product properties. These compositions are, in general, currently characterized by irregular distributions in primary-phase and secondary-phase grain size and porosity; and to a large extent these variations result from the character of particulate materials employed. Extensive particle-size, shape, and composition irregularities pose significant handicaps in the development of controlled character.

STATE-OF-THE-ART SUMMARY

Table 3 is a compilation of the Panel's assessments of the varieties of solids processes covered in this report, with respect to their important characteristics and capabilities. The elements of character selected are those considered pertinent to structural applications, including those considered important for maximizing strength and minimizing the scatter of strength.

In view of the wide variety of compositions processed, which sometimes dominate the character that results, regardless of the particular process employed, it is really appropriate to consider the tabulation as a rather average approximation of the over-all state of art.

DEVELOPMENT OF RECOMMENDATIONS

Solids-processing research has been undersupported in the past because it has been tied in with end-item needs as well as proprietary industry efforts, and thus has been directed toward a specific property requirement. Although certain characteristics and properties of materials will necessarily continue to be related only to process variables at the level of present understanding, it is important to realize that this type of approach is empirical and specific. A fundamental approach will relate process and material variables to the achievement of a particular character that, in turn, will determine the properties of materials. This approach is necessary to maximize finished-material performance and reproducibility and to facilitate the transition from laboratory results to quantity production and scale-up.

An assessment of the state of art has revealed the close interconnection that exists between the characteristics of particulates and the character that develops in sequential processing steps in solids processing. A quantitative understanding of this interconnection is lacking because of current limitations in characterizing particulates in a fashion that is quantitatively meaningful to subsequent body-character development. This results from limitations in analytical methods used to characterize particulates, and insufficient control (using available control procedures) of character of available particulate materials during preparation, whereby both chemical and physical characteristics often have been found to vary significantly and independently in source material.

In general, in the manufacture of commercial and high-purity ceramic ware, purposeful chemical additions are often made to source particulate material in an effort to negate undesirable effects of source-material inhomogeneities.

The recognition of the close interconnection between the preconsolidation, consolidation, and final-densification steps, therefore, leads to the most important recommendation—that broad research programs are needed to develop an understanding of interrelations in the essential processing steps and mechanisms with respect to starting raw-material particle characteristics. Emphasis must be given to the study of character evolution at each processing stage in relation to preceding and following steps to develop a general basis for materials-processing control. The objective is to improve the ability to evaluate quantitatively those variations in particulate composition and structure that contribute to character development and variability in in-process and finished ceramic bodies.

It is recommended that investigations in particulate characterization be carried out for specific types of available minimum 99.9% pure oxides, with emphasis initially on Al_2O_3 and MgO. Subsequent efforts should include higher-purity materials when they are available.

Efforts should be concentrated on the physics and chemistry of fine particles, together with the application or development of necessary techniques and instrumentation for a more sophisticated characterization. The work should subsequently include tasks aimed at relating the variations in particle characteristics to their influence on structure in subsequent stages of processing.

The following represent other recommendations for research in areas of science and technology, specifically separated in terms of preconsolidation, consolidation, and final densification, that also seriously limit achievements in solids processing.

Preconsolidation

The subject of ceramic-particle technology requires further consideration here and the areas of prime significance follow:

SYNTHESIS OF ULTRAHIGH-PURITY MATERIALS

The synthesis of ultrahigh-purity >99.99% pure oxides in limited quantities, in controlled submicron particulate form, is essential for use as chemical standards and for intrinsic studies concerned with, for example, nonstoichiometric effects, densification, kinetics, grain growth, and high-temperature strength.

It is recommended that investigations be supported leading to the initial preparation of 100-lb batches, in order of priority, of (a) ultrahigh-purity Al_2O_3, (b) ultrahigh-purity MgO, and (c) ultrahigh-purity BeO, each in controlled fine-particle (submicron size) forms.

Later, consideration should also be given to other oxides, such as ZrO_2, for which a significant processing program is currently under way, and to other compounds, e.g., nitrides, borides, and carbides.

IMPROVED CHARACTERIZATION OF PARTICULATE MATERIALS

It is recommended that investigations in particulate characterization be carried out for specific types of available ~99.9% pure oxides, with emphasis first on

Al_2O_3, then MgO, to improve the ability to evaluate quantitatively variations in particulate chemistry and character that contribute to character development and variability in a finished body.

In this connection, the following aspects are in need of greater understanding:

1. The interrelation among the different characteristic particle sizes as determined by different techniques, and further improvements in the techniques of particle-size distribution determination.

2. Improvements in the techniques of size-shape analysis and the quantitative description of particle shape and its relationship to the characteristic dimensions, including surface area.

3. Lattice imperfections in fine particles as affected by elastic stresses, chemical-variation dislocation, and space charges, including influence of interstitials and vacancies.

4. Crystal-structure distortions as a function of crystallite size.

5. Improvements in the techniques for determining chemical composition, with special reference to anionic species and variation at surface and interior particles.

IMPROVED UNDERSTANDING OF FLOW AND AGGLOMERATION
IN PARTICULATE SYSTEMS

Specific recommendation areas include:

1. Basic research into fundamentals of flow in particulate systems. Experimental and theoretical studies are needed to obtain general relationships between rheological behavior and the fundamental structure and compositional characteristics of particulate systems.

2. The problems of agglomeration of particles, characterization of agglomerates, their flow and behavior during consolidation, and their effect on the character of resulting ceramic products, are considered important and unresolved problems that are essential for study. Segregation in size leads to a gradient in densification, and the development of techniques is needed to prepare uniform agglomerates from particulates with size ranges from submicron to several microns, and to handle them in a manner that avoids segregation. This work is considered to be of an inventive nature.

3. A quantitative description of binder and moisture distribution is lacking in solids processing. Trade-off studies in binder or binderless-moisture-particle relationships are required in respect to their impact on consolidation processing. Exploratory studies aimed at establishing desirable levels are needed, again in relation to specific consolidation processing.

Optimization in agglomerate development and behavior can be expected to improve character and resulting properties for compositions at all levels of purity.

Consolidation

Consolidation processes have been identified as those unit operations in which loose particulate matter is formed into a coherent body. They deal with the general areas of forming, including slip casting, cold-pressing, extrusion, vibratory compaction, and high-energy-rate compaction.

These forming operations present particular problems in character uniformity and reproducibility. Density inhomogeneities are semiquantitatively known in some cold-forming operations; i.e., shrinkage, warpage and distortion data are available for a number of oxide compositions, but no known technique is available for fabricating material without density gradients. The elimination or control of density gradients is considered most important from the point of view of maintaining uniform character in subsequently processed compositions.

Specific recommendations include:

1. Basic research into the fundamentals of flow in particulate systems. The physics of flow in powders and pastes is virtually nonexistent and is relevant to all particulate-consolidation processes. The isostatic component of stress on

the local shear strength of particles and agglomerates, and the effect on general flow behavior, are unknown. Experimental and theoretical studies are needed, with the aim of obtaining general relationships between rheological behavior and the fundamental structural and compositional characteristics of particulate systems.

2. Studies of the structure and bonding in agglomerates and green bodies, with special reference to the deformation of agglomerates under applied pressure and to the strength of green bodies. Methods of characterizing agglomerates and green bodies require intensive study and include gas-permeability measurements, x-ray radiography, sound-velocity measurements, dye penetration, and impregnation and microscopy.

3. Fundamental research into the response of particulate systems to applied pressure, and development of methods to eliminate density gradients. Controlled-pressure slip casting and thixotropic casting, for example, offer the potential of uniform flow during consolidation. Mechanical and binder improvements in pressing and extrusion may significantly decrease density gradients.

Final Densification

The character that develops during final densification of a ceramic body is dependent, of course, not only on the specific firing treatment but also on the preceding processing steps and particulate-material character. While this increases the difficulty in correlating firing practice with character, enough work has been performed, as indicated in state of art discussions, to indicate the direction and needs for further effort in densification science and technology.

The Panel agrees with the conclusions reached in MAB report 195-M that the principal areas for which the necessary basic information is lacking are subsolidus equilibria for gases and solids, their effects on transport in crystal lattices, their segregation at grain boundaries, and consequent effects on grain-boundary diffusivities and mobilities.

1. Identification is needed of impurities and their effects on resulting character, especially in very-high-purity and ultrahigh-purity compositions. Impurities control and influence grain boundaries, phase boundaries, and nonstoichiometry. The characterization-of-boundary effects (including the influence of impurities; stresses and strains at boundaries; interactions of dislocation with boundaries; chemical variations at boundaries and surfaces; crystal-structure imperfections, including vacancies; interstitials; ions; electrons; holes in the vicinity of boundaries and surfaces; and space-charge influences near boundaries) are problems requiring a highly competent research approach from both theoretical and experimental points of view. The nature of these problems is similar to the ones related to the characterization of fine particles.

In this area there is a mutual dependence of processing and properties. Boundary effects are important for process and character development, and concurrently the processing methods used affect the boundary characteristics and resulting properties in an important way. Specifically, basic studies are needed of the effect of impurities and particulate character on over-all character evolution. The goal would be to determine the limits to which final body character can be controlled using the best controlled-purity materials available commercially.

2. Subsolidus phase relations and kinetics of phase interactions are important to ceramic processing and go beyond the usual determination of phase-equilibria diagrams, and include: the determination of solid solubility as a function of composition and temperature and the study of nonstoichiometric systems, e.g., metal-oxygen, metal-carbon, metal-boron, and metal-nitrogen.

Recent information indicates that the range of solid-solution stability in some oxide systems is substantially greater than was previously anticipated. Almost all the classic phase-equilibria work has been done measuring liquidus relations;

ceramic phase-equilibrium diagrams show little regard for subsolidus equilibrium in contact with metal systems where such equilibria have long been recognized as essential to controlled processing. Similarly, in systems in which there
is very limited solid solubility, solute segregation effects are found to have a
strong influence on processes taking place during sintering (such as in the development of Lucalox, transparent polycrystalline magnesia, yttallox, and zyttrite).

3. Further effort is required in the specific area of densification research.
The characterization of the changes in microstructure that occur during sintering or liquid-phase sintering would require the independent description, during
density change, of the pore shape and size, and the grain-size changes which
accompany it. There is no material for which a complete description of the
microstructure evolution has been made from the as-fabricated bulk compact
to the final density limit achieved after high-temperature firing. The analyses
of the mechanisms of material transport that have been conducted in many systems have been based on observations of neck growth between spheres, shrinkage
in powder compacts, or densification with observed grain growth during the later
stages of the process. From these studies, it has become apparent that the sintering process should, in general, be interpreted as being a complex mixture of
various mechanisms of material transport that can be operative. The current
understanding of character evolution is, therefore, predominantly empirically
based and systematic studies involving a complete description of evolution
during the various processing stages are required to enhance the understanding
of densification mechanisms and the prospects of predicting and controlling
character development.

The remarks apply as well to densification by hot-forming, where final-stage
densification mechanisms at the lower end of the pressure range are similar to
sintering. Initial-stage densification is not as clearly established, since several
mechanisms may be occurring simultaneously. The over-all densification
mechanisms at the higher end of this pressure range are not clearly established
either, although it is generally conceded that the plastic-deformation characteristics of the higher-symmetry materials become important. Further work
is needed to describe the densification kinetics and character development in
each of these areas. Specific needs are:

a. Determination of the mechanism in which pressing aids, e.g., LiF in MgO,
can dramatically lower the temperature and/or pressure required for full densification. Thorough understanding of this system and the possible extension to
other systems is of significant technological importance.

b. Fundamental studies of densification mechanisms throughout the entire
densification range, using 99.9% minimum-purity material. The role of the
various mechanisms in determining character evolution should be evaluated.
Similar studies should be made in a low-symmetry material (e.g., Al_2O_3) and
a high-symmetry material (e.g., MgO).

The area of preferred orientation in terms of phase, grain, and/or pore
structure deserves special attention. While this is, of course, well developed
in metals systems, current effort in this connection in ceramic technology is
still in a laboratory stage of development. The implications of preferred orientation in ceramic character can have far-reaching significance in the general
area of structural ceramics, as has already been accomplished in electronics
and magnetics. Effort is needed to explore in detail the various methods available for accomplishing preferred orientation, e.g., controlled sintering and hot-
working processes—rolling, forging, extrusion, and pressing, as well as cold-
forming followed by controlled recrystallization.

Scale-up and Quantity Production

In addition to the science and technology aspects cited above, there are special
needs for programs to enhance the capability for size scale-up and quantity
production.

The goal of fundamental understanding of processing is the capability of producing in quantity large or small pieces with desired character and properties, shapes, and dimensions. This capability has not generally been attained because manufacture of large ceramic products frequently presents or aggravates problems that are not serious in small sizes or thin sections. Rejects result from:

1. Nonuniformities of composition, density, and microstructure from point to point in the body and at the surface, which cause nonuniform physical and mechanical characteristics.

2. Presence of cracks, undesirable internal stresses, and other flaws that are large in relation to the microstructure.

3. Nonconformity to dimensional limits.

The problem of the occasional, isolated, large flaw should be emphasized because of our current inability to identify such flaws reliably.

Although fundamental knowledge of the nature and behavior of the material itself is necessary, the fundamental aspects of carrying out desired processes in a controlled way are particularly important in size scale-up or scale-down and quantity production. Some factors are:

1. Designing adequate production equipment.

2. Providing adequate sources and applications of energy to the process.

3. Providing adequate controls at all steps in the production, starting with raw materials and ending with the finishing of the final ceramic piece.

In addition to the areas covered in the discussions on the sciences and technologies underlying processing (which are important in attaining a given character uniformly), mass transfer, heat transfer, and development of internal strains are of importance.

Preconsolidation

Raw-material variability and lack of control and characterization of particles and agglomerates become more important with increasing size of products because these variables cause changes in shrinkage and ultimate properties in different locations of a large object. Problems related to raw-material and agglomerate variability require more sophisticated capability to characterize raw materials and aggregates. These problems have been discussed previously in the section on the areas of science and technology that seriously limit ceramic processing.

Even with adequate knowledge of the fundamental behavior of materials during processing, problems related to quantity production can arise because of batch-to-batch variability of materials and mixing. Invariably, in processing from ore to greenware, material variations occur that affect the characteristics of lots or batches at some points. Problem areas then become:

1. Adequate instrumentation for control of powder quality and variability by continuously monitoring a flow of fine particulate matter in gaseous or liquid suspension.

2. Agglomeration equipment that permits a more controlled range of agglomerate structure and rheological properties than that currently obtained.

3. Chemical-process equipment that duplicates capabilities available on a small scale in chemical-laboratory apparatus.

4. Materials-handling techniques and equipment that economically maintain ultrahigh-purity and uniform rheological behavior of suspensions, pastes, and plastic masses.

5. Comminution equipment that yields a controlled range of particle sizes.

Consolidation

Discussions indicated that present forming or consolidation techniques are, in many cases, inadequate for unusually large sizes. Slip casting of large hardware, although possible, presents difficulties in terms of particle segregation, drainage, inadequate green strength and density, and resulting nonhomogeneity. These may cause unsuitable properties during or after subsequent sintering. This method, however, has capabilities of forming sizes and shapes that are exceedingly difficult to accomplish with pressure-forming methods.

It is considered, for example, worthwhile to recommend the scale-up of shapes to several feet (>10 ft) dimension hardware in the commercial-composition categories. Current art is limited to 5- to 6-ft ware. Potential fabrication methods include slip casting and isopressing, and the state of art is adequate to consider such a project. While it is recognized that no immediate application may exist, the availability of such forms could precipitate their extensive application to radome and deep-submergence areas. The capital equipment requirement is significant and probably not available from private industry.

Scale-up of explosives and pneumatic - mechanical impaction processes does not appear to be an attractive possibility at the present time; fracture problems are dominant with most materials although the methods are useful in producing high-density agglomerates from ultrafine powders.

The yield and product quality - character from current production processes employing dry-pressing and isopressing, for example, can be improved by employing the in-process control measures indicated earlier, i.e., nondestructive test methods (x-ray radiography and ultrasound), to predetermine density gradients and flaws in green microstructure. Further effort is required to determine economic feasibility, and improvements in consolidation processing are needed to diminish or eliminate density-gradient development.

Final Densification

The ability to produce large shapes or large quantities of smaller forms effectively and efficiently is, of course, dependent on particulate character, preconsolidation, consolidation processing, and the actual firing operation, as previously discussed.

However, there are improvements in firing practice that, by themselves, can enhance the prospects for development of controlled-character ceramics. Besides the need for large-scale furnaces to fire ware of greater than 10-ft dimensions, there is a need for better control of temperature and temperature distribution in furnaces. Distortion due to prior processing of density gradients can be compensated for to some extent by improved firing practice. The minimization of contamination by furnace refractories and the control of atmosphere are also recommended as being considered important to investigate in relation to production of ceramic ware.

Recently, the state of art in hot-forming has witnessed significant achievements in terms of:

1. The current production of hot-pressed boron carbide-torso-armor shapes of a 1 to 2 sq ft area with compound curvature.

2. The semicontinuous hot-forming of long rods of dense ferrite materials in alumina dies.

3. The successful development, on a laboratory scale, of isostatic hot-pressing of ceramics.

4. The production of infrared transmitting compounds in a variety of sizes.

Despite these achievements, however, additional effort is required in order to appraise the hot-forming processes effectively in terms of mold life, tolerance control, shape opportunities, and resulting character, which are pertinent to technical-economic exploitation of the process.

Areas of investigation requiring study include:

1. Chemical interactions between die materials and materials to be completed under these conditions. While available thermodynamic data may be used in some instances to predict reactions, the rates for reactions and products of many reactions require empirical determination.

2. Fabrication and evaluation of suitable and reliable hot-forming dies. This

capability is particularly needed for scale-up operations involving uniaxial pressing and hot-extrusion. Potential materials include refractory oxides, carbides, borides, nitrides, and metals. At the present time moderate-pressure hot-pressing is done in graphite dies, which limit the attainable pressure. In the pressure range up to and beyond 100,000 psi and at temperatures up to 1,500°C, there is a clear need for the development of die materials that can be used with a variety of materials for forming materials with controlled character. In the case of hot-extrusion, higher temperatures and pressures may be required, imposing even greater demands on materials. Potential candidates would include refractory carbides and metals and deformation-resistant oxides, possibly in composite form. Development of these dies is necessary in such sizes and mechanical-property specifications that an intensive program for empirical development independent of a particular end-item product is warranted and required.

3. Development of continuous hot-pressing processes. Although the capabilities of hot-pressing have been demonstrated, the relatively high cost associated with its use as a batch process has been a deterrent to the further development and extensive use of this method of forming. The development of hot-pressing as a continuous production tool would play an important part in its use and warrants an empirical approach because of the great complexity of the process equipment.

Effort is also required in the further development of high-pressure isostatic hot-pressing.

Problems associated with the process and requiring investigation fall into the following categories:

1. Interactions between sheath or mandrel material and material being consolidated. This problem is important from the point of view of compatability in terms of chemical reactions, contamination of the bulk ceramic, and thermal expansion.

2. Sheath-material composition, forming, and design. This problem is important from the standpoint of mechanical stability during densification in order to ensure retention of the desired shape. Container composition, design, thickness, and plasticity at densification temperatures influence over-all mechanical stability, and more reliable canning materials and techniques are needed.

3. Vessel materials and design. Performance limits in terms of pressures and temperatures are also determined by vessel composition and design. Development of improved temperature control and uniformity is needed, particularly during pressurization of the autoclave.

ACKNOWLEDGMENTS

Appreciation is expressed to Michael Humenik, Jr. and Thomas J. Whalen of Ford Motor Company, William P. Shulhof and William Flock of General Motors Corporation, and James Hunt of Whittaker Corporation for their assistance as guest contributors at meetings of the Ad Hoc Committee.

BIBLIOGRAPHY

MAB Report 195-M, Ad Hoc Committee on Processing of Ceramic Materials (1963).

Critical Compilation of Ceramic Forming Methods, RTD-TDR-63-4069, January 1964, Univ. of Calif., Berkeley, California.

Critical Evaluation of Ceramic Processing at Sub-Conventional Temperatures, AF 33(615)-5124, Rocketdyne.

A Survey of Firing Processes and Their Critical Influence on Ceramics, AFML-TR-65-281, B.M.I., October 1965.

A Critical Survey of Characterization of Particulate Ceramic Raw Materials, AFML-TR-67-56, Univ. of Calif., Berkeley, California, May 1967.

Raw Materials for Refractory Oxide Ceramics, AFML-TDR-64-110, Univ. of N.C., July 1964.

Alumina Ceramics, AFML-TR-66-13, WPAFB, Ohio, January 1966.

APPENDIX TO CHAPTER 2

ANALYTICAL TECHNIQUES FOR REFRACTORY MATERIALS *

A considerable number of techniques are available for cation and elemental analysis of refractory solids that are sufficiently sensitive and precise to meet the demands of materials scientists. Analyses in the parts-per-million (ppm) range are standard, and analyses in the parts-per-billion (ppb) range are often possible with the limitation that there is a paucity of suitable reference standards. Methods for anion analysis are not nearly so well developed, and commercial materials often contain detailed results for metals and omit consideration of common anion impurities. Examples of such impurities are sulfate, carbonate, nitrate, chloride, and hydroxyl groups.

While the determination of gross impurities of cations may be routine, the determination of location can be extremely difficult in the low-concentration ranges. The microstructure of ceramic materials is generally such that the segregation of impurities at a grain boundary often is found to play a significant role in the properties of the material. The determination of a given impurity at a grain boundary is a difficult problem indeed, and becomes increasingly difficult as we move to considering fine-grained ceramic bodies. In Figure 1, for example, the grain-boundary-hardness profile of NiGa before and after exposure to oxygen is seen to change markedly.[1,2] The determination of the oxygen in the total sample of NiGa is not nearly such a problem as determining the segregation of oxygen at the grain boundary. In this case, there is significant change in hardness at 25 μ from the grain boundary; but if one considers the case where the grain boundary may be only a micron or less in cross section (and this is a large grain boundary for many conventional ceramic materials), then the determination of segregated impurities at this boundary by instrumental techniques such as the electron microprobe is virtually impossible. It is found in an example such as given above that nitrogen as well as oxygen may play a role in grain-boundary hardening, but there are extreme difficulties in analysis to determine nitrogen and oxygen simultaneously in this case, which compounds the difficulty. In general the problem is not so much in detecting the impurity but in determining the location of that impurity.

The instrumentation boom in recent years, which now includes the adaptation of developments from the laser beam to emission-spectrographic and mass-spectrometric analysis, can be utilized at least for determining the location of impurities down to the low-micron region. The electron microprobe can sometimes be used on a cross section as small as one micron, but as yet cannot be used successfully for soft x-ray elements. Thus, some of the elements of greatest interest, such as carbon, boron, oxygen, and nitrogen, cannot be determined routinely unless they constitute major concentrations in the matrix.

*This contribution was provided by Dr. C. T. Lynch, U.S. Air Force liaison representative to the Panel on Solids Processing.

54

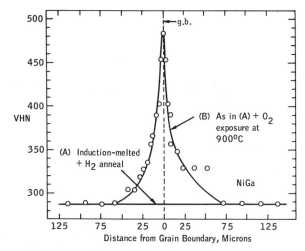

FIGURE 1. Grain-boundary-hardness profile in
MiGa before (A) and after (B) exposure to oxygen

Need for Standards

Before further discussion of some of the newer techniques and their limitations,
it is necessary to realize that no analytical technique is going to be better than
its standards. All materials scientists must be concerned with the lack of refractory-materials standards for doing analysis in the low ppm and ppb ranges.
Reproduced in Table 1 are the entire refractory-materials standards for materials listed in NBS publication 260, which is the catalogue of standard materials
issued by the Office of Standard Reference Materials of the National Bureau of
Standards.[3] Currently the Bureau is working on a series of four glasses that will
be doped with 50 elements at the levels of 50 down to less than 1 ppm. This is
important and should be followed up by serious concern for improving the standards for nonglassy oxides, borides, carbides, nitrides, and intermetallic compounds. Without such work it is useless to consider seriously the development
of ultrahigh-purity ceramic bodies since there really is no accurate basis for
comparing results of analysis on a laboratory-to-laboratory basis. There was
a conference on chemical compounds of certified high purity held in June 1959
at the National Academy of Sciences in Washington, D.C. It was sponsored by
the National Science Foundation and the National Academy of Sciences - National
Research Council. The recommendations made were the typical ones expected
for improving sources of standard materials, the characterization of these materials, and increasing the number of compounds covered in such a program.
Improving communications between individual researchers and materials sources
was also considered important. It took five years to get this report into print as
a government research report,[4] which seems indicative of the general speed
with which we have attacked this serious problem.

There are alloy-base standards such as Cu-base, Ti-base, and Al-base alloys
which in some instances can serve through the low ppm range for standards in
which the matrix of the ceramic does not influence the results. Even the methods
that have been considered relatively free of matrix effects, such as atomic absorption spectroscopy, have recently been found, on closer examination, to have
matrix effects that definitely limit the precision of our results when we start
pushing a given method to its lower sensitivity limits. Perhaps the best method
for matrix-free analysis is an activation analysis. There are other difficulties
with this very sensitive method, however, which are discussed later in this
report.

Table 1. Ceramic Materials[a]

Sample Nos.	Kind	Approximate Weight	Price	Sample Nos.	Kind	Approximate Weight	Price
76	Burned refractory (40% Al_2O_3)	60 g	$10.00	92	Glass, low-boron	45 g	$10.00
77	Burned refractory (60% Al_2O_3)	60 g	10.00	93	Glass, high-boron	45 g	10.00
78	Burned refractory (70% Al_2O_3)	60 g	10.00	165	Glass sand (low iron)	60 g	10.00
103a	Chrome refractory	60 g	10.00	1a	Limestone, argillaceous	50 g	10.00
198	Silica refractory (0.2% Al_2O_3)	45 g	10.00	102	Silica brick	60 g	10.00
199	Silica refractory (0.5% Al_2O_3)	45 g	10.00	104	Burned magnesite	60 g	10.00
89	Glass, lead-barium	45 g	10.00	112	Silicon carbide	85 g	10.00
91	Glass, opal	45 g	10.00	154a	Titanium dioxide	40 g	10.00

ANALYSES

Sample Nos.	Kind	SiO_2	Al_2O_3	Fe_2O_3	FeO	TiO_2	ZrO_2	MnO	P_2O_5
76	Alumina refractory	54.7	37.7	2.4	—	2.2	0.07	—	0.07
77	Alumina refractory	32.4	59.4	0.90	—	2.9	0.09	—	0.45
78	Alumina refractory	20.7	70.0	0.79	—	3.4	0.12	—	0.62
103a	Chrome refractory	4.6	29.96	—	12.43	0.22	0.01	0.11	0.01
198	Silica refractory	—	0.16	0.66	—	0.02	<0.01	<0.01	0.02
199	Silica refractory	—	0.48	0.74	—	0.06	0.01	<0.01	0.01

Sample Nos.	Kind	V_2O_3	Cr_2O_3	CaO	MgO	Li_2O	Na_2O	K_2O	Loss on Ignition
76	Alumina refractory	0.02	—	0.27	0.58	0.11	0.15	1.54	0.22
77	Alumina refractory	0.03	—	0.26	0.50	0.35	0.06	2.11	0.21
78	Alumina refractory	0.05	—	0.38	0.51	0.20	0.06	2.83	0.26
103a	Chrome refractory	—	32.06	0.69	18.54	—	—	—	—
198	Silica refractory	—	—	2.71	0.07	0.001	0.01	0.02	0.21
199	Silica refractory	—	—	2.41	0.13	0.002	0.01	0.09	0.17

GLASS ANALYSES

Sample Nos.	Kind	SiO_2	PbO	Al_2O_3	Fe_2O_3	ZnO	MnO	TiO_2	ZrO_2	CaO	BaO	Loss on Ignition
89	Lead-barium	65.35	17.50	0.18	0.049	—	0.088	0.01	0.005	0.21	1.40	0.32
91	Opal	67.53	0.097	6.01	0.081	0.08	0.008	0.019	0.01	10.48	—	—
93	High-boron	80.60	—	1.94	0.076	—	—	0.027	0.013	—	—	—

Sample Nos.	Kind	MgO	K_2O	Na_2O	B_2O_3	P_2O_5	As_2O_5	As_2O_3	SO_3	Cl	F	Loss on Ignition
89	Lead-barium	0.03	8.40	5.70	—	0.23	0.36	0.03	0.03	0.05	—	0.32
91	Opal	0.008	3.25	8.48	—	0.022	0.102	0.091	—	0.014	5.72	—
92	Low-boron	—	—	—	0.70	—	—	—	—	—	—	—
93	High-boron	0.026	0.16	4.16	12.76	—	0.14	0.085	0.009	0.036	—	—

GLASS-SAND ANALYSIS

Sample No.	Fe_2O_3
165	0.019

Table 1. (continued)

LIMESTONE, SILICA-BRICK, BURNED-MAGNESITE, AND TITANIUM-DIOXIDE ANALYSES

Sample Nos.	Kind	SiO_2	Fe_2O_3	Al_2O_3	TiO_2	MnO	CaO	SrO	MgO	Na_2O
1a	Limestone	14.11	1.63	4.16	0.16	0.038	41.32	0.23	2.19	0.39
102	Silica-brick	93.94	0.66	1.96	0.16	0.005	2.29	—	0.21	0.015
104	Burned-magnesite	2.54	7.07	0.84	0.03	0.43	3.35	—	85.67	0.015
154a	Titanium dioxide	—	—	—	99.6	—	—	—	—	—

Sample Nos.	Kind	K_2O	SO_2	S	P_2O_5	CO_2	C	Loss on Ignition	Density
1a	Limestone	0.71	0.04	0.25	0.15	33.53	0.61	34.55	—
102	Silica-brick	0.32	—	—	0.025	—	—	0.38	2.33 g/cm^3 at 25°C
104	Burned-magnesite	0.015	—	—	0.057	—	—	—	—

SILICON-CARBIDE ANALYSIS

Sample No.	Total Si	Total C	Free C	SiC	Fe	Al	Ti	Zr	Ca	Mg
112	69.11	29.10	0.09	96.85	0.45	0.23	0.025	0.027	0.03	0.02

[a]This group of standards is supplied in the form of powders, usually 100 mesh or finer. They are intended to provide materials for checking the accuracy of methods used in the analysis of similar materials, primarily in the glass and steel industries. Note that Silica-brick No. 102 is a density sample with density of 2.33 g/cm^3 at 25°C.

Method Sensitivity and Precision

Having standards at hand and a well-defined method is not the entire answer either. The analyst must understand the problem sufficiently to use the most appropriate available method and use it correctly. Analytical methods are often developed independently from the requirements of specific applications. The materials scientist in a field such as solids processing of refractory oxides needs to be aware of suitable developing techniques. The instrumentation explosion, a result of the electronic boom following World War II, is making available fantastically precise and sensitive physicochemical tools for the investigator with adequate understanding to take advantage of them. Commercial Nuclear Quadrupole Resonance Spectrometers are now on the market as an example. The spectra, however, are exceedingly complex and, like NMR and other resonance techniques, the results are usually poor for refractory solids.

Gas chromatography is a simple, sensitive, and excellent quantitative tool for volatile-materials analysis. Gas chromatography has great potential for analysis of adsorbed gases, metal chelates such as the β-diketonates, and sufficiently covalent salts such as many metal halides. Thus far it has received limited attention. There are an estimated 50,000 or more gas chromatography units in the world, making it possibly the most widely used instrumental tool, save perhaps the simple colorimeter and pH meter. Quantitative techniques are well established but the 1964 ASTM Committee E-19 got some sobering results when a sample mixture was sent to 32 major analytical alboratories for gas-chromatographic analysis.[5] These are shown in Table 2. Table 3 gives some data from an instrument laboratory on the type of results that can be

Table 2.

Compounds	Actual (%)	Found (%)	Standard Deviation	Relative Standard Deviation
Methyl ethyl ketone	12.0	11.96	0.907	7.6%
Methyl isobutyl ketone	17.2	17.87	3.288	18.3%
Toluene	16.9	17.84	4.516	25.3%
n–Butanol	31.5	30.04	5.666	18.8%
p–Xylene	22.4	22.29	1.885	8.5%

achieved using various quantitative methods.[5] Since the standards in Table 1 were accurately known to the 0.1% level, the relative standard deviation is also a measure of the relative accuracy of measurement. Now if we consider that the method is capable of 0.1 to 1% relative standard deviation as seen in Table 3, a 25% deviation for a simple hydrocarbon like toluene or 19% on n-butanol is discouraging. When a method such as emission spectroscopy is utilized, relative errors of 10% or more are expected in the ppm range. Practical errors on a laboratory-to-laboratory basis often exceed 100%. This is seldom considered by the scientist when an analyst's report is in front of him. Where no standard samples are available, it is impossible to perform a routine quantitative analysis on 20 or 30 elements in a matrix and come even close to the 10% figure. In these cases a 100% relative deviation is often optimistic. These thoughts must temper the "expert's" enthusiasm as he hopefully approaches more sensitive methods at the ppb level.

Electrical Methods—Problems in Nonspecificity

In addition to providing analytical data, a useful method should have some universality—an adaptability of determination in a variety of matrices. The method should also be commercially available. Electrical methods of analysis are at once singularly precise and sensitive, often are nondestructive, and are rapid. A list of a number of these methods and estimated detectability limits is given in Table 4.[6] Residual resistivity and the resistivity ratio ($R_{4.2°K}$ to $R_{273°K}$) are useful in determining purification of ultrahigh-purity materials. The use of electrical methods, however, is limited by the problem of nonspecificity. The Hall effect and conductance values do not tell the investigator what carriers

Table 3. Comparison of Integration Methods

	1	2	3	Average	σ absolute	σ relative
MODEL 471 DIGITAL INTEGRATOR						
n–Nonane	39.156	39.150	39.193	39.166	0.0716	0.184%
n–Decane	60.844	60.850	60.807	60.834	0.0227	0.037%
DISC INTEGRATOR						
n–Nonane	39.33	38.97	38.91	39.07	0.22	0.56%
n–Decane	60.67	61.03	61.09	60.93	0.23	0.38%
TRIANGULATION						
n–Nonane	40.77	40.68	40.07	40.51	0.38	0.94%
n–Decane	59.23	59.32	59.93	59.49	0.39	0.66%
WEIGHING PAPER						
n–Nonane	42.58	41.73	42.83	42.38	0.58	1.37%
n–Decane	57.42	58.27	57.17	57.62	0.58	1.01%

Table 4. Electrical Methods

Sensitivity Limit (M/liter)	Method
10^{-4}, 10^{-5}	AC polarography, chronopotentiometry, thin-layer coulometry
10^{-5}, 10^{-6}	Coulometry at controlled V, classical polarography, specific electrodes
10^{-6}, 10^{-7}	Linear sweep, derivative polarography, eddy-current decay
10^{-7}, 10^{-8}	Pulse polarography, amperometry, coulometric titrations
10^{-8}, 10^{-9}	Anodic stripping with hanging Hg drop
10^{-9}, 10^{-10}	Anodic stripping with thin-film electrodes or solid electrodes

are in the material. The results are nonselective. High-purity germanium, as originally developed, had 50 ppm of oxygen in it, but no one knew it was there because electrical measurements insensitive to oxygen constituted the test. The determination of the purity of water is a common example, where the nonconductor organics must be analyzed separately, otherwise conductivity water is not necessarily very pure. Electrical measurements for general determination of impurity distributions, purification, and general purity have great usefulness to refractory inorganic materials if the limitations are understood.

Ion-specific electrodes with treated membranes have considerable potential for future development. Electrodes are currently available for determinations of Cl^- to 10^{-5} moles per liter (M), Br^- to 10^{-6} M, I^- to 10^{-7} M, and Ag^+ to 10^{-6} M. New electrodes are being developed for sulfate, phosphate, sulfide, fluoride, and a variety of common metals.[7,8] The possibility for anion analysis makes this development particularly interesting. Hall effect and magnetic-susceptibility measurements have been made sufficiently to show their usefulness in studying variations in stoichiometry in some interstitial hard-metal compounds.

Wet-Chemical Methods

Wet-chemical methods are the backbone for standardization of instrumental techniques, a factor often overlooked by instrumentation analysts. Many wet-chemical methods have applicability to refractory-materials analysis through techniques of microanalysis. The field of catalytic analysis has been generally neglected but offers an excellent tool for low-ppm-range analysis. When, as is the general case, the catalytic reaction is first order with respect to the catalyst and the uncatalyzed path is of negligible rate, the rate of reaction for a great many reactions is proportional to the amount of catalyst present. Some examples are the determination of 0.1 to 10 ppm of iodide in solid sodium chloride utilizing iodide catalysis of the Ce(IV) oxidation of As(III).[9] The decomposition of H_2O_2 in alkaline medium is catalyzed by Mn, Pd, and Cu, providing a method for analysis of these metals by measurement of oxygen evolution with time.[10] Copper can also be determined at the ppm to parts per thousand (ppt) levels by the catalysis of the Fe(III) reaction with thiosulphate. Fe can be determined by its catalysis of the oxidation of p-phenylene diamine by H_2O_2.[11] The reaction of H_2O_2 with iodide in acid medium is catalyzed by many metals and has been studied for the determination of Mo, W, Fe, and V.[12] A prior separation is necessary in such a nonspecific case as this, but the sensitivity for Mo in terms of minimum detectability has been reported as 2.6×10^{-9} M, which is extremely low, i.e., in the ppb range.

The problems of determining free carbon in carbides and free boron in borides, and the general methods of refractory hard-metal analysis are in large measure those of wet chemistry.[13] The Kjeldahl method, sometimes reported in reviews as inadequate for nitrogen determination because nitride nitrogen is determined, is a good illustration. Nitrogen present in nitro or nitrate forms can be determined by prior sample treatment with a salicylic acid - sulfuric acid mixture followed by a reduction of the nitro compounds to amines with thiosulfate.[14]

One of the major problems in analysis is the determination of free carbon in the carbides and free boron in the borides. The insolubility of free graphitic carbon in acid mixtures that can be used to dissolve these compounds is widely used as a method of analysis. Critical evaluation of results indicates there is a small error due to incomplete dissolution of the sample and/or partial oxidation of the graphite. The method of determining free carbon is, however, superior to the methods that have been developed for determining free boron in the borides. New wet-chemical methods have been developed in recent years, however, for some of these compounds. Free boron has been determined in boron carbide by a method based on the different rates of oxidation in acid solution of free boron and carbide-bonded boron.[15] The oxidation of amorphous boron into boric acid has been used to determine free boron in zirconium diboride, with a relative error of less than 1%.[16] In this particular study a hydrogen peroxide - nitric acid solution was employed. This solution and other oxidizing solutions such as potassium iodate, cerium sulfate, and sulfuric acid, partially dissolved refractory diborides of titanium, niobium, and tantalum, for example, so that an accurate free-boron analysis was not achieved.[16] More work should be done on differential-dissolution techniques to develop a satisfactory free-boron determination for all these compounds. A simplification in metal determination in refractory borides has been reported wherein the metal is complexed and the boron titrated directly.[17] This eliminates a precipitation step in the determination. Another new technique is pyrohydrolysis to determine total boron as the acid. The latter method eliminates the solubilization step.[18]

Difficulties in the analysis of ZrB_2-$MoSi_2$ composites are apparent from the results of wet-chemical analyses recently obtained.[19] This is an example of refractory material on which data generation was being accomplished where the chemical techniques of analysis were inadequate. The analytical results were so erratic that attempts were made to use emission-spectrographic and electron-microprobe techniques for quantitative determinations. Neither of these methods is comparable in precision to wet analytical methods.

Before proceeding to the new instrumental techniques, a few further examples of analytical problems should be considered to delineate some of the demands now being made.

Phase Equilibria and Stoichiometry

The zirconium-carbon phase diagram shown in Figure 2 is particularly interesting because of the broad single-phase field of zirconium carbide from 38.5 to approximately 50 atomic percent carbon.[20] This is an interstitial compound where carbon atoms occupy the interstitial sites of the fcc lattice. The significance of this broad homogeneity range is that approximately one-fourth of the interstitial sites can be empty without a change in phase. Extreme care must be exercised in preparing a zirconium-carbide body with given stoichometry. Zirconium carbide is presented here as an example of the specificity that may be demanded in the process step when the material of desired characteristics is close to a phase boundary.[21] For zirconium carbide, a material containing 39 atomic percent carbon would not melt below 3,300°C, although a body containing 38 atomic percent carbon would produce a liquid phase at 1,850°C. In the zirconium-carbide system this 1 atomic percent difference in carbon is equivalent to approximately 3.5 ppt by weight. This small weight change is extremely dif-

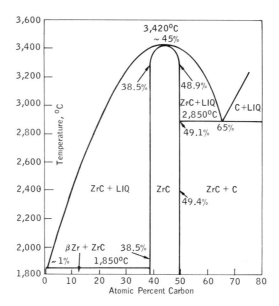

FIGURE 2. Zirconium-carbon phase diagram

ficult to control in the complicated operation of high-temperature processing. At the other side of the zirconium-carbide homogeneity region, the boundary between zirconium carbide and zirconium carbide plus carbon changes with temperature from 49.4 at 2,400°C to 48.9 at 3,250°C. A starting composition of single-phase zirconium carbide containing over 49.1 atomic percent carbon would contain a liquid phase at 2,850°C, which is 500°C below the expected melting point for the material. Since impurities may affect the zirconium-carbon ratio, they become increasingly important whenever a material with a composition close to the phase boundary is desired.

The stoichiometry of compounds of AgMg and NiAl has a tremendous effect on the ductility of the material. A fractional excess of these two, Mg or Al, embrittles their respective intermetallics and significantly increases the grain-boundary hardness over the grain-bulk hardness. In Figures 3 and 4, the variation of hardness with stoichiometry for these intermetallics is shown.[22] Ternary solute additions have been found to modify the grain-boundary hardening effect, which further complicates the consideration of the mechanism responsible for increased hardness. The point is well taken, however, that stoichiometry and the specific nature and location of the impurities in these intermetallic compounds are often the most important factors determining strength and duc-

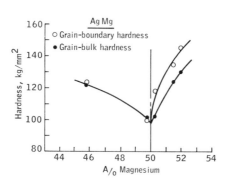

FIGURE 3. Bulk and grain-boundary hardness of AgMg as a function of composition

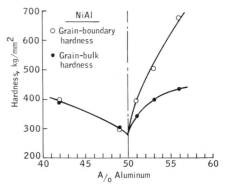

FIGURE 4. Bulk and grain-boundary hardness of NiAl as a function of composition

tility. The demands placed on analysis are being met by improvised alterations to existing wet analytical techniques.

The determination of nitrogen at the grain boundary was accomplished by a controlled dissolution of the individual grains at a measured rate, followed by determination of nitrogen in the dissolved sample. It is difficult to determine oxygen and nitrogen simultaneously.[23] A method for this determination in refractory metals was recently reported using a dc-carbon-arc gas-chromatographic technique.[24] The refractory metal was fused with a platinum flux, and the liberated oxygen and nitrogen were analyzed by gas chromatography. This is an example of a recent approach to refractory metals, which might have interesting ramifications in the analysis of inorganic materials and intermetallic compounds. The measurement of rate of evolution of the gas vs time should give equally good analytical data for grain-boundary vs matrix impurities as are obtained by time-dissolution experiments. Since the analysis is by gas chromatography, the results would be much easier to obtain.

Instrumental Methods

The workhorse method for instrumental analysis is emission spectroscopy, which serves as an excellent qualitative tool but has definite quantitative analytical limitations. Inherent in this analysis is the problem of electric spark-arc stability. The laser-beam microprobe certainly offers an additional tool for microanalysis of ceramic materials. Used in conjunction with an emission spectrograph it gives localized impurity analyses of a volume of material 50 μ in diameter by 25 μ in depth. With further refinement, this area-depth limit can currently be reduced to half, and potentially a 1 to 2 μ cross section must be considered possible. The sensitivity limit of emission spectroscopy is close to 1 ppm for most elements. The demands for low ppm into ppb-range analyses have led to increased use of more sensitive techniques for trace analysis. Foremost of these is the mass spectrograph. New sources for utilizing the mass spectrograph for refractory materials are the spark and the ion beam.[25] Ppb sensitivities are easily obtained for all elements except adsorbed gases (e.g., O_2, N_2, and trace hydrocarbons) and water, where the background interference is severe. For other elements a 1 ppb sensitivity limit is the experimental limit when good technique is used to enhance signal-noise ratio. An example of this is the split-plate technique to reduce fogging of analytical plate by the high intensity of the primary beam of the matrix element(s). At a routine nominal 20-kV excitation potential, consideration must be given to the variable energy distribution of ions of various materials. Ions may be present at 18-22 kV for an element such as Si and sharply close to 20 kVA for Ge. This gives rise to relative sensitivity coefficients, and results must be corrected accordingly. Difficulties in trace analysis from laboratory to laboratory become apparent in the large scatter in results using spark-source double-focusing mass spectrographs. Knowing a trace element to a factor of 10 is often the case under favorable conditions. Some problems encountered are due to the small amount of material sparked and analyzed, which is not representative of the whole sample. Most standards in practice are not homogeneous under such mass-spectrographic analysis. Results for matrix elements are always considerably better, and have been reported within 5% standard deviations for ideal examples. On the positive side is the use of spark-source mass spectrometry to determine impurities in nonconducting ceramics.[26] A high-purity gold probe was placed close to MgO in conducting mount. With a minimum projection of the MgO beyond the sample holder, a 50 kV, 1 Mc rf spark was struck between the gold probe and the MgO, producing a low-yield spark. As the sample temperature increased, a high-yield spark was obtained. The probe may be moved about to analyze different regions. A conducting matrix is not necessary for the analysis, but all other method limitations apply.

62

Neutron-activation analysis is an extremely sensitive tool for trace analysis and should be widely employed whenever standard methods can be established.[27] Advantages include the lack of matrix effects, which makes standards simple and obtainable; the use of large or small samples; high precision and accuracy (better than ±10% relative precision routinely); and no need for sample preconcentration or pretreatment. Difficulties include the nature of equipment required, with the associated radiation hazards. The specimen, after activation, often contains long-lived isotopes that make subsequent routine handling impossible. Some isotopes (such as one for F with τ 1/2 of 10 seconds) have such short half-lives that short irradiation times are necessary, which creates experimental problems with other isotopes requiring longer irradiation before obtaining the gamma-ray spectra.

Many light elements are not adequately activated by thermal neutrons (C, N, and O, e.g.) and need high-energy gamma-ray activation (using a linear accelerator). This produces short-lived isotopes, which are hard to discriminate spectrally. Sensitivity is also much lower using a linear accelerator (by a factor of 100, which puts many ppb limits back in the ppm range). Some activities such as ^{24}Na produce gamma spectra that interfere with and obscure other activities. For these reasons, the emergence of atomic-absorption spectroscopy coupled with the classic flame-emission technique for lighter elements seem to offer much more potential. The technique is almost as sensitive as neutron activation. Matrix effects are fairly small, and development of standards is not difficult. The method is very good quantitatively, utilizes simple apparatus, and is rapid and reproducible. For refractory-materials analysis it should become a principal quantitative tool following qualitative - quantitative estimate work by emission spectroscopy.[28]

The range of coverage and sensitivity for the atomic-absorption and flame-emission techniques as recently reported is indicated in Figure 5. This application is extremely broad already, after only a few years of commercial development. Hollow cathode lamps are now available for some 70 elements, and multiple-element lamps are being made. One is now made, for example, for Cr, Co, Cu, Fe, Mn, and Ni. Another is available for Ba, Sr, Ca, and Mg. Over 25 such combinations are produced. As multibeam pass instruments are developed, simultaneous determination of a number of elements will be possible by atomic absorption, as can now be done with x-ray fluorescence. X-ray fluorescence per se is not a good trace-analysis tool for most elements, owing to significant matrix effects. The detection limits for a number of elements are given in Table 5.[28] A recent comprehensive study of igneous-rock standards by atomic-absorption and x-ray fluorescence analysis for principle elements shows the former method equally as good on a routine basis for principle elements. For trace elements in igneous materials, results were favorable to those obtained

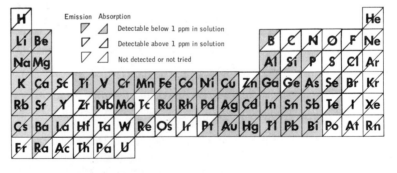

FIGURE 5. Detectability of the elements of emission and atomic-absorption flame photometry.

Table 5. Detection Limits in Atomic Absorption

Detection Limit (μg/ml)	Element	DetectionLimit (μg/ml)	Element
0.5	Aluminum[a]	0.01	Manganese
0.2	Antimony	0.5	Mercury
1.0	Arsenic	0.2	Molybdenum
1.0	Barium	0.05	Nickel
0.05	Beryllium[a]	1.0	Palladium
0.2	Bismuth	0.5	Platinum
0.01	Cadmium	0.005	Potassium
0.01	Calcium	0.3	Rhodium
0.05	Cesium	0.02	Rubidium
0.01	Chromium	1.0	Selenium
0.15	Cobalt	0.02	Silver
0.005	Copper	0.005	Sodium
1.0	Gallium	0.02	Strontium
0.1	Gold	0.5	Tellurium
0.5	Indium	1.0	Titanium[a]
0.05	Iron	0.2	Thallium
0.15	Lead	2.0	Tin
0.005	Lithium	0.5	Vanadium[a]
0.003	Magnesium	0.005	Zinc

[a]Requires organic solvent and oxyacetylene burner.

colorimetrically. This is indicative of the broad range over which atomic-absorption analysis can function. It is the specificity of the spectral determination that makes it superior to colorimetric methods. Very few color complexes can be found specific to one element, making prior sample treatment necessary to separate interferences. In atomic absorption the low degree of experienced matrix effects makes the spectral determination specific only to the element employed in the hollow-cathode source lamp.

Infrared spectroscopy is usually thought of in terms of organic analysis. The development of instruments for analysis in the medium- and far-infrared regions of the spectrum place many inorganic compounds within analytical possibility. The refractory oxides have significant spectral changes in the medium-infrared region for phase changes, such as anatase and rutile TiO_2, and mono-clinic and cubic ZrO_2. Figure 6[29] shows the change in frequency of a principal absorption peak obtained for various rare-earth oxides in the 500 to 600 cm^{-1} region. As yet, the infrared spectra of refractory compounds has received limited attention.

Nuclear magnetic resonance has generally proven disappointing in studying inorganic solids. As magnets get larger, however, the potential for useful analyses should increase. Nuclear quadrupole resonance is insufficiently developed at this stage for any conclusions on its usefulness for these materials. It is an extremely complex method to understand, though, which places limits on its impact. The achievement of measuring the existence of gamma-ray emission without recoil of the admitting or absorbing nucleus ranks as a central advance of this decade. The Mössbauer effect is of tremendous importance because the supremely sharp gamma-ray lines enable measurements of the Mössbauer effect with great precision. Very small influences on the nuclear electric and magnetic properties can be detected. The method has a definite applicability to inorganic solids, commercial instruments are now available, and as more scientists become familiar with the techniques and interpretation, it should develop into an important tool. It is essential that interest in analysis of trace elements be translated into experiments to build a base of experience for the method. Light elements are unsatisfactory, however, because gamma-ray energies E

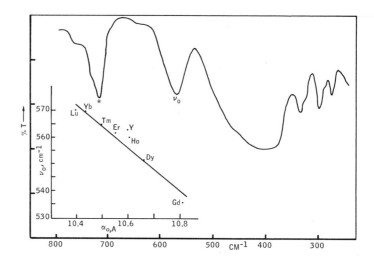

FIGURE 6. Spectrum of a normal type C rare-earth oxide, ytterbia (graph shows a plot of frequency against unit-cell dimension of type C oxides)

tend to be high, increasing the recoil energy ($\sim E^2$). In this case, light elements include all the first three principal series elements and some of the transition elements, which makes it an important limitation.

X-ray diffraction is an applicable tool when the cross section for analysis is fairly large. On a practical basis, this limit is often as large as 40 μ, and it is difficult to realize effective analyses at less than 20 μ. This means that the present state of the art of the current techniques is such that it cannot be used to determine localized impurities or segregated phases in fine-grained materials. The development of electron-microscope equipment with electron-diffraction devices, however, has provided a tool for analyzing below 1 μ in cross section for a skilled operator using thin-film-transmission, or, in some cases, reflection techniques. This method must be considered as potentially the most exciting of the instrumental methods for locational analysis.

The electron microprobe can routinely analyze to cross sections of 1 μ with a limitation that elements of low atomic number ([11]Na and below) cannot be satisfactorily analyzed. Soft x-ray methods are available that can be used to analyze for the light elements provided reasonable concentrations (for example, 1% C in Fe) are present. When one considers trace analysis, however, light-element determinations by the electron microprobe are very unsatisfactory. An indirect method of measuring the beam current from the specimen is used to estimate light-element concentrations, since the backscatter electron effect in the specimen is proportional to the average atomic number of the material on which the beam impinges. This, of course, is a qualitative method and cannot be considered good quantitative practice. The laser beam and the ion beam can be used as source exciters for a number of instrumental methods. Some mention has already been made of this, and there are additional possibilities, such as the use of the laser beam with a mass spectrograph. This has been used with good results on graphite analysis.[30] A laser beam could also be coupled with atomic-absorption equipment, thus eliminating problems associated with the flame and offering locational determination. Practical limits of cross sections with a laser beam are thus far unsatisfactory, but it should be within the state of the art to develop a 1-μ cross-section capability.

In conclusion, the purpose of this report is to give some dimension to the problems associated with developing satisfactory techniques for trace analysis of refractory solids. Without attempting to cover every possible method or potentially interesting method, it is hoped that a sufficient breadth and depth have been given to this treatment so that reasonable conclusions may be drawn.

REFERENCES

1. A. U. Seybolt and J. H. Westbrook, Acta Met., 12, 449, 1964.
2. A. U. Seybolt and J. H. Westbrook, "Oxygen-Induced Grain Boundary Hardening in the Intermetallic Compounds AgMg, NiGa, and NiAl," Plansee Proceedings, 1964.
3. NBS Publication 260. Office of Standard Reference Materials, NBS, Washington, D.C. Available from U.S. Govt. Printing Office, Washington, D.C., 20402.
4. Report on Conference on Chemical Compounds of Certified High Purity, NAS, 22-23 June 1959, Washington, D.C. NSF, NAS-NRC, 1964.
5. J. M. Gill and H. M. McNair, Aerograph Research Notes, 1, Fall, 1965.
6. H. A. Laitinen, "Trace Characterization by Electrochemical Methods," Trace Characterization, Chemical and Physical, 75-107, NBS Monograph 100, edited by W. W. Meinke and B. F. Scribner, U.S. Govt. Printing Office, Washington, D.C., 1967.
7. E. Pungor, J. Havas, and K. Toth, Z. Chem., 5, 9 (1965).
8. G. A. Rechnitz, M. R. Kresz, and S. B. Zamochnick, Anal. Chem., 38, 973, 1966.
9. E. B. Sandell and I. M. Kolthoff, Microchim. Acta, 1, 9, 1937.
10. T. Shiokarva and S. Suzuki, Sci. Rep. RITU, 3, 419, 1951.
11. H. Goto and S. Suzuki, Sci. Rep. RITU, 3, 429, 1951.
12. K. B. Yatsimirskii and L. P. Afanaseva, J. Anal. Chem. (USSR), 11 [3], 327, 1956. [English Translation]
13. O. W. Kriege, "The Analysis of Refractory Borides, Carbides, Nitrides, and Silicides," Los Alamos Scientific Laboratory, LA-2306, 1959.
14. W. C. Pierce and E. L. Haenisch, Quantitative Analysis, 3rd edition, 140, John Wiley and Sons, Inc., New York, 1948.
15. Ye. Ye. Kotlyar and T. N. Nazarchuk, J. Anal. Chem. (USSR), 15, 207, 1960.
16. L. N. Kugay, "Chemical Properties and Methods of Analyzing Borides of Transition and Rare Earth Metals," Trans. Acad. Sci. Ukranian SSR, Institute of Metal Ceramics and Special Alloys. Seminar on Heat-Resistant Materials, No. 6, Kiev, 1961.
17. V. G. Shcherbakov, R. M. Veytsman, and Z. K. Stegendo, "Analysis of Titanium, Chromium, and Zirconium Borides," Trans. Acad. Sci. Ukranian SSR, Institute of Metal Ceramics and Special Alloys. Seminar on Heat-Resistant Materials, No. 6, Kiev, 1961.
18. L. M. Litz and R. A. Mercuri, J. Electrochem. Soc., 110, 921, 1963.
19. F. M. Anthony and W. H. Dukes, "Selection Techniques for Brittle Materials," Bell Aerosystems Company Report No. 2178-900204, June 1964.
20. R. V. Sarah, C. E. Lowell, R. T. Dolloff, "Research Study to Determine the Phase Equilibrium Relations of Selected Metal Carbides at High Temperatures," WADD TR 60-143, Part IV, February 1963.
21. C. T. Lynch and J. J. Krochmal, RTD Technology Briefs, 1, [10], 1, 1963.
22. J. H. Westbrook and D. L. Wood, "Effect of Basic Physical Parameters on Engineering Properties of Intermetallic Compounds," WADD TR 60-184, Part III, July 1962.
23. E. Booth, F. S. Bryant, and A. Parker, Analyst, 82, 50, 1957.
24. R. K. Winge and V. A. Fassel, Anal. Chem., 37, 67, 1965.
25. G. D. Nicholls, A. L. Graham, E. Williams, and M. Wood, Anal. Chem., 39, 584, 1967.
26. A. J. Socha and M. H. Leipold, J. Am. Ceram. Soc., 48, 463, 1965.
27. A. A. Smales, "Radioactivity Techniques in Trace Characterization," pp. 307-336, in Trace Characterization, Chemical and Physical, NBS Monograph 100, edited by W. W. Meinke and B. F. Seribner, U.S. Govt. Printing Office, Washington, D.C., 1967.
28. Data on atomic absorption taken primarily from several recent issues of the Atomic Absorption Newsletter.
29. N. T. McDevitt and W. L. Baun, "A Study of the Absorption Spectra of Simple Metal Oxides in the Infrared Region 700 to 240 cm^{-1}," RTD-TDR 63-4172, January 1964.
30. P. D. Zavitsanos and L. E. Brewer, "Chemi-Ionization and Chemi-Excitation in the Oxidation of Gaseous Carbon," G. E. Rpt. R 66SD64, December 1966.

PANEL ON SOLIDS PROCESSING

THOMAS VASILOS, <u>Chairman</u>
Manager, Material Sciences Department
Avco Space Systems Division

Members

ROBERT LOUIS COBLE
Associate Professor, Ceramics
Department of Metallurgy
Massachusetts Institute of Technology

LAURENCE E. FERREIRA
Director of Research
Coors Porcelain Company

DOUGLAS W. FUERSTENAU
Professor, Metallurgy
Department of Mineral Technology
University of California

S. EDWARD HATCH
Eastman Kodak Company
A&O Division, Research Department – Hawkeye

LIAISON MEMBER FROM THE MATERIALS ADVISORY BOARD
AD <u>HOC</u> COMMITTEE ON CERAMIC PROCESSING

ALEXIS G. PINCUS
Scientific Advisor
Ceramics Research
Illinois Institute of Technology Research Institute

LIAISON REPRESENTATIVES

MORTON I. KLIMAN
C&OM Division, AMXRE-CMR
U.S. Department of the Army
Natick Laboratories

C. T. LYNCH
Air Force Materials Laboratory
U.S. Department of the Air Force
Wright-Patterson Air Force Base

ARAM TARPINIAN
(Army Liaison Representative from
August 25, 1965 to September 1966)

IRVING MACHLIN
Materials Engineer
Naval Air Systems Command
Materials and Processes Branch
U.S. Department of the Navy

HUBERT B. PROBST
National Aeronautics and Space
  Administration
Lewis Research Center

PROFESSIONAL STAFF

DONALD G. GROVES
Staff Engineer
Materials Advisory Board

CHAPTER 3

Report of the Panel on Fluid Processing

ABSTRACT

This panel report documents an intensive study of the characteristics, capabilities, and limitations of fluid processes for the fabrication of ceramics—those processes in which the immediate precursor of the solid product is largely or completely in the liquid or vapor state.

For achieving maximum qualities of performance, uniformity, and reproducibility of oxide ceramics in respect to structural-applications needs of the Department of Defense, the most broadly promising and versatile fluid processes fall in the glass-forming and glass-crystallization, single-crystal, chemical-vapor-deposition, and molten-particle-spray classifications. Of these general process types, the first and last are the least costly, and the inherent capability of the last is the least clear because of its relatively primitive foundation in scientific understanding at the present time. Numerous individual fluid processes have excellent potential for satisfying specific combinations of character and configuration.

A list of pertinent areas of basic research and a program of applied research and engineering development are recommended relative to oxide ceramics for structural applications, through advancement of fluid processing capability and through the foundation of process development in a science of ceramic processing. Most of the recommended research utilizes aluminum oxide and refractory-glass compositions.

SUMMARY OF RECOMMENDATIONS

Fluid processing of oxide ceramics is usually freed from dependence on the physical nature and behavior of particulates. A number of such processes are capable of the incremental building up of a dense mass, providing a unique resource for coating, surface-finishing, and joining, as well as an opportunity to form very large shells or sheets of high uniformity. Fiber and filamentary forms of oxides are only obtainable by these means. The vitreous or glassy state, the single crystal, and the short-range-order internal structure are achievable in most cases exclusively by fluid processes. In polycrystalline oxides, both single- and multiphase, certain of these processes yield finer and more uniform microstructures than can be approached by the processing of particulates. In many cases, zero or near-zero porosity is typical.

A number of structural ceramics of present importance to the Department of Defense are made by fluid processing: bulk glass and crystallized glass, coating materials, glass monofilament, boron coaxial monofilament, bulk single crystals, and short single-crystal fibers. Many more refractory and structural applications of fluid-processed oxides are possible if appropriate research is conducted to remove certain processing deficiencies, to increase levels of product performance, or to adapt known methods to economical production of desired configurations.

Approximately forty-five variants of fluid processing were recognized in an intensive survey of process capabilities and limitations. Attention has been given to those types of processes that exhibit good prospects for achieving superior mechanical performance, uniformity, and reproducibility in their oxide products, on grounds of their physicochemical nature and the controllability of their parameters. In each case, opportunities for enhancement of these and other qualities, such as ability to form special configurations, were listed and the appropriate research identified. These processes were then examined for suitability of their products to recognized, important structural-applications needs of the Department of Defense, and the number of research objectives was accordingly reduced.

Program of Applied Research and Engineering Development

A Priority Program of Applied Research and Engineering Development of Fluid Processes for oxide ceramics was thus constructed, every task of which recognizes the needs of the Department of Defense and the inherent opportunities of fluid processing for fabricating candidate materials of improved performance and reliability over present levels. In most cases, superior qualities of uniformity and reproducibility can already be achieved. In any event, the approaches to higher performance and to these qualities are the same: systematic research into combinations of material composition and rigidly controlled processing parameters, guided by extensive and sophisticated characterization and definitive property testing. In a number of cases, such systematic investigations of the process - parameter ⟶ character ⟶ property relations have never been performed; consequently, the potential of these fluid processes has never been realized.

This Applied Research and Development Program consists of eight areas of investigation of a variety of kinds, depending on the nature of the need and the capabilities of the candidate process considered. Where technological achievement seems likely, process economy dominates. Where the probability of achievement is more difficult to assess, process economy is ignored and redundancy of exploratory investigations is built in. The benefits obtainable through pursuit of the recommended program include:

1. High likelihood of major and timely improvements in oxide-ceramic technology and of the exploitation of these improvements in various systems.

2. Saving of future wasted effort otherwise attendant on hasty material and process development conducted within hardware programs.

3. Accumulation and spreading of an increased rate of ceramic-technology advancement through its firm foundation in scientific knowledge and method.

The recommended program is subdivided into two groups of four task areas, those in the first group addressed to bulk forms of oxides and those in the second group to four other ceramic-oxide configurations of importance. It is recommended that all of the first group be undertaken at one time, and that individual tasks from the second group be mounted at appropriate times thereafter, in order to preserve the values of coordination and mutual support designed into the Program. Other recommendations are:

1. Preservation of the listed initial research objectives as separate from any immediate and specific hardware goal; if possible, administration of all tasks of Group I as a coherent program, as opposed to disjointed individual projects.

2. Inclusion in all tasks of extensive use of material characterization and process-parameter measurement throughout processing, and of interpretation of process ⟶ character and character ⟶ property relationships based on the most sophisticated scientific knowledge available.

3. Investigation of process ⟶ character ⟶ property relations in respect to variability (uniformity, reproducibility) as well as to mean values; interpretation leading to effective, instrumented process control.

4. Attention to validity of property test methods, as to both mean values and variation.

The eight recommended R&D areas are listed below.

GROUP I: BULK CONFIGURATIONS

1. Simultaneously investigate and explore new refractory, high-modulus glass compositions (probably nonsilicate) and techniques of nucleation and crystallization to yield extremely fine grain size ($\lesssim 0.01\mu$) upon complete crystallization. The ultimate objective is bulk form. Special problems will attend the handling and forming of molten refractory material in addition to those of controlling nucleation and crystal growth and avoiding premature devitrification.

2. Investigate systematically all the process variables of: an electric-flame (i.e., "plasma") method; and the liquid-fuel-fired method of high-velocity molten-particle spray deposition of Al_2O_3, including the use of programmed substrate heating and postfabrication annealing. The objective is a large, thick (to 1 in.), dense free-standing body of high strength, consistent with high deposition rates. Special problems will be: elimination of porosity and achievement of good interparticle bonding; uniform particle temperature, velocity, and size; atmosphere; and mold parting.

In addition, two follow-ons are recommended for consideration as these first tasks mature: spraying of refractory-crystallizable glass compositions, as a means of quenching in the vitreous state for subsequent crystallization; and spraying of admixtures of Al_2O_3 or glass with an extremely finely subdivided foreign phase (C, Pt metals, refractory metals, or carbides) for grain-growth inhibition.

3. Investigate chemical vapor deposition (CVD), or combined physical vapor deposition (PVD) and CVD methods, for depositing Al_2O_3, or for codepositing Al_2O_3 with inert foreign atoms (e.g., C, Pt metals) to yield 1/4 in.- to 1/2 in.-thick free-standing bodies of high density and extremely fine grain size, high modulus, and high strength. Special problems will be reagent control, nodular and uneven growth, mold-parting, and internal stress.

4. Develop shaped-crystal techniques for growing single-crystal Al_2O_3, spinel, or yttrium aluminum garnet, directly in useful form and nearly to tolerance, e.g.: shaped-crucible variant of the melt-freezing method to form blanks approximating finished articles such as turbine blades or leading edges; and a float variant of the melt-freezing method to form discs or sheets approximating windows. Requirements include high strength, high bulk and surface perfection, and often transparency. Special problems will be crucible reuse, heat-flow control, and economy.

GROUP II: SPECIAL CONFIGURATIONS

1. Joining of Ceramics. Develop techniques for high-strength butt welding of 1/4 in.- to 1/2 in.-thick Al_2O_3 sheet stock by high-velocity molten-particle spray processes, including the use of controlled substrate temperature. This area of study depends on and must follow task I-2.

2. Fiber and Filamentary Ceramics for Reinforcing. Advance techniques for the production of long fibers and, especially, monofilament forms of oxides. Objectives are high elastic modulus, high strength, and preservation of these qualities to high temperatures. Recommended approaches include the following:

(a) Investigation of crystal-withdrawal techniques, by the freezing or flux method, to grow single crystals (Al_2O_3 or other) in continuous-filament or long-fiber configurations. Special problems attend virtually every aspect of these processes.

(b) Investigation of CVD methods to form, on a refractory-metal wire, a coaxial Al_2O_3 or Al_2O_3-base composite coating of extremely fine grain size or short-range-order (SRO) structure and full density. Special problems will be the danger of "snowing out," uniformity, and cost. This area of study should follow task I-3.

(c) Investigation of anodizing and fused-salt electrolysis from appropriate chemical systems, followed by annealing as necessary, to yield a refractory (non-Al) oxide of extremely fine grain size or short-range-order structure and high density as a deposit on metal wire. Special problems will be foreign atoms and porosity in deposit.

(d) Development of techniques for drawing (possibly including nucleating and crystallizing to extremely fine grain size approaching SRO) filaments of new refractory high-modulus glass compositions; also includes fiber "finishing," and evaluation. This area of study depends on and must follow task I-1.

3. Reinforced and Prestressed Ceramics. Develop techniques for depositing dense fine-grained Al_2O_3 (or Al_2O_3-base composite compositions) as a sheet sequentially on both sides of an array of stretched refractory metal, or boron, or carbon reinforcing filaments. Recommended approaches include the following:

(a) High-velocity molten-particle spray processes. Special problems will be bonding, elimination of porosity, and uniformity of thickness. This area of study depends on and must follow task I-2.

(b) CVD or combined CVD/PVD processes. Special problems will be bonding, avoidance of "snowing out," and uniformity of thickness. This area of study depends on and must follow task I-3.

4. Powders for Solids Processing. Addition is needed to the arsenal of particulate oxides, of unique and favorable characteristics, to be used as feed material in conventional solid processes for fabricating ceramics. The approach recommended is to develop and evaluate fluid processes peculiarly suitable to the preparation of fine crystalline powders, especially where high chemical purity and sinterability to high final density are important considerations. Fluid processes worthy of further investigation for preparing Al_2O_3 powders or mixed powders include:

(a) The "sol-gel" process.
(b) CVD methods and "snowing out" the oxide from halides or metal organics.
(c) Arc or induction plasma-spraying of decomposable or combustible particles into an appropriate atmosphere, and "snowing out."

Also, for reference, Table 9 (p. 123) lists all the applied research objectives in need of early attention to advance all fluid processes of special interest. Cognizance of progress in these areas for the next five years or more may disclose new subjects of interest; some subjects will be natural follow-ons to the recommended program above.

Basic Research

Selected areas for basic scientific investigation pertinent to this program are listed in Table 11 (p. 126). These are primarily physical and structural studies of Al_2O_3 and refractory glasses above and below the liquidus, and studies of the mechanisms and phenomena involved in nucleation and crystallization of these materials.

INTRODUCTION

For purposes of this Report and to fix interfaces among Panel study activities, the following definition was adopted:

Fluid Processes are those in which the immediate precursor of the solid product is largely or completely in the fluid (i.e., liquid or vapor) state.

In most cases, the "solid product" is identical with the term "ceramic" or "ceramic material." However, in incidental cases, fluid processing is inherently suitable either for surface finishing or for the preparation of raw materials (i.e., particulates) for use in solids processing. The "ceramic" definition was employed to establish the scope of this Panel study, while the latter opportunities for utilization of specific fluid processes were not overlooked in their evaluation.

Fluid processing has primarily been examined with respect to the fabrication of oxidic compositions and relative to the present and potential needs of the Department of Defense for structural applications of oxide ceramics.

Structural Applications are those in which either the primary or an important secondary consideration in the use of the material is its ability to respond, within specified limits, to a large stress of whatever origin. Often this requirement occurs at high temperature.

Needs of the Department of Defense in this area were considered in terms of the kinds of subsystems or components in which oxidic ceramics may figure. One index of fluid-processing evaluation is, accordingly, the ability to produce materials in various useful forms or configurations and sizes, and to useful tolerances.

The translation of load-bearing capability into specific material and microstructural objectives of ceramic processing is difficult, beyond a number of general quantitative relationships and the direction of present qualitative reasoning. Nevertheless, the objectives of achievement of improved performance, uniformity, reproducibility, and reliability provide substantial guidance for assessment of fluid-processing capabilities.

Performance (i.e., superior mechanical behavior) is treated here on the basis of the present state of understanding of the behavior of refractory brittle materials. Recognized important areas of processing capability consequently include: the chemical compositions and chemical purity achievable; the ability to prepare multiphase or composite as well as simple materials; the ability to produce polycrystal, single-crystal, glass, or "short-range-order" (sometimes called "amorphous") internal structures; the achievement of very low to zero porosity and small mean grain size of polycrystals.

Uniformity is taken to mean control of such elements of material character as the preceding and their variation within a part, including both surface and bulk character, and control or elimination of the occasional defect (e.g. tramp material, large pore, crack).

Reproducibility here means control of variability from part to part in quantity production.

Reliability is the product or consequence of uniformity and reproducibility.

Since the ultimate purpose of the Report is to point the way toward advancement of performance, uniformity, and reproducibility at reasonable cost, the economics of processes must be considered. Research and development are required for this advancement, and a critical, objective view must also be taken of the potential values of R&D versus the investment of time and money that will be required.

Basic Research into the physicochemical phenomena pertinent to fluid processing is considered. The purpose is to relate areas of basic research as closely as possible to potentially fruitful consequent advancements of specific fluid processes.

Applied Research and Engineering Development programs of an even more specific and more immediate nature can be described for advancement of the most attractive fluid processes and the realization of their potential with respect to the desired configuration and character of products.

The Objectives of the Panel Study are therefore:

1. To assess the present state of achievement and attempt to forecast the

ultimate achievement capability of fluid processes, primarily for the production of oxidic-ceramic materials relative to recognized needs of the Department of Defense for structural applications of ceramics.

2. To identify those fluid processes and their oxidic products that are most likely to contribute significantly to technological capability in the defined areas of application, and to predict the kinds of research and development work necessary for important practical advancement of technology through advancement of these selected processes.

3. To recommend basic and applied research and engineering development activities for Government funding. Those activities recommended must be related to established needs of the DOD in the defined areas of application of ceramics and must provide unusual opportunity or probability for fulfillment of those needs. The recommendations must also be disposed to place ceramic processing on a firm foundation of science.

General Aspects of Fluid Processes

The outstanding technical distinction between fluid processing and solids processing is that the former is usually freed from any dependency on the structure and behavior of particulate solids. This can result in a major technological or economic advantage.

Numerous fluid processes are capable of the incremental building up of a condensed body. In these cases there are unique opportunities for the production of very large objects with high uniformity, for fabricating coatings and other composite structures, and for material addition, patching, and joining.

Fluid processes on the whole have achievement capabilities of zero or near-zero porosity. This is of tremendous significance in the matters of strength and transparency.

The glassy state, the single crystal, and the short-range-order structure are achievable in most cases exclusively by fluid processing. In the domain of polycrystals, certain fluid processes have achieved finer and more uniform grain sizes than can be approached by the processing of particulates.

These general considerations are indicative of the importance of fluid processing of ceramics to the Department of Defense. However, most of the above, and other general statements, have some exceptions. Also, fluid processes as a group encompass a wide variety in the present state of advancement, from those that are basically somewhat understood and technologically sophisticated (e.g., glass-forming) to some that are only presently undergoing research (e.g., anodic sparking), or undergoing engineering investigation with a relatively weak foundation in research (e.g., some spray-deposition processes). Without resorting to the ultimate in specification, viz., a particular process for a particular component and performance requirement, the Panel has therefore attempted to make relatively specific assessments of the pertinent product characteristics and of process sophistication for each of a number of individual types of fluid processes.

Organization of the Study and Recommendations

Relatively detailed and comprehensive assessments of the present state of art have been made. These studies are presented largely in narrative form (p. 73). They are then condensed, summarized, and brought into relation with specific Department of Defense needs in the Development of Panel Recommendations (p. 111).

For convenience, fluid processes have been subdivided into two major classifications:

Bulk Processes, in which a mass of material is prepared in the fluid state and then allowed cool in its final configuration into a rigid body. Examples are fusion casting of crystalline ceramics and the forming of glass.

Incremental Processes, in which the condensed body is built up by the successive transport and deposition of particles from a fluid onto a solid surface. Examples are vapor deposition, the growth of single crystals by precipitation or freezing, and molten-particle spray processes.

The studies and the development of recommendations are organized under five subclasses of Bulk and Incremental Processes, as follows:

Bulk
1. Fusion and Freezing
2. Glass and Glass-Crystallization Processes
Incremental
3. Gas-Phase Molecular Transport
4. Liquid-Phase Molecular Transport
5. Molten-Particle Spray Processes

Bulk Fusion and Freezing is so termed to indicate that the process of crystallization is concurrent with "solidification," and the immediate product is crystalline.

Bulk-Glass and Glass-Crystallization Processes comprise first, the basic glassmaking process, and second, the treatment of "solidified" glasses of certain compositions in such a way that controlled nucleation and growth of crystals take place within the sensibly rigid glass. The latter is therefore an extension of the former.

Incremental Gas-Phase Molecular Transport comprises processes in which there is simply a forward and reverse change of state of the deposited material: solid $\longrightarrow$ gas $\longrightarrow$ solid (PVD), and those in which a chemical reaction or decomposition occurs at the point of condensation (CVD). The transported and deposited particles are molecules or atoms.

Incremental Liquid-Phase Molecular Transport is further subdivided into three types of processes: melt-freezing, in which a solid is grown by freezing on a defined interface from a liquid of essentially the same composition; solute crystallization, in which the composition that freezes or precipitates is one component of a more complex melt composition; and electrolytic, in which a cathodic or anodic reaction is involved in the deposition and the liquid-transport medium is an electrolyte. The transported and deposited particles are of molecular dimensions in all cases.

Incremental Molten-Particle Spray Processes are those in which a solid is transported in the form of largely to completely molten particulates in a high-velocity hot-gas stream, and freezing occurs as these impinge on a surface. Subdivisions are made according to how the gas is heated or propelled—the "detonation" method, combustion flames, or electrical flames (often called "plasmas"). Typical sizes of the transported particles lie between 1 and 100 μ.

STATE OF THE ART

Bulk Fusion and Freezing

Of the many approaches to the consolidation of materials of all kinds into useful shapes, solidification from a melt is by far the most common technique. This is certainly true for metals, organics, and glasses. Crystalline ceramic materials, conversely, are more usually consolidated by solid-state techniques. This survey examines the present bulk melt-freezing processes for crystalline ceramics, attempts to determine the reasons for their limited use, and develops possible opportunities for the use of melt-freezing processes for the consolidation of ceramic materials.

Two process classes are considered under the present heading:

Production of fused grain. In general, production of fused grain requires means of melting the material and solidifying it under conditions that result in the required internal structure. The massive solid is subsequently crushed and ground to the desired particle size. The maximum obtainable dense-grain sizing is determined by the distribution of gas inclusions, while the minimum is a matter of the economics of comminution.

Whereas the casting process is inherently able to provide material with a number of unique characteristics, the only characteristic utilized in the majority of present industrial fused-grain processes is the ability to obtain particles of a desired size that are essentially dense and free of connected porosity. Such a product has been shown to be resistant to chemical attack, and to be volume stable, up to near its melting point. Thus, fused grain is used to an increasing extent in premium refractories where corrosion resistance, volume stability, and density are of primary importance. Examples are fused-alumina brick in electric-furnace roofs and fused UO_2 in nuclear-fuel elements. Because microstructure is not generally controlled, mechanical properties are usually poor. A few examples of attempted microstructural control during solidification exist, such as in a recently introduced fused-grain basic refractory; but even in such instances, the control exercised has been minimal.

Production of polycrystalline shapes. The material is melted and solidified as in the production of fused grain. However, the additional configuration requirement may add significantly to the difficulty of the process.

Present industrial processes for fusion-cast shapes largely utilize only the high density or lack of interconnected porosity and the volume stability characteristic of melt solidification processes, without controlling to any extent the microstructure, and without exploiting the ability to produce large shapes. Thus the application of fusion-cast shapes is largely limited to areas where corrosion resistance and volume stability are paramount, such as glass-tank refractories and, more recently, oxygen steelmaking refractories. Since high density also results in maximum thermal conductivity, UC and UO_2 rods have been cast for nuclear-fuel elements; and since optical transmission of transparent polycrystalline materials is primarily limited by light scattering of small pores, infrared windows of halide compositions have been made by solidification from the melt. In all the present applications, however, microstructure, with the exception of porosity, is not closely controlled, and thus mechanical properties are generally poor. Major problems in production of large refractory blocks are control of macroposity and prevention of thermal-stress cracking during solidification and cooling to room temperature. Macroporosity results from gas exsolution and volume change on solidification, usually high for oxides. Shrinkage cavities can be overcome by the choice of compositions showing minimum volume change (complex oxides), mold design, or the addition of nucleating agents to obtain a relatively uniform "Swiss cheese" structure. Dissolved gases are removed from the melt by heating in vacuum, where feasible. Cracking is reduced by slow cooling, of more than a week for large shapes.

Dimensional control is usually poor: Blocks are ordinarily cut to shape.

RAW MATERIALS

Since raw materials are melted, their original physical structure is destroyed and therefore largely unimportant. Selection is based on chemical composition. There is a practical preference for dense materials to simplify loading operations. Incongruently melting compounds and materials of high vapor pressure or very high melting point cannot be fabricated by this technique. The latter two limitations are not fundamental, but a reflection of the present state of technology.

THE MELTING PROCESS

By definition, a stable melt of reasonable volume is required in this process class. The volume can be as small as 20 cm^3 for casting of carbide nuclear-fuel elements, or as large as 10-20 tons for the production of refractory blocks. A variety of melting techniques that can be characterized by the melt container and the power source are available. Crucible techniques are technically simpler but require a nonreactive, high-melting-point crucible, a requirement that severely limits choice when refractory oxides are to be melted. Platinum is useful up to about 1,450°C; above this temperature iridium is the only known container meeting all requirements, although tungsten and molybdenum are usable in some instances, provided the atmosphere is carefully controlled and some tungsten - molybdenum contamination can be tolerated. Iridium (mp 2,454°C) is usable to about 2,200°C, and crucibles as large as 5 in. in diameter by 7 in. high are commercially available, although costly (~ $15,000). Nonporous Ir coatings on graphite and tungsten that promise larger crucibles and lower initial cost have been developed. Conventional containers for higher-melting oxides are not likely, although osmium is at least theoretically useful up to 2,600°C. Graphite is a good crucible material for the carbides.

Heat sources available for crucible processes include oxyhydrogen, electric resistance, and induction heating, with the last-named being preferred because it affords close control both of melt temperature and the atmosphere surrounding the melt.

Crucibleless processes utilize a skull of the same material to contain the melt, backed by a water-cooled (usually metal) container. Energy may be introduced into such systems via two electrodes, either by establishing an arc between them (arc heating) or by utilizing the conductivity of the melt (resistance heating). For oxide melts, carbon electrodes that are slowly consumed are generally used. Very large melts of oxides are commercially produced by this technique. However, melt control is very poor: Reduction of oxides takes place, and the temperature of the melt is nonuniform and uncertain. It is, moreover, very difficult to scale down this system to melts of only a few pounds.

Other methods for heating of skull melts have been proposed, including the use of electron-beam techniques, very-high-frequency induction coupling directly to the melt, and arc-imaging techniques. Although promising, none has so far reached the useful stage. For electrically conducting carbides, cold-crucible techniques developed for metals are applicable and have been used successfully.

Atmosphere above the melt is usually uncontrolled in commercial oxide-melt processes. Yet the interaction of molten oxides with the atmosphere is substantial: Such melts dissolve appreciable quantities of gases. The technology to control atmosphere and to vary its total pressure is available. Such control seems essential for the fusion and freezing process to yield high-performance ceramics.

SOLIDIFICATION

Whereas the melt can be solidified in the melting container, and thus no pouring is necessary (such an approach is often followed in the production of fused grain), in general the melt is poured into a mold of suitable shape, where solidification takes place. Either permanent molds (graphite, precious metals, or water-cooled metals) or "sand" molds can be used. As will be discussed later, however, control of the rate of solidification and cooling is essential to obtain high-quality oxide structures; thus, at least for simple and small shapes, nonreactive "hot" metal molds are needed.

Surprisingly little is known about properties of liquid oxides. The density is less than that of the solid, but the volume change on solidification varies substantially. Generally the change is largest, between 15 and 25%, for simple close-packed oxides, and least, approximately 10%, for complex oxides such as spinels and garnets with a relatively open structure. Viscosity, on the other hand, tends to be higher for complex-oxide melts, although little quantitative data are available. Melts are electrically conductive, and gas solubility is generally high. But except for glass-forming oxides, essentially no data are available.

Striking characteristics of oxide melts are the degree of supercooling achievable before stable nuclei are formed and the relative insensitivity of oxide melts to foreign nucleating agents. Supercooling of melts by as much as $300\,^{\circ}C$ is not uncommon. Whereas such behavior is very useful in growing oxide single crystals (and helps to explain the relatively perfect crystals achievable under quite primitive conditions), it also contributes to the large grains typically obtained in cast polycrystalline structures.

Whereas the mechanisms of nucleation and crystal growth of oxides are probably essentially similar to those of metals, physical properties that control the quantitative behavior are quite different. For example, the thermal diffusivity of oxides is a factor of 10 to 100 times lower than that of metals. Therefore, without substantial modifications, metallurgical techniques are not directly applicable to the freezing of ceramic systems.

When a single-phase oxide melt is poured into a cold mold, heterogeneous nucleation occurs at the mold surface. Very quickly, favorably oriented crystals take over, and columnar growth of very large grains results throughout most of the volume of the casting. The solidified ingot will crack along grain boundaries and can easily be separated into individual grains. An entirely different structure will result if a melt is solidified in the crucible used for melting.

Because of the high degree of supercooling obtainable and the small number of nuclei ordinarily formed, in a single-phase system grains will grow rapidly to a very large size. Often only 10 or 20 such grains will be present in a 50 to 100 cm^3 volume. If, however, nucleating agents such as metallic solid particles are present in such a melt, the grain size will be significantly smaller. In a two-component mixture, equiaxed grains of smaller size can result because of constitutional supercooling. Eutectic mixtures on solidification give rise to structures quite similar to metallic eutectic melts, although very little information is available on the various types.

Because of the high volume change in freezing of oxide melts, shrinkage cavities are very large and usually centrally located unless special precautions are taken to cause unidirectional cooling. Relatively large bubbles are present throughout a solidified mass because of the change of gas solubility on freezing. These bubbles can be avoided by melting under reduced pressure, and ingots of large grain size, but quite transparent, can be produced by this means. Unless solidification takes place very slowly, thermal gradients within the system build up to high levels; and since little plastic flow takes place in the cast piece, cracking usually results.

OPPORTUNITIES AND AREAS FOR FURTHER STUDY

Until relatively recently, the major limitations of bulk-solidification techniques have been technological. That is, means to melt oxides under controlled conditions and without contamination, and of solidifying such melts under controlled conditions, have not been available. Such limitations no longer apply, at least for volumes up to 2,000 cm^3. The use of precious-metal crucibles and molds in combination with induction heaters allows precise control of the process.

The most serious limitation is the difficulty of obtaining fine grain size, because of the combination of a large degree of supercooling, sparse nucleation, and the low thermal conductivity of oxide ceramics. However, these limitations appear to be real primarily for single-phase systems. Whereas single-phase, single-component ceramics are presently preferred when fabricated by the more conventional solid-state processes, complex compositions are preferable for bulk fusion and freezing techniques. Eutectics or peritectics will result in microstructures both finer and unique in texture. Another approach to overcoming the problem of coarse grain size in cast ceramics is the use of solid solutions in which the solubility decreases rapidly with temperature. Work in Germany during World War II has shown that coarse-grained spinel, with a fine precipitate of alumina, does not behave as a coarse-grained ceramic, but the effective grain size is proportional to the separation of the precipitate particles.

There are, furthermore, many applications for which large grain size is not a detriment per se. This is true of applications in which mechanical strength is less important than other properties such as density or optical transparency. Infrared components, lasers, and light-source envelopes provide some examples of such applications.

A most striking characteristic of the fusion and solidification process for ceramics is the lack of hard information about the process and of physical data on liquid and solid oxides near the melting point. Support should be given to a continuing long-term fundamental study of the properties of liquid oxides and of solidification mechanisms.

Some other applied research and development areas that merit exploration include:

1. Additional means of controlling uniform nucleation and crystallization, e.g., the use of applied pressure at about the normal melting point to cause freezing (viz., utilizing $\Delta(PV)$ in place of ΔE to drive the reaction), and the use of programmed cooling of molds to control the freezing rate.

2. Additional means of adjusting grain size and texture after freezing, e.g., subsolidus heat treatment or hot-working of appropriately chosen compositions.

3. Additional means of achieving different configurations, e.g., dipping a porous body in a molten-oxide bath (i.e., infiltration), or repeatedly dipping a hot form to build up a shell configuration.

In spite of recent progress and of foreseeable future improvements in fusion-casting methods, it would appear that technical superiority, especially for structural uses, will be difficult to obtain.

In most cases, accomplishments of research will be relatively specific regarding the compositions to which the methods are applicable. Emphasizing that this statement pertains only to the "structural ceramics" objective and its general advancement, it is probable that applied research can be more fruitfully devoted to selected solids-processing methods and to other fluid-processing methods than to fusion casting. Nevertheless, there will continue to be a number of specific products and applications (especially where transparency is important) that justify advancement of this processing technology.

Bulk Glass and Glass-Crystallization Processes

Glass has been broadly described as a product of inorganic fusion whose structure is random beyond about 8 Å, although some uncertainty and controversy remain as to the actual extent of "short range order" in vitreous materials.

Many of the applications of glass take advantage of its inherent transparency in the visible region, while special formulations can extend this transparency into the ultraviolet, infrared, and microwave regions. Among other useful properties of glass are high resistance to chemical attack, high hardness and resistance to mechanical abrasion, thermal stability up to 1,000°C, low electrical and thermal conductivity, zero porosity and permeability, and low density (commonly from about 2.5 to 3.5 g/cm^3). Glass can also be made chemically and physically homogeneous on an almost atomic scale.

The theoretical strength of vitreous silica has been estimated to be nearly 3×10^6 psi. Although this number indicates the potential value of glass as a structural material, all glasses, under normal use conditions, are susceptible to breakage by the concentration of tensile stresses at imperfections. Cracks, scratches, or other surface flaws usually act to reduce transverse glass strength to a few thousand psi. Acid polishing, protective coatings, and the introduction of thermally or chemically induced surface compressive stresses are some methods now used to preserve at least a portion of the very high intrinsic strength of glass.

Although glasses containing a dispersion of one or more crystalline phases have been known since ancient times, crystallized glasses or "glass ceramics" of technical importance are relatively new. Within about the last decade a growing number of highly crystalline products have been made by the controlled nucleation and crystallization of special glass compositions. By the controlled heat treatment of certain glasses, a large number of minute crystal nuclei can be produced in a uniform dispersion, many of which subsequently act as growth centers during a bulk crystallization process.

The principal significance of the development of technical glass ceramics is that substantial improvements in the properties of glass can be achieved through a simple heat-treating sequence. Modification of the following properties can be effected through the crystallization of glass: mechanical strength and hardness, chemical durability, thermal expansion (either lower or higher than the parent glass), thermal and/or electrical conductivity, transparency in the ir or microwave regions, and thermal stability. Much of the important visible transparency of glass can often be maintained through the crystallization process by careful control of the parent-glass composition and its heat treatment.

THE GLASSMAKING PROCESS

Common commercial glasses are made from inexpensive and abundant raw materials. Minerals and chemicals of appropriate grain size and purity are initially prepared by crushing and sizing. Mixing of the particulate batch materials is then accomplished, in order to achieve a high rate of batch solution and a high degree of homogeneity in the molten state. Preparation of the batch, and its delivery to the melting tank, can be fully automated.

During the continuous glassmaking process, batch materials are heated, in a container or tank lined with refractory oxides, to above the liquidus temperature (usually about 1,200-1,600°C). The molten glass passes from the melting portion of the tank to the "finer" section, where it is degassed (i.e., bubbles are removed). Homogenization is finally accomplished by stirring and thermal agitation. The melt is cooled to an appropriate viscosity while passing through an orifice out of the tank into the forming equipment. A continuous industrial melting unit may produce hundreds of tons of high-quality glass daily. Platinum is used as a refractory-containment material to produce the purest, most homogeneous glasses (e.g., for optical and ophthalmic uses).

As a glass-forming melt cools, the fluid changes continuously to a viscous or plastic state in which the glass may easily be formed into various shapes. In industrial installations, glass is fed continuously into high-speed spinning, casting, blowing, drawing, rolling, pressing, or other automatic forming equipment. This equipment is complex and expensive, and the molds require special high-temperature metals to withstand the severe thermal environments that are encountered.

The finished glass article is normally reheated to relieve any residual stress caused by thermal gradients encountered during cooling. Portions of the finished article may be remelted at any time to accomplish localized viscous flow for the correction of defects or for polishing. Forming and subsequent processes must take place rapidly enough that devitrification to the equilibrium crystalline assemblages does not occur.

VARIETY OF GLASSES AND GLASS-FORMING CAPABILITIES

The bulk of the commercial glass industry can be divided into four general sections: (a) flat glass, which includes most of the window glass produced; (b) container glass, which includes bottles of all kinds; (c) specialty glass; and (d) fiber glass. Approximately 25% of the industry's total dollar volume ($3 billion in 1966) is accounted for by flat glass, 38% by container glass, 20% by specialty glass, and 17% by fiber glass. Table 1 lists some properties of a selection of commercial glass compositions.

Fused silica is probably the most widely known of the advanced technical glasses. It is the most refractory (annealing point 1,050°C), and its low coefficient of thermal expansion ($5.5 \times 10^{-7}/°C$) underlies many applications in which the ability to withstand large temperature gradients is important. Its elastic modulus is relatively high (10.5×10^6 psi) and its density is low (2.20 g/cm^3). It has a very low dielectric constant and power factor (3.8 and 1×10^{-5}, respectively, at 1 Mc), and is highly transparent from near-ir to uv wavelengths. The forming-and-working methods for vitreous silica are basically similar to the processes for more ordinary glasses, but with unique quantitative differences.

Although silicate glasses (complex compositions containing silicon dioxide) are by far the most common, over 60 of the chemical elements have been incorporated into glass. The following refractory oxides, either alone or in combination with other oxides, can be quenched in bulk from the molten to the vitreous state:

Al_2O_3	GeO_2	P_2O_5	SnO_2	TiO_2
B_2O_3	Nb_2O_5	SiO_2	Ta_2O_5	V_2O_5

In addition, nonoxide glasses containing such anions as tellurides, arsenides, sulfides, fluorides, selenides, and antimonides can be made. The use of high pressures during melting has made possible the production of glasses containing large quantities of volatiles, such as chlorides, bromides, iodides, water, carbon dioxide, and hydrogen.

Composition control of common silicate glasses can be held to within fairly

Table 1. Properties of Some Commercial Glasses

	Soda Lime Silicate	Alkali Barium Silicate	Medium Borosilicate	Heat Resistant Borosilicate	Alumino Silicate
Coeff. of linear exp (0 to 300°C)	$92 \times 10^{-7}/°C$	$89 \times 10^{-7}/°C$	$46 \times 10^{-7}/°C$	$33 \times 10^{-7}/°C$	$42 \times 10^{-7}/°C$
Annealing temperature (constant viscosity)	510°C	445°C	480°C	565°C	715°C
Density (g/cm^3)	2.47	2.64	2.28	2.23	2.52
Young's modulus (psi)	10×10^6	9.8×10^6	8.2×10^6	9.1×10^6	12.7×10^6
Log volume resistivity (at 250°C)	6.4	8.9	9.2	8.1	11.4
Dielectric constant (1 Mc and 20°C)	7.2	6.3	4.9	4.6	7.2
Power factor (1 Mc and 20°C)	0.009	0.0017	0.0026	0.0050	0.0038

close tolerances. Batch-solution rates and rates of volatility of melt constituents normally determine the amount of composition control that is possible. Using special precautions, control can often be achieved to within a few parts per million of certain major batch ingredients, and to within less than one part per million of minor constituents. Uniformity of composition during the glass melting-and-forming process depends upon the homogeneity of the batch as delivered to the tank, grain size and distribution of batch raw materials, solution rates of the various batch components, and melting time and temperature. Stirring (usually with platinum-clad molybdenum equipment) is used to achieve a high degree of uniformity in some commercial glasses, especially optical glasses. The degree of purity that is obtainable during the making of glass is primarily dependent upon the purity of the batch materials used, but is also contingent upon batch-handling procedures and purity of the refractory melting container. Certain optical glasses are currently manufactured with a total impurity level of less than one part per million.

As in-process control, glass composition is monitored along with several important and easily measured physical properties. The temperatures in various parts of the tank and in the forming equipment are continuously recorded for a running history of the melting-and-forming operation. The control of defects (e.g., bubbles, unmelted batch, and devitrification or "cord") is made simple through the examination of the transparent glass immediately after forming. These defects can be related to faulty tank operation and quickly eliminated.

In addition to bulk or massive shapes, glass can be made continuously in the form of tubing, rod, sheet, ribbon, foam, fiber, and beads. All these can be made with reproducibly high quality and uniformity. Although bulk glass can be applied during forming as a coating on certain substrates, the coating process is usually initiated from the quenched state. A glass powder or frit is generally sprayed on the article to be coated. Subsequent firing produces a smooth continuous glassy coating or glaze. Particulate glass can also be slip cast or pressed into shape and fired to produce a sintered body with controlled degrees of consolidation.

Shrinkages, normally large in conventional ceramic processing, are quite small in the glassmaking process. Precision forming is therefore possible with very high accuracy. Glass can be machined (i.e., ground) to close tolerances, but not without some difficulty, owing to its hard and brittle nature.

Although articles of almost any size and shape can be made from glass, it may be impossible to cool unusually thick or massive sections rapidly enough to prevent devitrification and, at the same time, uniformly enough to eliminate thermal cracking. Special glass compositions, however, can be formulated with sufficient stability and low thermal expansion to permit fabrication in sections exceeding one foot in total thickness. Softening and reworking of manufactured glass articles are also limited by devitrification, which occurs most readily upon reheating.

GLASS-FORMING ECONOMICS

When manufactured in large quantity, glass is among the cheapest of materials. The costs of basic raw materials and melting are low, usually not more than a few cents per pound; but large, high-temperature melting tanks and automatic forming equipment require high capital expenditures. Refractory costs can be high, especially when platinum is used. For new glass products, special forming equipment must usually be designed and built. The cost of finished glass articles is thus extremely sensitive to production volume, the cost per item dropping rapidly as volume increases. The glass-forming process therefore cannot compete in cost with most of the conventional ceramic-forming techniques unless production volume is high.

GLASS CRYSTALLIZATION

In the manufacture of crystalline ceramics from glass objects, a heat-treating cycle, normally consisting of a low temperature (600 to 900°C) and a high temperature (900 to 1,300°C) portion, is required. For some compositions containing dissolved Ag, Au, and Pt, for example, the thermal treatment is preceded by ultraviolet "photosensitizing," the effect of which is similar to that of exposing a photographic emulsion. The low-temperature soak is designed to produce the desired number of crystalline nuclei, and the second hold is required to accomplish crystallization of the main portion of the glass. Depending on composition and the crystalline assemblage desired, the total heating cycle can range from a few hours to many days.

Although the internal structure of glass is commonly thought to be essentially random, certain structural inhomogeneities often become apparent during annealing. A phase separation is commonly observed in the form of a two-liquid composite, where droplets of one glass composition are dispersed within a matrix of the other or both phases are continuous. An example of this behavior occurs in the sodium borosilicate system, in which a sodium borate phase is rendered cocontinuous with a 96% silica glass during a special heat treatment. This is an example of a deliberate phase separation; others often occur spontaneously in glass forming. Liquid-liquid phase separation has a marked influence on the nucleation and growth of crystalline phases.

A special requirement in glass crystallization is that it must occur with a minimum amount of deformation. Heating to higher temperatures to hasten the process could produce an intolerable amount of sagging, necessitating the use of expensive forming hardware to maintain the proper shape during crystallization.

The number of glass compositions that can be effectively crystallized and the range of uses for the product materials are being increased rapidly. Table 2 samples the list of "technical" and "nontechnical" glass ceramics as of 1966.

Crystallization of glass can produce composite ceramics of various grain sizes, shapes, orientations, and distributions. Control of the microstructure of glass ceramics is achieved through careful selection of glass composition and heat treatment. Little is known of the bonding that occurs between a growing crystal and its parent glass, but there is no detectable porosity in glass ceramics that contain even a very small amount of residual glass. The range of grain size in glass ceramics is from the edge of resolution of the electron microscope (i.e., about 20 Å) to several microns and even up to the millimeter size range. The desirable orientation is generally random, although oriented crystallization beginning at the surface of a glass can be achieved with certain compositions. For very small crystal sizes the shape is generally almost spherical, but as the crystals grow they assume a more angular or euhedral geometry. Control of the variety and number of crystal phases can be achieved through selection of composition and heat treatment. Glass ceramics can be obtained by crystallization to the point where virtually no residual glass remains.

Limitations with respect to size and shape are somewhat more restrictive for glass ceramics than for the common glasses. This is because glass ceramics are necessarily designed to crystallize in a very short time upon reheating. Especially in the case of refractory compositions, some of the glass-forming methods cannot be used. The reworking by softening of a finished glass-ceramic article is also limited by the necessity of partial remelting to the glassy state; therefore, such operations must precede crystallization and may interfere with it.

During crystallization a volume densification of less than 3% is generally encountered, allowing fairly close dimensional control during glass-ceramic

Table 2. Some Commercial Crystallized Glasses

Commercial Identification	Crystal Phases	Properties	Application
Corning 8603	$Li_2O \cdot 2SiO_2$, SiO_2	Photochemically machinable	Fluid amplifiers, molds for printing plates
Corning 9606	$2MgO \cdot 2Al_2O_3 \cdot 5SiO_2$, SiO_2, TiO_2	Low expansion, transparent to radar	Radomes
Corning 9608	β-spodumene solid solution, TiO_2	Low expansion, good chemical durability	Household cooking utensils
Corning 9611	α-quartz solid solution	Very high strength	Structural members
Neoceram (Japan)	β-spodumene solid solution	Low expansion	Household cooking ware
Owens-Illinois Cer-Vit	β-quartz solid solution	Zero expansion at ambient temperatures	Telescope mirror blanks
Anchor-Hocking Cookware	β-spodumene solid solution	Low expansion	Household cooking ware
Corning 0303	$Na_2O \cdot Al_2O_3 \cdot 2SiO_2$ $BaO \cdot Al_2O_3 \cdot 2SiO_2$	High strength	Tableware and dinnerware
Corning CYKOL and CYKO2	Sodium niobate	High dielectric constant	Miniature capacitors
Corning 9690	β-spodumene solid solution	Low expansion	Gas-stove burners
Corning 0333	β-spodumene solid solution	High strength, weatherability	Building cladding

processing. Machining methods are the same as for conventional ceramics.

Glass ceramics are often somewhat stronger than the original glass, as a result of the randomly dispersed crystals, which tend to impede the initial growth of microcracks. The achievable ultrafine grain size, together with the zero-porosity characteristic of glass, presents a combination of microstructural features not broadly found via any other ceramic process. Variation of other specific properties at will over a substantial range, as for example the expansion coefficient, is already practiced. One present limitation in thermomechanical properties, which may be overcome as more compositions are explored, is that of high-temperature strength owing to the presence of a residue of glass (predominately SiO_2) at the grain boundaries.

The primary inherent advantage in a process that produces crystalline ceramic materials from glass is the controlled internal nucleation, which makes possible the greatest homogeneity known for a polycrystalline ceramic system, assuming of course that the parent glass is homogeneous. The combination afforded by the various glass-forming resources, together with the variety and precision of microstructure control by glass crystallization, is unique. The impact of these combined capabilities is just beginning to be felt in the technical-ceramics area, and advanced glass ceramics are regarded as one of the most important classes of materials for further development by both Government and industry.

FINISHING OF GLASS CERAMICS

Having no porosity, glass ceramics are very suitable for strengthening by prestressing techniques similar to those employed with glass. Through carefully controlled heat treatments or subsequent chemical processing, compressive surfaces have been developed on many glass-ceramic materials. The most common procedure involves immersing the glass-ceramic body in a molten salt to effect ion exchange, which in some cases also involves a crystalline phase transformation. The surface compressive layer formed results in modulus of rupture strengths up to as much as 10 to 20 times the original glass-ceramic strength. Some examples are:

1. An Mg-Al-Si-O composition nucleated with TiO_2 to give a body comprised of α-quartz, spinel, and enstatite; ion-exchanged with Li (for Mg). A low-expansion β-quartz phase is grown in the surface layers. Modulus of rupture: original, 15,000 psi; strengthened, 140,000 psi.

2. An Li-Al-Si-O composition nucleated with TiO_2 to give a body comprised of β-spodumene and rutile; ion-exchanged with Na (larger) for Li (smaller) without phase change. Modulus of rupture: original, 12,000 psi; strengthened, 90,000 psi.

3. An Na-Al-Si-O composition nucleated with TiO_2 to give a body comprised of nephelite and anatase; ion-exchanged with K (for Na). The phase kalsilite (of 10% larger specific volume than nephelite) appears in the surface layers. Modulus of rupture: original, 15,000 psi; strengthened, as high as 200,000 psi.

As is also typical with glass, these higher strengths owing to surface compression are accompanied by a decrease in the scatter of strength values about the mean.

OPPORTUNITIES FOR RESEARCH AND DEVELOPMENT

Refinement of processing techniques of glass melting and forming could increase the quality and uniformity of the product. Innovations in processing equipment are required for new product concepts. Tanks to melt greater volumes of high-quality glass, higher-temperature glasses, or glasses of unusual or highly corrosive composition, are among the important future needs of the glass industry. Other methods of forming, e.g., molten-particle spraying, should be further investigated.

Opportunities to achieve Young's modulus values above 25×10^6 psi and to maintain high strength values at temperatures of 1,000°C and above lie in the exploration of new glass compositions, including, in particular, nonsilicate compositions. Rapid-chilling methods may be necessary to preserve these in the vitreous state for use or for controlled crystallization.

New high-modulus compositions should find ready use as filaments if they can be preserved in the vitreous state. The role of crystallized high-E glasses as filaments is still indistinct, requiring further research; it is certain that complete crystallization and extremely fine grain size will be required.

Exploration of nucleation and crystallization in unusual glass-forming systems is therefore needed. This research is sure to produce new high-performance glass-ceramic materials for structural and many other applications. Extension to more refractory compositions is important. Achievement of the finest of grain sizes ($\lesssim 0.01\mu$) with complete crystallization is necessary. Study of the changes in the internal structure of glass as it is being heat-treated is also needed, because proper control of heat treatment can produce a variety of new and interesting microstructures for each glass composition studied.

Of basic significance are studies of the phenomena of nucleation, growth, and phase separation relative to the structure of glasses. From this work it is expected that new ways may be found for controlling crystallization to produce glass-ceramic materials.

Instruments of investigation and instrumental means for process control appear to be adequate except for the direct observation of critical nuclei.

An invaluable contribution would be the compilation of a reference work that lists glass and glass ceramics and their properties for all known compositions so interested parties can keep abreast of developments in this field.

Incremental Gas-Phase Molecular Transport

The fluid processes for ceramic forming included in this section are: (a) Physical Vapor Deposition (PVD), i.e., direct condensation of atomic or molecular vapor, including sputtering; and (b) Chemical Vapor Deposition (CVD), i.e., the formation of a solid product from gaseous compounds by chemical reaction at a surface. Impregnation is a variant of (b) in which a gaseous material is allowed to interact with a particulate aggregate in such a way as to bond and consolidate the aggregate; Reactive Sputtering, e.g., sputtering of a metal in an oxygen-, nitrogen-, or other gas-containing atmosphere, is a hybrid of (a) and (b), and Ion-Plating is a variant of (a), in which vaporized materials are ionized and the ions are driven by an electrical potential to the surface to be coated.

These processes were conceived and developed for purposes of coating. While they are adaptable to the building up of free-standing thin-walled shapes, their deposition rates are in many instances too slow to consider for the fabrication of massive ceramic objects. Variants of these processes include the coating of small particles in a fluidized bed, in which the reactant gases are components of the fluidizing stream; and the preparation of particulates by conducting the reaction in the gas phase (termed "snowing out") and collecting the product.

The most important general advantages and disadvantages of PVD and CVD processes are listed in Table 3. A more detailed discussion follows.

COMPOSITIONS

The compositions of materials that can be formed by these processes are varied but depend on some measure of volatility either of the desired material itself (PVD) or of a material that will react subsequently to give the desired product (CVD). A few examples of the compositions that can be formed are given in Table 4. Many homologues remain to be explored.

CONFIGURATIONS

The range of configurations that can be formed or treated by incremental gas-phase processes depends upon the availability of arrangements for bringing the gas into contact with a substrate. The uniformity of the product will depend upon the uniformity of that contact. Several limitations should be considered:

1. PVD is a line-of-sight process becuase of the molecular-flow mass transfer at the low pressures of operation that are made necessary by the low volatility of the materials of interest. Therefore, for uniform coatings the substrate must be uniformly exposed to the vapor source.

2. CVD occurs by reaction whose rate can be affected by the interdiffusion of reactants to the surface and reaction products away from the surface through a boundary layer. Thus, in CVD the dynamics of vapor flow is of primary concern, and the control of vapor flow is important.

3. Even in impregnation, where the gas flow may be in one direction (i.e., all the reactant is consumed), it may be necessary to limit the rate of surface reaction so that uniformity is attained. Further, even small quantities of non-reactive gaseous impurities can form a barrier and restrict access of the reactant gas into the interior of a porous body, thus limiting the depth to which uniform penetration can be achieved.

Thin films ($0.01\,\mu$ to $1\,\mu$) are used for optical, electronic, and emissivity-control purposes. Coatings ($1\,\mu$ to $250\,\mu$) are used to impart abrasion resistance and corrosion resistance to surfaces. The thinner coatings and films require

Table 3. Advantages and Disadvantages of Incremental Gas-Phase Processes

Process	Advantages	Disadvantages
PVD	Relatively cold substrate	Heat-sensitive substrates must be force-cooled for rapid deposition
	Ideal for thin films of metals and some ceramics	Range of achievable ceramics limited
	High-vacuum ambient ideal for cleanliness	Must be carried out in high-vacuum equipment
	Rate of deposition well controllable	Rates of deposition limited to 0.01 in./hr
	Condensation patterns are predictable	Is line-of-sight process with no "throwing power"
	Uses readily available form of high-purity feed material	Mechanical feeding of rod, wire, or particles needed for continuous operation
	Sputtering permits deposition of materials of low volatility	Sputtering occurs at very low rate
	Adaptable to formation of dispersed two-phase systems	Control of relative rates of evaporation of two components is difficult
Ion plating	Adhesion improved over that of PVD	Requires additional complexity of equipment relative to PVD
	Rate of deposition comparable to PVD	Rate of deposition limited
CVD	Substrate does not have to be cooled	Substrate must be heated, thus preventing application to many plastics and other materials
	May be carried out at atmospheric pressure	Most vapor-feed compounds are sensitive to air oxidation or hydrolysis
	Applicable to the deposition of a large number of ceramic materials	Feed materials are toxic and/or expensive
	Variety of controlled morphologies attainable	Anisotropic deposits lead to thermal stress
	May be used to minimize stress at high operating temperature due to thermal-expansion mismatch	Good thermal-expansion match of deposit with substrate required
	Adaptable to formation of some very fine two-phase dispersions	Component of feed vapor may constitute undesirable contaminant
	Up to 10-fold advantage over PVD in rate of deposition in some cases	Limited rate of deposition (0.01 to 0.1 in./hr)
	Throwing power exceeds that of PVD	Limited throwing power
Impregnation	Gives isotropic product	Limited composition range of applicability
	Relatively thick sections can be fabricated	Since body must be porous to introduce one reactant, some connected porosity in final body is inevitable

Table 4. Examples of PVD and CVD Products and Their Forming Reactions

Product	Reactants	Reaction Temperature
Boron	B (PVD)	$T(evap) \geq 2150^\circ C$
	$BCl_3 + H_2 \rightarrow B$	$T(substrate) \geq 900^\circ C$
Carbon	C (PVD)	$T(evap) \geq 2750^\circ C$
	CH_4, etc.$\rightarrow$C	$T(substrate) \geq 1000^\circ C$
Silicon	Si (PVD)	$T(evap) \geq 1600^\circ C$
	$SiI_4 \rightarrow Si$	$T(substrate) \geq 1000^\circ C$
Oxides	$AlCl_3 + CO_2 + H_2 \rightarrow Al_2O_3$	$T(substrate) \geq 1000^\circ C$
	Al alkoxides $\rightarrow Al_2O_3$	$T(substrate) \geq 300^\circ C$
	SiO_2 (PVD)	$T(evap) \geq 2000^\circ C$
	$TiCl_4 + H_2O \rightarrow TiO_2$	$T(substrate) \geq 600^\circ C$
Carbides	SiC (PVD)	$T(evap) \geq 1900^\circ C$
	$SiCl_4 + CH_4 \rightarrow SiC$	$T(substrate) \geq 1200^\circ C$
	$CH_3SiCl_3 \rightarrow SiC$	$T(substrate) \geq 1000^\circ C$
Borides	$TiCl_4 + BCl_3 \rightarrow TiB_2$	$T(substrate) \geq 1000^\circ C$
Nitrides	$BCl_3 + NH_3 \rightarrow BN$	$T(substrate) \geq 1000^\circ C$
Silicides	$MoCl_5 + SiCl_4 + H_2 \rightarrow MoSi_2$	$T(substrate) \geq 1000^\circ C$
	$Mo + SiI_2 \rightarrow MoSi_2$	$T(substrate) \geq 800^\circ C$

the transport of only very small amounts of material and can be effectively applied by either PVD or CVD. PVD is preferred for thin films because the distribution of material transferred from source to substrate is easier to predict, and the substrate temperature can be varied independently. For heavier coatings where the substrate temperature constraints are acceptable, CVD is preferred because of the greater available rate of mass transfer.

Individual pieces or mandrels to be coated can be mechanically translated and rotated relative to the vapor source for uniform exposure. For deposition on a continuous sheet, staggered or banded vapor sources are used to establish uniformity.

Certain coatings, films, and surface-layer modifications can be formed on various shapes by the variant known as the "pack-cementation" process. For example, siliconizing of molybdenum or tungsten gives a silicide coating. Recent research in the pack cementation of Al_2O_3 by Cr_2O_3 utilizes the lower coefficient of expansion of the Al_2O_3 - Cr_2O_3 solid solution to give a compressively stressed surface layer on cooling.

In such processes, the parts to be coated are embedded in a mixture of powdered reactants and inert diluent. The entire pack is raised to an elevated temperature, where a CVD reaction takes place via the vapor phase. Slurry or paste packings are also used. The use of a fluidized pack can improve the uniformity of the coating. Also, the economy of semicontinuous operation is one factor favoring the fluidized pack over the static pack.

Because of its higher mass-transfer rates, CVD should find a greater range of applicability than PVD for forming free-standing shell structures or sheets by means of deposition on a mandrel—as illustrated in the deposition of pyrolytic-carbon nose cones. Impregnation is also of utility in the bonding of certain materials, for example by the reaction with nitrogen of preformed green compacts of Si_3N_4 or SiC admixed with silicon powder.

In order to produce shell, sheet, or tube structures of uniform thickness by

PVD or CVS it is necessary to control the effective exposure of the substrate to the vapor. Shell structures most suitably formed are those that can be rotated about an axis of symmetry.

These processes are important in the preparation of ceramic fibers. In the context of this discussion the term "fiber" refers to both whisker and filament forms of material. One technique used for filament preparation entails the continuous coating of wire. For example, 0.005-in. continuous filaments of high-strength boron are formed by hydrogen reduction of boron trichloride on a 0.0005-in. resistively heated tungsten core wire passing axially through a tubular reactor, counter-current to the vapor flow. Other filamentary materials may be formed similarly.

"Whiskers" in the present context are single crystals of material having an aspect (length-to-width) ratio sufficiently high to be of interest in composites ($\geq 100:1$) and having small enough diameter to exhibit exceptional strength. Whiskers are formed by two detailed mechanisms of deposition:

1. Normal whisker growth. There exist for many materials ranges of temperature and supersaturation (actual reactant to product ratio relative to equilibrium value) that favor whisker growth over other morphologies. Whiskers can be nucleated on a suitable substrate and their growth continued as long as conditions are not changed or until prohibitive impurity assimilation occurs on the growth surface.

2. VLS (vapor-liquid-solid) mechanism. Whisker growth may also occur by the VLS mechanism, in which a droplet of solvent material at the tip of the whisker participates in the growth, and the depositing atoms are transported from the vapor through this droplet to the growing solid.

Single-crystal platelets useful for reinforcing purposes may also be grown by CVD in a controlled range of conditions.

The ranges of temperature and supersaturation suitable for growth of whiskers and platelets by these techniques impose two important constraints on such processes. First, the required supersaturations are obtained at low reactant concentration and consequently at low rates of material transport. Second, because of reactant depletion, it is difficult to maintain the required conditions over a large-volume production unit.

Vapor-deposition processes are used for the formation of solid particles directly from the vapor phase. These can vary in size from 10 Å to 1,000 Å depending upon the conditions (temperature, supersaturation, and dwell time). Very fine metal powders are being prepared by "snowing out" of a concentrated beam of vacuum-evaporated metal. By analogy, finely powdered ceramic materials can be prepared by the oxidation, carburization, or nitriding of a beam of metal vapor or by, e.g., hydrolysis of a halide or decomposition of an alkoxide. Some powders could be formed by direct evaporation and condensation of the ceramic material itself.

Most of the vapor preparation of ceramic powders is presently by the chemical route, usually by a flame process. The most familiar is the formation of carbon blacks by the pyrolysis of hydrocarbons. More recently the oxidation-hydrolysis of silicon tetrachloride and titanium tetrachloride has been used for production of the corresponding oxides for pigment and reinforcing-agent applications. Suitable procedures could probably be devised for the formation of very fine powders of many oxides, carbides, nitrides, borides, and silicides.

Vapor-deposition reactions on suitably agitated particles are being used for encapsulation, and this use is expected to increase as new applications for coated particles are devised. The coating of nuclear-fuel particles (100μ to 500μ diam) with pyrolytic carbon for fission-product retention is an important example. Oxides and other coatings are being applied by CVD, and some metal coatings by PVD. Applications in the processing of composites of high uniformity are among the most attractive.

DIMENSIONAL CAPABILITIES

The dimensional capabilities of vapor-deposition processes with respect to particulates and fibers have previously been discussed to some extent. No practical limitations exist in the formation of continuous coated-substrate filaments. Whiskers greater than 1 in. in length are a minor fraction of the usual product. By improved understanding of the mechanisms of growth, means of extending the length of such whiskers may be devised. However, unless fibers are very long, so they can be woven, the 1 in. length is adequate for fiber-reinforcing applications.

In the coating of particles, limitations in dimensional capabilities are encountered as the substrate size is decreased below about 50μ. Very small particles tend to coat as agglomerates, rather than discretely, unless special arrangements are made to provide proper interparticle agitation. Particles in the micron range have been coated.

In the coating of extended surfaces and the formation of shell structures by vapor deposition or reactive sintering, the size of the object to be formed or coated is limited only by the facilities available for processing. The use of multiple vapor injectors and/or exhausts becomes necessary as the size of the object to be processed is increased. There are, however, definite limitations in the thickness of coating or shell. These are related to deposit morphology as discussed herein. In most CVD systems, surface protrusions that extend out into the gas stream are sites of increased deposition rate. Therefore, one may expect increased surface irregularity with increased thickness. Furthermore, vapor-deposited materials tend to be anisotropic. That is, nucleation and growth can occur with some degree of preferential orientation of the crystallites relative to the deposit surface. Thus, any basic anisotropy in the crystallites will be additive and will result in a new anisotropy in the final product. In a closed structure, anisotropy in thermal expansion will lead to internal stress when the object is cooled from the deposition temperature to room temperature or is heated above the temperature of deposition.

Even in isotropic materials, deposition can occur with defects in the material. To the extent that these have a pattern of preferred orientation, the structure may be internally strained and may crack at some characteristic thickness.

When the above factors are considered along with the economic limitations of low deposition rates, it is improbable that layers of vapor-deposited materials greater than one or, at most, a few inches in thickness will be practical. In many cases, the reasonable limit will be a small fraction of an inch.

The extent to which a porous powder compact can be impregnated by vapor-deposited materials or by a gaseous reactant for reactive sintering depends on many factors, including the pore size and continuity and the nature of the reactions employed. However, the upper limit of thickness of the order of inches appears to apply, and the limit will be much lower if near-zero final porosity is the objective.

MORPHOLOGY

The morphology of vapor-deposited materials is primarily determined by the fact that there is but one growth interface. Material may be incorporated in the growing deposits either by the direct addition of molecules (heterogeneous surface reaction) or by precipitation of solid particles which have "snowed out" in the gas phase ("homogeneously" nucleated material). The heterogeneous nucleation of new grains may or may not be epitaxial or rheotaxial. However, the heterogeneous growth process is epitaxial. Thus, any orientation preference in the nucleation and growth mechanisms is reflected in preferred orientation in the final product.

Grain size in the deposited material depends upon the competition of the nucleation and growth mechanisms for material from the vapor phase, and is modified by whatever grain growth occurs in the material already deposited. The latter, as well as being a function of temperature, is specific to the material and its as-deposited morphology, which determines the driving force for grain growth.

Both the nucleation and heterogeneous growth processes for a given material are functions of temperature and supersaturation (actual reactant to product ratio relative to equilibrium value). Since the over-all rate of growth is also dependent upon supersaturation as determined by the reactant concentration and the rate of supply of reactant to the surface, one may have to limit the rate of deposition to attain a desired morphology, or, conversely, accept a compromise in morphology for economically favorable deposition rates.

The uncontrolled precipitation of gas-phase-nucleated material on a growth surface is often troublesome. Since this type of material invariably has the form of agglomerated submicron spheres, its incorporation leads to voids in the deposits. The surface protrusions previously mentioned can originate from precipitated particles. Since gas-phase nucleation is favored by increased supersaturation, increasing reactant concentration to increase over-all rate of deposition can lead to such problems. However, when the precipitation can be controlled it may be useful, as in forming continuously nucleated pyrolytic graphite or the porous "cushion" layers of pyrolytic carbon applied in coated nuclear-fuel particles.

The introduction of foreign material may limit grain size in the as-deposited product by "poisoning" the growth process. This can be used to advantage if properly controlled.

Vapor-deposited materials have been shown to exhibit two types of unique resistance to grain growth; both are related to their unique morphology.

1. In a preferentially oriented deposit of columnar grains, grain growth at elevated temperature is limited by the lack of driving force for growth between the low-angle grain boundaries.

2. Because of the very fine dispersions of stable second-phase material (impurity materials or those purposely added) attainable by vapor deposition, it is frequently possible to restrict grain growth with very small amounts of foreign material.

Considerable variability can be obtained in deposit morphology by the control of deposition temperature and reactant concentration. This is particularly true of reactions that can be made to go over a wide temperature range, or when several reactions are available to give the same product. For example, alumina can be obtained from hydrolysis of aluminum chloride as a porous amorphous material, dense amorphous material (glass), or a macrocrystalline deposit with one or another (c- or a-parallel) preferred crystallographic orientation relative to the deposition surface.

The codeposition of compatible materials is possible and gives interesting heterogeneous products. For example, carbon can be codeposited with BeO to give a grain-growth-resistant product.

INTERFACE CONSIDERATIONS

The structure at the interface between substrate and deposit is closely related to the characteristics of nucleation and early growth. Problems are specific to the process and conditions, and generalization is difficult. However, control of substrate-surface cleanliness is important. In PVD, ion- or electron-bombardment cleaning, followed by coating at pressures of 10^{-6} torr, permits adequate control in many cases. In ion plating, the highly energetic impact of ions with the substrate constitutes in situ cleaning, to which improved adhesion is attributed. However, a greater nucleation density relative to that in simple PVD may be a factor.

In CVD the presence of reaction intermediates at the interface may lead to poor adhesion (e.g., $TaCl_2$ at the interface between a tantalum substrate and molybdenum deposited by hydrogen reduction of molybdenum chloride). The generally lower nucleation density of CVD relative to PVD leads to more adhesion problems with CVD. Where the substrate can be heated to the point of substrate-coating interdiffusion, adhesion is improved.

One of the basic limitations of any process that yields a composite product (coating and substrate or shell and mandrel) is the tolerance for thermal-expansion mismatch of the components. Where the composite is used at low temperature, a PVD process may be preferred, since the substrate is not heated appreciably in coating. However, where the end use carries the composite to high temperatures, the deposition temperature requirements of CVD may not be a problem, and indeed may be an advantage, in minimizing thermal stress at the service temperature. The problem of thermal-expansion mismatch must be dealt with intelligently in all the situations described above.

MASS RATES OF FABRICATION

Vapor deposition is limited relative to some other ceramic-forming processes in the attainable rates of deposition, the primary factor in determining economics. Part of this limitation derives from the obvious fact that the gaseous form of matter is of low density, and large volumes must be handled for a given weight of solid product. Where the morphology of the product is compatible with a high rate of production (carbon blacks and flame-process TiO_2), or where morphology is not a factor (fluidized-bed production of granular UO_2 by hydrolysis of UF_6), the cost of processing can be as low as a few cents per pound. However, in order to obtain a dense product or a product with controlled morphology, limitations in production rate must be accepted. Thus, a growth rate in CVD of 0.1 in. per hour (attainable in deposition of dense tungsten) is considered very rapid; but more often, to prevent premature reaction and "snowing out," or to obtain some desired morphology, one must settle for 0.001 to 0.01 in. per hour.

In PVD, the advent of electron-beam heating has permitted very high rates of evaporation of materials at the source (e.g., 0.002 in. per second). However, very-high-power densities are required for this localized heating, and geometrical constraints limit the amount of evaporating area that can be exposed to the substrate on which condensation takes place. Deposition rates of 0.001 to 0.01 in. per hour are practiced. At higher rates, one encounters problems with removing the heat of condensation and radiated heat from the substrate. Forcing the rate of mass transfer can lead to splattering of the boiling metal and in some cases to gas-phase nucleation of material that can precipitate on the surface to give an inferior product.

Sputtering or reactive sputtering by ion bombardment is an inherently slow process, 1/10 to 1/100 as rapid as vacuum evaporation - condensation.

UNIFORMITY AND REPRODUCIBILITY

The present levels of uniformity and reproducibility of PVD processes and products are evidenced by the strong trend toward the use in aerospace applications of very complex microelectronic circuitry produced by PVD thin-film techniques. By contrast, in CVD the complex dependency of deposition rate and morphology on temperature, pressure, composition, and vapor-flow conditions can lead to definite problems with uniformity and reproducibility, which must be solved on an individual basis. In principle these are surmountable by good process design and control, and in a number of cases this has been demonstrated.

Ion-plating and vapor impregnation are not used widely enough to permit judging their capabilities with respect to uniformity and reproducibility on the basis of experience. However, the problems in ion-plating would be expected to be comparable to those of PVD, and in impregnation, to those of CVD.

IN-PROCESS CONTROL

In the PVD of thin films (as well as in sputtering and ion-plating), the film thickness can be monitored with high sensitivity up to a few microns by the change in vibrational frequency of a piezoelectric crystal as material is deposited on one face. The crystal is placed so that it receives a known fraction of the vapor being condensed. Thicker films may be monitored by weighing devices.

In CVD, such devices are not used because the requirement that the substrate be heated limits their range of adaptability, and the deposit thicknesses for which CVD has its greatest utility are beyond the range of such instruments. They could be used for thin films deposited by low-temperature ($< 500°C$) reactions.

In-process control of CVD is mainly based on monitoring the gaseous by-products of the chemical reaction. With proper control of the process variables, this gross rate of reaction can be related to deposit thickness. Control of thickness in the range of ± 15 to $\pm 3\%$ can be attained, depending upon the system involved.

No devices exist for the in-process monitoring of morphology in CVD processes. Because of the complex relation of process variables to the rate of deposition and morphology in CVD, control of uniformity, reliability, and reproducibility are best approached through control of process variables in a manner specific to each application.

OPPORTUNITIES FOR RESEARCH AND DEVELOPMENT

Betterment of the trade-offs between morphology and deposition rates is achievable by specific R&D programs. Widening of the arsenal of CVD feed materials is similarly achievable, and improvements in the engineering of processes will follow intensive process-development programs with specific end-item objectives.

The CVD method is one of few processes available for fabricating large shell structures of high uniformity out of high-modulus materials, and filaments of high modulus, high strength, and low density, and for material addition and other finishing operations. The most important objectives of applied research should be to adapt the conditions that have been developed largely for particle coating and impermeability to yield similarly dense, extremely fine-grained or short-range-order structures in oxides for large, thick, free-standing layers, and for coatings on refractory metal filament.

Some efforts to prepare particulates by CVD processing have seemed successful, but few have been accompanied by adequate characterization and evaluation of the product for solids processing use. One of the most fruitful outcomes of such research should be the ability to prepare sinterable oxide powders of very high purity.

As the demand for CVD materials increases, the cost will come down. However, the complexity of some synthesis processes leads to minimum costs that may still be appreciable. For example, aluminum chloride, the cheapest form of votatile aluminum, costs $1.00 per pound of contained aluminum in tonnage quantities, but the cost of tri-isobutyl aluminum at a large tonnage level is expected to be no less than $2.00 per pound of contained aluminum.

The most effective expenditure of basic research funds would be directed toward improving the understanding of nucleation and growth mechanisms. This should open the way for improvements in attainable morphologies and increased rates of production for a given morphology.

Incremental Liquid-Phase Molecular Transport

For the purposes of this report, a ceramic process employing incremental liquid-phase molecular transport is defined as one by which a solid ceramic material is formed incrementally by the deposition of, and/or surface reaction with, molecular-size units from a liquid. The majority of practical processes that fall into this category are concerned with the growth of single crystals, in either bulk or fiber (e.g., "whisker") forms. However, some of the processes included in this report yield polycrystalline shapes or films. Two basic processing categories are included: either the product and the liquid medium from which it is formed are of sensibly identical composition, or the compositions of the product and its liquid precursor are different.

Three general groups of processes are discussed herein: Melt-Freezing for the preparation of single crystals, Crystallization of a Solute from a Solvent, and Electrolytic Processes. Specifically excluded from treatment are those processes (e.g., electrophoretic deposition) that involve incremental liquid-phase transport, but in which a bonded ceramic product is apparently not achievable. Also excluded from consideration are those crystallization processes that use comparatively common solvents and occur at ordinary temperatures and pressures to yield a granular product. The only exceptions to this exclusion are processes (e.g., so-called "sol-gel") that fit into one of the three general groups just mentioned and that can be used to produce refractory ceramic materials in the form of particulates as feed material for subsequent solids processing. Brief descriptions of these process groups follow.

Melt-Freezing (Single Crystals). Comparatively large bulk single crystals are produced from melts of essentially the same composition by controlled seeding and growth. The term "seeding" denotes the initiation of single-crystal growth by any nonspontaneous means, such as the use of a suitable single-crystal fragment or the deliberate termination of the growth of all but one grain of a polycrystal assemblage started in a comparatively small volume located at one extremity of an originally all-liquid system.

Seeding is usually controlled by any or a combination of the following procedures: selecting seed crystals of the desired morphology; using a crucible or tubular container, the lower extremity of which forms the tip of a cone (as in the Stockbarger method), or is drawn into a capillary, or extended beyond a narrow restriction (as in the Tammann and Bridgman methods); maintaining the melt temperature at a suitable value within the so-called metastable range, where spontaneous nucleation is repressed; excluding from the vicinity of the melt any extraneous nucleating materials; and orienting the seed lattice properly with respect to the growth direction.

Growth can be controlled by resorting to some combination of the following means: control of the melt temperature, maintenance of proper temperature gradients in both the crystal and the melt in the neighborhood of the growth surface, use of special containers for physically confining the growth of the crystal, control of the rate of movement of the melt - crystal boundary through the zone of the furnace within which the controlled growth temperature prevails, and use of impurities (e.g., poisons or catalysts) that tend to affect growth habit. Those processes that involve zone-melting of one sort or another also belong to this group. Zone-melting processes are also used to produce polycrystalline materials of high purity.

Crystallization of a Solute from a Solvent. This group of processes features the separation of crystals from a liquid medium of sensibly different composition from that of the crystal. It includes three kinds of processes: (a) crystallization of bulk single crystals from solutions (either aqueous or nonaqueous) under comparatively mild conditions of temperature and pressure, and growth of bulk and fiber forms of single crystals by so-called flux methods, viz., by the use of molten inorganic solvents such as salts, metals, and oxides, at elevated temperatures and ordinary pressures; (b) hydrothermal crystallization near the critical point, interpreted in a broad sense to include solvent systems other than those based upon water (e.g., those based on NH_3, H_2S, or HCl); and (c) sol-gel processes.

Electrolytic Processes. Included in this group are anodic processes, electrolytic deposition from molten-salt baths, and codeposition of ceramic particles with electrolytically deposited metals. These processes are mainly limited to the application of coatings. However, dense polycrystalline bulk forms have been made, and schemes have been proposed that employ electrolytic processes for the preparation of continuous filaments of an amorphous or polycrystalline ceramic on a metallic-wire substrate.

MELT-FREEZING (SINGLE CRYSTALS)

Growth of large bulk single crystals from a melt of the same composition has been spurred tremendously in recent years, primarily by electronic and optical needs. There has been a substantial commercial effort in addition to large organized Government programs in this area. Developments of an engineering nature and a growing body of more fundamental knowledge have resulted in the capability of growing large, relatively pure, and for many purposes quite adequately defect-free single crystals. Here, four variants of melt-freezing are treated in order: viz., (a) crucible methods, (b) withdrawal techniques, (c) flame and plasma fusion, and (d) zone-melting.

Crucible Methods

For the crucible methods (Stockbarger, Tammann, and Bridgman techniques), the bottom of a crucible or tubular container that holds the melt is formed into the apex of a cone, drawn into a capillary, or extended beyond a narrow restriction. Ordinarily, the container with the melt is lowered from the hot zone of a vertical furnace at a controlled rate through a negative temperature gradient. Alternatively, the crucible is held stationary while the hot zone is raised. Horizontal modifications have also been used successfully.

Nucleation of the crystal phase begins at or very near the lowest extremity of the container. Because of the shape of the tip, that particular crystal that is oriented such that the upward component of its growth velocity is greatest eventually predominates and becomes the single crystal. It is possible to adjust the angle or curvature of the tip to control the orientation of the prevailing crystal. The Bridgman and Stockbarger techniques have produced inorganic single crystals (e.g., NaCl, KCl, and CaF_2) well over one foot in longest dimension.

There are three possible rate-limiting factors, any one of which may determine the maximum rate at which single crystals can be grown by crucible methods: (a) the net rate at which the latent heat of solidification, liberated at the melt-crystal interface, is distributed to cooler surroundings; (b) the maximum forward velocity of that particular molecular (or atomic) reaction that has the slowest rate in the sequence of steps comprising the over-all crystal-growth process; and (c) the size of the temperature interval corresponding to the metastable zone in which crystal growth can essentially occur in the absence of extraneous nucleation.

Factor (a) will be found to limit the maximum rate of production of oxides in most cases. It is dependent upon such parameters as the size of the crystal; the magnitude of the temperature gradient maintained in the furnace; the respective temperatures of the melt-crystal interface, the crucible walls below the melt-crystal interface, and the surroundings that are in a direct line of sight of that portion of the crucible below the melt-crystal interface; the thermal conductivity and transparency of the crystal phase; the rate at which the crucible is lowered through the temperature profile; the furnace design; and the emittance of the crucible and the furnace interior.

Factor (b) will generally be unimportant unless a highly viscous liquid is involved. It has been stated that crystals may grow from the melt as fast as the velocity of sound in the liquid. However, it is obvious that this can only occur when no multibarrier diffusion, surface nucleation, or reconstructive transformations are required.

Factor (c) can be tremendously important. If the metastable zone is too short in a given compound, growth of single crystals of the compound by crucible methods may be precluded. And even if growth of single crystals is not ruled out by this factor, it may severely amplify the problem of process control by restricting the temperature range within which satisfactory processing can be obtained.

There is a technical limit to the size of single crystals of any given compound that can be grown within a reasonable time. Heat released at the melt-crystal interface must travel both axially and radially through the crystal and out of the lower portions of the crucible in order for growth to proceed. For most ceramics the thermal conductivity is small. Furthermore, comparatively inert metal crucibles with smooth interior walls must almost always be used to minimize thermal resistance and make satisfactory separation of the product crystal from the container feasible. But smooth metal surfaces generally have high reflectance values, so any thermal transmittance the crystal may offer could be of little moment. Consequently, from heat-transfer considerations alone, the large magnitude of the temperature difference required will restrict the diameter of single crystals that can be grown. In addition, this temperature difference generates stresses within the crystal during the growth process, which increase in magnitude with crystal size and are therefore more likely to damage larger crystals than smaller ones.

Withdrawal Techniques

In withdrawal techniques (e.g., the Czochralski method), a comparatively cool rod, usually with a selected seed affixed in a desired orientation, is lowered into a crucible until the tip makes contact with the melt. Hydrodynamic conditions at the meniscus must be kept constant so that the melt-crystal interface is stable; therefore, various methods are used to rotate either the crucible, the crystal, or both, to accomplish this. Frequently, the crucible is restrained from vertical movement as the crystal grows and is withdrawn from the upper surface of the melt. Growth velocity (and therefore withdrawal rate), presently ranging from 1/4 in. to 1 in. per hour, is governed entirely by the net rate at which heat flows up and out of the vicinity of the melt-crystal boundary through the columnar crystal. However, it is necessary that the inherent linear growth rate of the crystal in the direction of withdrawal be enormously larger than in other directions; if it is not, the crystal will propagate laterally to the container wall early in the process, making withdrawal impossible. As is the case with the crucible methods, the temperature interval corresponding to the metastable zone must be wide enough that spontaneous nucleation of crystals will not occur in the melt or at the melt-crucible interface.

Withdrawal methods avoid the difficulties that accompany the removal of the product from a container as in the crucible methods. These techniques permit the preparation of relatively strain-free and defect-free crystals, largely because the nature of the process is such that the crystal is annealed as it is pulled, in the heat of the furnace. For example, dislocation-free silicon crystals have been produced by withdrawal methods. Although Czochralski rubies grown along the c-axis may have subgrain misorientations as large as $0.5°$, any other growth direction yields crystals with very little misorientation (e.g., 30 seconds of arc for a crystal grown at 60° to the c-axis). The dislocation count on the basal plane of rubies grown along the c-axis is typically 10^5 to $10^6/cm^2$, as compared with $10^3/cm^2$ for growth in any other direction. The number of visible scattering sites (i.e., voids or inclusions larger than about $0.5\,\mu$ and causing large-angle light scatter) is typically no more than $1/cm^3$ in present Czochralski rubies. The longitudinal variation of Cr_2O_3 content in Czochralski rubies can be controlled to less than 7% of the Cr_2O_3 concentration over 8 in. of length. Typical radial variation of the solute concentration is approximately 3% of the average concentration over the radius of 0.6-in.-diam crystals.

In the Czochralski process, the growth habit of crystals that facet strongly (e.g., garnets) is affected by impurities. Crystals grown from an impure melt show essentially no faceting and tend to be round cylinders. Faceting is generally an indication of purity. This would be expected from considerations based on thermodynamics. An undesirable result of faceting is the change in distribution coefficient over the area of the facets owing to the high growth rate. This causes a thin (1-2 mm diam) cylindrical region, which is compositionally different but structurally the same as the rest of the crystal, to form within the crystal, parallel with the growth axis.

Impurities may adsorb on the surface of a growing crystal, occupy sites at which crystal-forming species would ordinarily enter the crystal (i.e., "poison" the surface), and thus retard the growth of the crystal normal to that surface. Such posioning need not be uniform from one surface of a crystal to another, nor need the extent to which the growth rate is altered be the same for the various surfaces; hence, impurity-induced growth-habit modifications may stem from poisoning.

Czochralski ruby and sapphire crystals having 2-in. diam and 12-in. lengths are examples of the largest crystals that have been grown by withdrawal techniques. Crucible size is the major technical limitation of the size of crystals that can be grown by the Czochralski method; destructive phase change is another. Use of a crucibleless process involving, for example, electron-beam heating would be advantageous, and given reasonable time for development, almost any size oxide crystal could be grown.

At the other end of the scale, sapphire filaments 5-20 mils in diameter and up to 6 in. in length have been grown by means of a relatively new variant of the withdrawal method, viz., the "floating-orifice technique." The method features drawing the crystal from the melt through a small molybdenum ring $(0.8 \le id \le 1.6$ mm) that floats on the surface of the melt, apparently held there by its weight (which stops upward movement) and the surface tension of the liquid (which prevents it from sinking). Growth is dendritic and does not require meniscus control. The method should lend itself to continuous processing and allow the preparation of filaments that are indefinitely long. Withdrawal rates up to 150 mm/min yield satisfactory crystals. Preliminary measurements of the mechanical properties indicate elastic modulus values of $(30-50)$ $\times 10^6$ psi (vibrating reed technique), 25×10^6 psi (flexure technique), and a tensile strength of 125,000 psi.

Compositions produced by withdrawal methods include ruby, sapphire, garnets, scheelites, stoichiometric spinel, yttrium vanadate, lanthanum aluminate, lithium niobate, and lithium tantalate. Present costs reflect a small market for oxide single crystals combined with the high costs of research and development. Were the market to expand significantly, costs of about $50/lb could be expected for bulk-crystal forms.

Flame and Plasma Fusion

In all these processes, particulate ceramics pass through hot gases and become molten, much as in melt-spraying processes. The molten particles fall against a melt puddle maintained atop a boule, which is the single crystal. The boule is carefully withdrawn from the hot zone of an insulated enclosure and into a region maintained at a lower temperature, satisfactory for annealing. As the boule is withdrawn, the liquid at the melt - crystal boundary solidifies as an addition to the boule, and the melt is continuously replenished by molten particles from above. The Verneuil method, which generally utilizes an oxyhydrogen or oxyacetylene flame, is typical. Within recent years, both arc-plasma and induction-plasma devices have been used with some success in modified Verneuil processes.

In crucible and withdrawal processes, the crystal necessarily remains for such a time in the heated portion of the furnace that substantial annealing occurs. Conversely, the nature of flame or plasma fusion processes is such that special provision must be made to insulate the crystal against excessive heat loss over a distance of several inches from the melt - crystal interface. Otherwise, large temperature differences will occur in the crystal and give rise to large internal stresses that cannot be relaxed in the cooler portions of the crystal. These stresses may crack the crystal. Furthermore, the number of structural imperfections in the final product is reduced by appropriate annealing. Hence, the annealing stage is particularly critical in any flame- or plasma-fusion process.

Sapphire and ruby synthesis is the most common example of the use of these methods, although single crystals of strontium titanate, rutile, nonstoichiometric spinel, and some rare-earth oxides have also been grown. Sapphire and ruby crystals of approximately 1-in. in diameter and 12-in. in length are now common. Rutile crystals have been grown to 3/4 in. x 8 in., and others to 1/2 in. x 2 in. or 3 in. Such crystals show varying amounts of substructure, 0.5 to 2° misorientations being common in Verneuil products. Very large crystals free from such major defects are extremely rare. Porosity, however, can be very low—approaching nil. Completely cohesive, but nevertheless visible, laminae frequently show up in the boules. Transparency is high and characteristic of the spectral behavior of the crystal lattice. Bi- and multicrystals have also been produced by Verneuil methods, enabling important basic studies of "grain boundaries" to be made.

Zone-Melting

Zone-melting is a technique in which a molten zone is made to traverse the length of the solid charge, which generally is in the shape of a rod or bar. This has been done both by moving a heater over a stationary charge and by moving the charge through a fixed hot region. Usually, the charge is contained in a tube or chamber to achieve special atmospheric control. This is especially the case if undesirable reaction of either the solid or molten material with ordinary air is likely to occur, the material exhibits a high vapor pressure in the molten condition, or the material is toxic and containment is a matter of good safety practice. Tube or boat containers must be used if the viscosity and surface tension of the melt are such that excessive loss of the melt would occur simply from flow out of the zone.

Several heating methods have been used for maintaining a molten zone of satisfactory thickness. Among them are chemical or plasma flames, ring-shaped electrical-resistance heaters placed coaxially with the charge, and high-frequency induction heating. For the purification of metals and semiconductors, high-frequency induction heating has generally been the most trouble-free approach and is widely used. It is not suitable, however, for less-conductive ceramics. Within the last several years, electron-bombardment heating has enjoyed a certain vogue becuase it has a number of advantages. It is clean, capable of comparatively high-power-density heating, and relatively easy to control as long as the vapor pressure of the molten material is not excessive. Very recently a special hollow electrode has been developed that, it is claimed, makes feasible the processing of even dielectric ceramics. If this claim is a valid one, the development may have important effects on ceramic technology.

The float-zone-melting of elements and of refractory carbides and nitrides, for example, has met with considerable success in the processing of Si, Ge, UC, TiC, ZrC, and many other compounds. Bulk single crystals in the form of rods up to 1/2-in. diam or larger are articles of commerce. Extension into other compositions, including some oxides, will probably be fruitful; however, the preparation of filamentary crystals by zone-melting, while it has been done in the laboratory on a small scale, does not appear to be practical.

The most widely known application of the zone-melting process is in the production of ultrapure semiconductor materials. In this case, zone-melting assumes the role of a fractional crystallization process. As the hot zone traverses the rod, it sequentially melts the material entering its forward boundary, mixes the newly melted material with that already molten, and crystallizes the material leaving its after-boundary. The distribution coefficient for impurities between the newly formed crystal phase and the liquid of the molten zone is usually such that the concentration in the crystal is a fraction of that in the liquid. Therefore, the material crystallizing in the wake of the zone is less contaminated with impurity than that melting at its vanguard. The molten zone itself, of course, accumulates impurities, and after the necessary number of passes have been made, the short length of rod at the end to which the impurities were swept is cropped. Semiconductor materials of extremely high purity are obtained by this method. Sizes of the material produced range to diameters in inches and lengths in feet. Use of this method for purification of nonconductor ceramics would be enhanced by the success of the special hollow electrode already mentioned.

General Comments about Melt-Freezing Processes

Some impurities may be removed in the fusion process, but solution of atmospheric gases in the melt may occur, with consequent effects on the crystal, which depend, e.g., on the rate of freezing. In general, condensed impurities in the feed material are found in the crystal (randomly distributed in the case of Verneuil, but tending to be segregated toward one end or toward subboundaries in Bridgman and Czochralski crystals) if the entire quantity of feed stock is crystallized. Multiple-pass zone-melting methods are expected to provide a more satisfactory means of impurity removal.

Before the advent of the floating-orifice technique, the use of any melt-freezing process to grow free filamentary crystals was severely limited by crystallization habit. This and other novel methods of growing filaments by melt-freezing will need to be evaluated as they are developed, relative to other methods such as vapor deposition and crystallization from a solvent.

Freezing to produce single crystals requires that: (a) the melt be of relatively stable composition; (b) the vapor pressure above the melt not be impractically high; (c) the various interface conditions of limited undercooling, nucleation, growth, and heat management, for example, be met; (d) subsolidus phase changes be either absent or fortuitously controllable; and (e) the melt not tend to vitrify rather than crystallize upon cooling. For refractory materials the melting point constitutes a general problem, in that high temperatures must be achieved concurrent with precise temperature and gradient control, adequacy of materials of construction or containment, and freedom from contamination. In connection with requirements (a) and (b) above, it is interesting to note that single crystals of such materials as GaAs, PbTe, PbSe, As, and certain phosphides with melts having high ($\sim$20 atm) vapor pressures have been made to sizes of multiple inches in length and diameter by special techniques. In one such technique, the crystal was pulled from a crucible through a protective liquid (e.g., B_2O_3 for PbTe and PbSe). A float-zone-melting method was used for the high-vapor-pressure phosphides.

CRYSTALLIZATION OF A SOLUTE FROM A SOLVENT

Growth from Solvents at Ordinary Pressures

Growth of crystals from a solvent system (in some instances referred to as a "flux") can produce some important advantages over controlled freezing. Ordinarily the motivating factor is the reduction of temperature, either to escape from the restraint of very high melting points (e.g., graphite) or to avoid a troublesome subsolidus phase change (e.g., BeO). Control of the rates of undesirably rapid reactions in series and/or parallel with the key process reactions may be the reason for resorting to the use of certain kinds of solvent systems. For instance, unwanted spontaneous nucleation can sometimes be avoided in the growth of single crystals by embedding the seed crystals in a matrix of inert gel. Calcium tartrate, lithium iodide, and cuprous oxide are examples of single crystals that have been grown by this means. Reactants are placed at diametric external boundaries of the gel mass and diffuse through the gel to the seed crystal to react and feed the growth process. By carefully situating the seeds in the gel at correct distances from the reactant reservoirs, and controlling concentration gradients of the reactants and the temperature, extraneous nucleation can be suppressed.

Other considerations of either practicality or convenience often suggest a solvent method. Among these is the occasional occurrence of a strongly preferred growth habit from a flux, from which filamentary crystals can be grown.

Disadvantages or problems arising from the use of a complex melt composition include its inevitable effect on the chemical composition or purity of the crystals, the introduction of boundary-layer concentration effects, susceptibility to inclusions, and consequent restrictions on growth rates attainable. Both engineering and fundamental scientific handicaps are accentuated in flux growth of crystals relative to freezing methods; nevertheless, the technique is being employed successfully in a number of instances, when sufficient care has been exercised to understand and place limits on the growth parameters. Although refractory crystals grown by such means are characteristically small in most cases, it is evident that this results from engineering (and cost) limitations rather than any inherent physics. Large single crystals (up to 240 lbs in the case of alum, 46 lbs in the case of $NH_4H_2PO_4$) have been grown synthetically from solvents.

Examples of current small-scale practice include graphite, BeO, various spinels, rare-earth orthoaluminates, garnets, ThO_2, Al_2O_3, and a number of electronically, optically, or magnetically active crystals in bulk or platelet forms. Also, long (up to approximately 2 in.) slender (approximately 0.2 mm) crystals of Al_2O_3, ZrO_2, TiO_2, and BeO have been grown. The BeO crystals were very pure. Major contaminants were Si, B, and Al, which were present in amounts less than 50 ppm.

Growth of reasonably large sapphire and ruby single crystals has been accomplished from a cryolite (i.e., Na_3AlF_6) solvent. The liquidus diagram for cryolite-alumina shows a eutectic at 962°C and approximately 11% Al_2O_3, which is indicative of the temperatures at which processing can occur. A mixture of 87.5 wt % Na_3AlF_6 and 12.5 wt % Al_2O_3 was melted with 3% chromia (1,040°C). A platinum crucible was used. A clear solution was obtained, then a 1/8-in. diam sapphire seed crystal was immersed through the top of the liquid. The temperature was then lowered at 1.5°C/hr, allowing the crystal to grow on the stationary seed. When 960°C was reached, the crystal was removed from the liquid and cooled to room temperature in the furnace. The size of the crystal obtained was 1/2 in. x 1/2 in. x 3/16 in. From this, a calculation of the rate of growth can be made: roughly 10^{-3} in.^{3} or 10^{-4} lb per hour. Several Laue patterns taken over the entire area of the single crystal matched perfectly, having no orientation differences or spot distortion. These results indicate a high degree of crystal perfection.

Two general modifications of flux growth of crystals predominate. The more common and more primitive involves saturating the solvent with the compound to be crystallized, then slowly cooling the entire mass to nucleate and grow one or a crop of crystals in a single batch. Generally, when single crystals of reasonable size are sought, the crystallization is initiated by selected seed(s), and the temperature (and therefore the supersaturation) is controlled to avoid spontaneous nucleation.

The other, more sophisticated, method has been less practiced but embodies the flexibility and potential for control desirable for long-range development. In this case, a constant temperature difference is maintained along one (ordinarily vertical) dimension of the solvent, a nutrient source of the crystal composition is placed at one end, and one or more crystals are grown at the other. Under suitable conditions, crystals should be able to be "pulled" from such a system, as for example in the Czochralski freezing method previously described. In the case of crystallization from solvents under comparatively mild conditions, this second modification can be arranged in such a way that the nutrient and growth sections are in more widely separated locations, connected by piping. If this is possible, more positive control can be maintained over the growth process, since the saturated fluid from the nutrient section can be pumped through filters and heat exchangers on the way to the growth system. Whether this could be successfully applied to processes using, e.g., molten salts, metals, and oxides as solvents is not known and would depend a great deal on the specific case (e.g., the solvents used or the temperatures required).

One variant of those methods involving growth from a solvent deserves special mention here. It is the so-called "traveling solvent" process, also a variant of the zone-melting technique already discussed. A flux, or solvent composition, is placed over a single-crystal base that is oriented to give growth along the desired direction. On top of the flux is the polycrystalline material that is to be melted and then crystallized as single-crystal material in extending the single-crystal seed. The flux moves along in the molten zone, which traverses the polycrystalline material.

Hydrothermal Crystallization

Hydrothermal crystal growth is a special case of the general solvent class. Nature provides numerous examples in which very large oxidic crystals have been achieved by this means. Hydrothermally grown natural quartz and beryl single crystals weighing as much as 5 and 19 tons, respectively, have been found. The essence of the basic process lies in the equilibrium attainable between the oxy- and the aqueous hydroxy- form of a large number of compositions, and in the high mobility of the hydrogen atom involved in this equilibrium. Supercritical water is the common solvent, or transport medium. Variants of the hydrothermal process include some homologues of water: NH_3, H_2S, and HCl, for example.

It can be argued that hydrothermal processes are necessarily distinguished from other, more moderate, environmental variants of chemical reaction systems by being operated above the critical point; and, in any event, a physical distinction exists at this point in the governing phase diagram for the system. An important advantage of hydrothermal crystallization is that the use of pressure as a variable adds an important dimension to process control and allows variations in product character not always possible with other methods.

100

Some critical conditions are:

Compound	Critical Temperature ($^\circ$C)	Critical Pressure (atm)
H_2O	374	218
NH_3	132	112
H_2S	100	89
HCl	51	82

A knowledge of the phase system under critical or supercritical conditions is essential to better than empirical-methods development; however, since the equipment requirements are similar for both phase investigation and crystal growth, it is not uncommon that both are investigated simultaneously. Autoclave apparatus is essential; and beyond the matter of phase relations and the corresponding selection of nutrient, solvent, and operating conditions, autoclave development has largely paced the achievements of the method.

Factors that influence autoclave materials and design include: ability to resist attack at high temperatures and pressures by acids, bases, and oxidizing agents; ease of leak-tight assembly and disassembly; sufficient mechanical strength, ruggedness, and durability at temperature; size, relative to the size of crystals to be grown and allowing for necessary temperature gradients to achieve material transport from nutrient to seed regions; provision for measurement and control of parameters; safety of operation; and cost. Some of the most important accomplishments of the past, and areas in which further development is needed, are in trouble-free closures and "cold-wall," or more properly termed, insulated-wall (internally heated) designs.

Crystals that have been grown by hydrothermal means include a large number of compositions. Some of those in which substantial size has been achieved (ranging from multiple millimiters to multiple inches in dimensions) are:

Al_2O_3 (ruby, sapphire)	CdO	SiO_2 (quartz)
$AlAsO_4$	CdS	V_2O_3
$AlPO_4$	Fe_3O_4	V_2O_4
$Be_3Al_2Si_6O_{18}$ (beryl)	NaCl	$ZnFe_2O_4$
BeO	$NiFe_2P_4$	ZnO
CaF_2	PbO	ZnS

The process is characteristically slow relative to freezing of the molten compound, and although fibers of materials such as sodium amphibole have been grown in lengths up to 4 in., it appears impractical to grow whiskers in quantity and economically by this means relative to other approaches. The uniform distribution of dopants has been fraught with difficulty and requires much more advanced knowledge of the basic aspects of material transport. Better knowledge and understanding of the solubility of compounds in supercritical fluids is needed. Only batch processing is feasible at present, and the autoclave-chamber dimensions limit production capacity and the sizes of crystals that can be produced. Lack of better closures also limits the hydrothermal approach.

The Sol-Gel Process

The sol-gel process has been used to produce particulate spheres of thoria, alumina, urania-thoria, zirconia, and plutonia. The example given here is the process for thoria. This consists of four steps: (a) steam denitration of thorium nitrate to prepare an easily dispersible (peptizable) thoria powder; (b) dispersion of the thoria powder to a nitrate-stabilized sol in water; (c) careful evaporation of the sol to form a gel; and (d) calcination of the gel at the relatively low temperature of 1,150°C to form large dense particles of oxide.

Satisfactory thoria for sol preparation can be made in several ways. However, the simplest procedure is the hydrothermal denitration of thorium nitrate. This is ordinarily accomplished at about 475°C in a horizontal rotary batch denitrator. Thorium nitrate solution and superheated steam are fed to the denitrator, and, at the end of a 3-hour period, a granular, free-flowing, off-white thoria is obtained, which contains residual nitrate to the extent of 0.08 NO_3^-/ThO_2.

The thoria from the denitrator is easily suspended in dilute nitric acid at 80°C by the shearing action of a centrifugal pump, which breaks apart the loose agglomerates of oxide to form the sol. The most important single factor that determines dispersal or flocculation is the pH. The optimum range for dispersal is $2 < pH < 4$. At $pH \lesssim 2$ the thoria particles dissolve slowly, while flocculation begins to occur at $pH \gtrsim 4$.

If the oxide contains significantly less than the optimum amount of nitrate, dispersion is incomplete. Significantly greater-than-optimum nitrate contents result in a soft flocculent precipitate that can be dispersed by addition of water. However, oxide particles made subsequently from such sols are glassy, fraught with cracks, and unsuitable.

The sol is evaporated to dryness in shallow trays at 135°C for approximately 24 hours. A sol depth of 3/4 in. is used. The resulting gel breaks into fragments 2-3 mm in dimension.

Calcination of the ThO_2 gel at 1,150°C is optimum so far as maximum densification is concerned. This process requires about 4 hours. At the gel stage the particles have specific gravities of 5 to 6 and still contain water and nitrate. Rapid calcination of these particles does not cause further fragmentation, and the rate of temperature rise during the calcination step does not appear to be a critical factor.

The final granular material is polycrystalline, with crystallite sizes of approximately 2,000 Å (measured by x-ray diffraction line broadening). The density of each particle is high (99% of theoretical), and the B.E.T. surface areas are low (0.01 m^2/g). Electron microscopy reveals crystallite sizes of about 5,000 Å. The discrepancy may be due to strain-broadening of the x-ray pattern.

The product of the sol-gel process is admirably suited as feed material for solids processing. Its high density and free-flowing qualities result in excellent green densities of pressed and extruded bodies and consequently in low firing shrinkage. Densification by sintering or pressure sintering results in matured ceramics of nearly theoretical density.

As noted, the sol-gel process has to date been explored almost exclusively in the nuclear ceramics field. Extension of the range of compositions into refractory structural ceramics should be carried out; success with Al_2O_3, TiO_2, and several other oxides seems very likely.

ELECTROLYTIC PROCESSES

Specific kinds of processes to be discussed under this category are anodic processes, including anodic-spark synthesis of ceramic coatings, and electrolytic deposition from molten-salt baths.

Anodic Processes

The most common anodic process is so-called "anodizing" in which an oxide-conversion coating is formed on the surface of a metal that is used as the anode in an aqueous electrolyte bath. While coatings can be generated on the surfaces of many different metals (e.g., Al, Mg, Ti, Sn, Cd, and Ta) by this method, the specific application that has been most successful and widespread in its use is that involving aluminum and its alloys.

Baths reportedly used for anodizing aluminum include chromic, sulfuric, boric, phosphoric, oxalic, malonic, sulfamic, succinic, tartaric, fumaric, glutaric, and adipic acids. The cost of the acid is an important aspect of the process economics, so several of these acids do not find wide commercial use. Two general kinds of coatings may be achieved, depending upon the conditions imposed—either a porous coating, or a hard comparatively impermeable one called a "barrier" layer. Generally, the greater the solvent action is, the thicker and more porous will be the coating. Also, higher current densities tend to yield more-porous coatings. The nature of the coating also varies somewhat depending upon which acid is used. Thicknesses are commonly of the order of tenths of mils from chromic- or sulfuric-acid baths. Film thicknesses achieved from boric-acid baths are typically in the thousandths of mils. Infrared analyses of barrier layers formed on aluminum from various baths indicate that hydrogen is an integral part of the coating. Evidence collected indicates that the barrier layer has a trihydrate composition, and as anodizing progresses further to produce the porous layer, the Al = O double bond forms. It is proposed that the "parent" layer of the porous structure is actually a barrier layer that has undergone a conversion form a tight-cyclic to a lower-molecular-weight decyclic molecular structure. Anodized coatings can be very hard and wear-resistant. The process is limited to the making of relatively thin coatings, but has also been used for the complete conversion of the metal (e.g., fine wires) to oxide.

On some metals (e.g., Mg) the quality of the coating, while not as good as with aluminum, is sufficient to render the metal more useful. Additional work needs to be done to characterize the coatings formed on metals and alloys other than those based on aluminum.

Anodic-spark discharges may occur if the breakdown voltage of a barrier film on an anode is exceeded. Such barrier films may consist of an oxide or other compound of the anode metal (e.g., Ta_2O_5 on Ta, CdS on Cd), or may consist chiefly of material deposited electrolytically from the anion constituent of the electrolyte (e.g., Al_2O_3 films deposited on various metals from solutions of sodium aluminate). Anodic sparking is under investigation as a means of obtaining dense refractory forms of metal oxides and sulfides, for example, as coatings.

In the anodic-sparking process a low voltage first applied to the cell causes initial passage of current and ordinary anodizing. This current then decays as a result of the formation of the barrier film on the anode surface. Next, the cell voltage is increased, causing further passage of current, with an accompanying increase in the thickness of the barrier film. The film thickness increases almost linearly with the applied voltage until the film becomes unstable. The instability of the coating is believed to be due to the build-up of internal stresses in the film and the onset of dielectric breakdown. Voltages required for dielectric breakdown are ordinarily of the order of a few hundred volts. Finally, continued passage of current at voltages exceeding the breakdown value gives essentially continuous sparking and localized high temperatures. The high temperatures give rise to interactions involving the electrolyte constituents, the anode metal, and the intervening coating. The voltage-vs-time curve is almost flat in the region where anodic sparking occurs (at voltages up to 500 V).

The spark sites migrate over the anode surface. It is presumed that this is due to sealing of the spark channel with ceramic products. Some anions, e.g., PO_4^{-3} in aqueous solutions, seem to promote movement of the sparks over the surface, causing the formation of more uniform coatings. Improvements in coating uniformity appear to result when alternating, rather than direct, emf is applied.

The composition of the spark reaction product depends upon the anode and the electrolyte constituents. However, accurate predictions of all the constituents that will comprise the products cannot be made at present. Alpha phases are generally obtained. This is indicative of very high temperatures in the anode sparks. Metals that readily form anodic-barrier oxide films (e.g., Al, Ta, Nb, Zr, Ti, Si, and the rare-earth metals) and have refractory oxides, usually yield coatings containing such oxides. If the electrolyte contains an anion that forms a stable insoluble compound with the anode metal, it is likely to occur in the coating (e.g., MgF_2; CdS; ZnS; $MgAl_2O_4$; $MgSiO_4$; $Cd_2Nb_2O_7$; various aluminum silicates; and sulfides, aluminates and vanadates of rare-earth metals).

Advantages of anodic-spark coating processes are: ease of application; coverage of interior surfaces; bulk heating of the object being coated is not required; and there is a wide range of possible compositions. The disadvantages are: coatings are limited to thicknesses of about 12 mils (a few minutes are required for deposition of a mil of coating); coatings are porous, although they tend to protect and the porosity can ordinarily be corrected by postdeposition sealing procedures; precise control of coating composition is presently lacking; and the process is inapplicable, in some cases, to assemblies involving several metals.

Electrolytic Deposition of Ceramics from Molten-Salt Baths

Considerable work has been done on molten-salt systems, but relatively little has been found dealing in any direct way with the deposition of ceramics. What was found, however, gives reason to believe that this will be a particularly important area for futher research and development.

A pertinent example is in the electrolytic growth of dense self-supported UO_2 shapes. Polycrystalline cylinders greater than 1/2 in. in diameter and 3 in. in length have been grown by electrodeposition from molten-chloride (LiCl and KCl) solutions of uranyl chloride. Graphite electrodes 1/4 in. and 1/8 in. in diameter were used. The product was dense—up to 99% of theoretical. It was composed of radially oriented columnar grains. Chemical purity was reasonable, with melt components LiCl and KCl present in amounts of less than 50 ppm of the cation and as low as 200 ppm of the anion. Both density and purity of the product improved with increasing temperature and with decreasing deposition voltage.

OPPORTUNITIES FOR RESEARCH AND DEVELOPMENT

The nature of undercooled liquids needs to be better understood. In some systems there is evidence that significant structural differences exist between normal and undercooled liquids. For example, for a number of associated liquids the activation energy for viscous flow changes abruptly as the liquid is cooled through the solidification temperature, even though no crystallization occurs. This phenomenon is not observed in so-called nonassociated liquids (e.g., benzene or toluene). It needs to be determined how general this behavior is. The phenomenon itself needs to be understood. The manner in which the differences between normal and undercooled liquids affect the course of nucleation and growth phenomena in crystallization needs to be ascertained.

The literature abounds with theoretically derived relationships for the crystallization rate, both in nucleation and in growth. In many cases, the models upon which these relationships are derived are in obvious conflict. In those cases where the general form of the derived relationship is inadequate to describe simple experimental data (e.g., rate vs temperature or rate vs time), it is easy to rule out faulty models. But the ability of a derived equation to describe the available experimental results successfully is a necessary but not a sufficient test of the validity of the underlying model. For example, two equations of obviously conflicting origin can agree equally well with the available data. This is the case with a number of relationships for the crystallization rate. The opportunity for further research is in the design of new critical experiments and the acquisition of new data to test the existing postulates. This work would not only test the validity of extant relationships, but should eventually provide the tools necessary to calculate nucleation and growth rates from a knowledge of system parameters.

Data on the properties of oxide liquids near the melting point would be of value. This would include changes in volume, structure, and transport properties that occur on melting and freezing.

The development of crucibleless processes for withdrawal techniques of crystal growth would be most worthwhile. This would result in better control of the crystal chemical composition as well as in larger-size crystals.

Recent work with metals has shown that, for example for turbine blades, metal single-crystal structures have properties superior to those of fine-grained cast structures. The same apparently holds for oxides. Since it is possible to obtain single-crystal oxides by freezing, the fabrication of shaped single crystals and the suitability of these for structural components should be explored. This direct forming of single crystals to a useful shape appears to be within reach. For example, in the Stockbarger and similar methods, if the main crucible cavity is shaped to produce a "blank" ceramic object (e.g., turbine bucket or leading edge), much wasteful and costly grinding can be eliminated. Some success has been achieved in forming cylinders by the Verneuil method and in forming disc or sheet crystals by a "float" modification of crucible growth. These important approaches need to be further investigated and developed.

Development of low-cost means of refining ceramic raw materials would be a boon to both DOD and commercial ceramic processing. Purity of available raw materials and the costs associated with present refining methods constitute major limitations in the economical production of high-purity single crystals.

The mechanisms involved in the deposition process in anodic sparking need to be determined. Further, the anodic-spark product needs to be more adequately characterized, and related to processing parameters. For example, the dependence of coating composition and properties on electrolyte and anode compositions, and electrochemical process variables, needs to be revealed. This understanding needs to be extended to systems other than oxides.

The successful obtainment of dense UO_2 shapes from fused-salt electrolytic techniques indicates that this method should be extended to other oxide systems. The same need for extension to more compositions of interest exists for the sol-gel process.

The potential of synthetic hydrothermal growth of crystals for large size, as exemplified in many natural crystals, requires engineering advancement. Furthermore, satisfactory control of dopant concentration and distribution has not been achieved for crystals grown hydrothermally. This is probably also a limitation that can be overcome by the development of better and/or larger apparatus. However, it is conceivable that the problem could be overcome in other ways, e.g., by use of high-purity nutrient and programmed auxiliary feeding of the dopant to the autoclave during the process. The nature of super-critical fluids and the solubility of ceramic materials therein need to be known and understood better. Also, the kinetics of dissolution and crystal growth in a hydrothermal situation need to be investigated in greater depth. In particular, the roles of "mineralizers," temperature, pressure, intense magnetic fields, and the hydrodynamics of the fluid in the autoclave require study.

Methods of growing filamentary single crystals from the melt and from fluxes need to be further developed. For example, it may be that the floating-orifice technique, which enjoys a certain success for obtaining filaments of single crystals from melts, can be adapted to grow continuous filament of high-modulus crystals from fluxes. Exploratory work to find improved fluxes also needs to be pursued, while the constant-temperature-gradient method and means of adapting it to the growth of very long fibers should be explored.

Molten-Particle Spray Processes

One type of fluid processing that has received only a minimum of attention for the forming of free-standing ceramics is the molten-particle spraying process. In this process the structure is formed by projecting small, high-speed, largely to completely molten particles against almost any solid substrate. When the particles strike the cold surface of the substrate, they flatten and freeze, building up a solid ceramic structure. Free-standing shapes and coatings can be formed by the process, although when a free-standing shape is desired, a substrate is selected that can be removed after spraying, generally by chemical dissolution at present.

SPRAYING METHODS

The five processes currently in use for applying coatings, which could presumably be used for forming solid ceramics, are listed in Table 5. A brief description of each follows.

Oxyacetylene Powder Gun

Several hand-operated guns of this type are available. Costs of the equipment are nominal. Basically, the guns operate in a manner similar to an oxyacetylene welding torch, except provision is made for aspirating a controlled flow of a ceramic powder into the flame along with the acetylene. The ceramic

Table 5. Some Processing Parameters for Molten Particle Spraying Processes

Spray Process	Materials That Can Be Sprayed	Usual Particle Size in Spray (μ)	Max Particle Velocity (ft/sec)	Usual Porosity of Deposit (Vol %)	Surface Finish of Deposit (rms μ-in.)	Deposition Cost[a]
Oxyacetylene powder gun	Ceramic powders with MP <5000°F	1 - 45	150	10 - 15	150 - 300	Low to medium
Oxyacetylene rod gun	Selected ceramic rods with MP <5000°F	1 - 30	600	6 - 10	200 - 300	Medium
Liquid-fuel gun	Selected ceramic powders with MP <5000°F	1 - 20	1,000	1 - 20	150 - 300	Low
Detonation gun	Selected ceramic powders	1 - 20	2,500	0.5 - 1.0	50 - 100	High
Arc-plasma gun	Almost all ceramic powders	1 - 45	1,500[b]	3 - 15[d]	75 - 125	Low
Induction-plasma gun	Almost all ceramic powders	1 - 45	[c]			

[a]Estimated costs for spraying alumina: low $10/lb, medium $40/lb, high > $1,000/lb
[b]Obtainable through high chamber pressures.
[c]Probably very low without a nozzle. Gun manufacturer states high velocities can be obtained if nozzle is used.
[d]Low value of 3% obtainable with high chamber pressures.

particles melt in the flame and are directed against a substrate to give a solid layer. Spraying distances are normally 3 to 4 in. Cooling of some substrates is required. Powder feed must be closely controlled. Low feed rates lead to inefficient operation; high rates lead to incomplete melting of the particles.

Oxyacetylene Rod Gun

Ceramic in the form of a sintered rod is fed into an oxyacetylene flame at a controlled rate. Melting occurs at the rod tip. When the force of the hot gas stream exceeds that of the surface-tension force, the molten material is torn away from the tip and atomized into small droplets. These droplets are then accelerated by high-velocity air introduced at the nozzle to propel the particles at high speed to the substrate. Spraying by this method is not continuous, but rather intermittent, with intervals of as long as 0.005 sec between bursts. Spraying rates tend to be low. However, it is the only process where complete melting of the ceramic can be 100% assured, since it is impossible for the gun to spray until the molten ceramic forms at the rod tip.

Liquid-Fuel Gun

A relatively new approach to molten-particle spraying is being developed for forming the refractory linings of oxygen converters in steel mills. The experimental gun now in use operates with a liquid fuel plus oxygen. The water-cooled gun is 3 in. in diameter by about 3 ft long. Heavy fuel oil has been used successfully. With such a fuel, the powder is mixed with the oil to give a suspension, resulting in a much higher concentration, more uniform distribution of particles in the flame, and better heat transfer than are obtained in any other spraying method. Spraying is done while the substrate is at 1,500°C. Rates are 5-10 lbs/min with the present gun; however, a new design with a gun 8 in. in diameter by 5 ft long is expected to spray at 250 lbs/min.

Alumina, mullite, silica, and some other oxides have been sprayed. Porosities of the deposits can be varied by changing spray parameters. The minimum porosity so far achieved is about 1%, although porosities up to 20% can be obtained. Maximum particle velocities are estimated to be about 1,000 ft per second. Deposit efficiencies are approximately 75% at the present time.

Detonation or "Flame-Plate" Method

This method uses a shock wave to propel the particles. The powder that forms the coating is fed in a stream of nitrogen into the rear of a 5-ft-long water-cooled stainless-steel tube. An explosive mixture of oxygen and acetylene is metered into the tube at the same time, and at the right instant the mixture is ignited by means of a spark plug. The process is discontinuous, the explosions occurring at a rate of about four per second. Because of high noise levels, the operation is carried out in a blockhouse by remote control. Coatings are formed by moving the part to be coated in front of the gun orifice. Particle velocities are very high, and the substrate need not be placed close to the tube nozzle. Working distances of three to four feet are common. The high particle velocities result in low-porosity structures. There is little evidence of the "flattened-particle" structure that can be detected in ceramics formed by other spray processes.

Arc-Plasma Gun

In this equipment a high-intensity direct-current arc is maintained in a closed chamber having a water-cooled copper nozzle or orifice at one end. A gas (usually helium or argon) is introduced into the chamber at a constant rate.

The gas is heated by the arc and is expelled from the orifice as a high-temperature high-velocity plasma. Particles of the ceramic material are injected into the plasma by means of a small amount of the carrier gas through an opening in the nozzle. Introduction of the powder at the nozzle rather than in the arc crater means that the particles are subjected to only brief periods of heating—also, not all particles reach the hot core of the plasma. Thus, regardless of the high temperature of the plasma, complete melting is not easily achieved, especially in the case of the larger particles. Because of these effects, claims that a plasma gun is capable of spraying satisfactory deposits of any material, no matter how refractory, have not always been borne out by experimental evidence.

The high temperature of the plasma creates problems of substrate heating, and some means of cooling the substrate is often required. In some cases, cooling air can be employed to deflect the hot gases without seriously affecting the temperature or trajectories of the particles.

Induction-Plasma Gun

The induction-plasma gun is a recent development. The operating principle is the same as that of the high-frequency induction heating of metals. A plasma-forming gas is fed into a refractory-lined enclosure which is surrounded by an induction coil. A conductive load (arc) is first produced within the enclosure by an ignition system. The rf field then couples to the hot conductive gas. Powder for spraying is fed by means of the carrier gas into either the top or bottom of the enclosure. Claimed benefits for the gun include large plasma diameter and freedom from nozzle problems. Particle velocities, however, are low unless a restriction or nozzle is placed at the outlet end to create higher pressures in the enclosure.

COMPOSITIONS

Almost any oxide, carbide, boride, nitride, or silicide that does not decompose or vaporize on heating can be sprayed by one or more of the spraying processes mentioned previously. Each material normally requires pretesting to determine the optimum conditions with respect to, e.g., carrier gas, power, and gas settings. Loss of stoichiometry sometimes occurs when spraying carbides. However, this can be corrected in most cases by adding methane to the gas stream to produce a carbon-rich atmosphere.

Loss of stoichiometry also occurs with some oxides, hafnia and titania being notable examples. This loss is usually reflected by an anion deficiency.

In general, pure metal carbides yield poorly bonded deposits, probably because of lack of complete melting. Admixtures or impure powders are required to achieve suitable structures for materials of this type. Oxidation during spraying must be avoided.

The purity of the deposited material is dependent on the purity of the ceramic introduced at the gun. This can be high or low, depending on individual requirements. Impurities may be introduced during spraying by gas adsorptions and/or gas reactions. The presence of water vapor in fuel-burning guns presents the threat of the formation of some hydroxide, although its presence has not been reported in the deposits. Also, the possible formation of nitrides in deposits formed by certain spraying processes cannot be overlooked.

The spray processes lend themselves readily to the formation of multiphase structures. Mixed oxides, and cermets consisting of both ceramic and metal phases, can be formed. However, if thermal properties of the two materials are widely different, it is sometimes necessary to introduce the materials to the spray gun at different points or to spray simultaneously from two guns, each spraying a different material.

Fiber-reinforced composites can be prepared by spraying techniques. One problem that has not been overcome, however, is how to spray the matrix material on the underside of the fiber. Unless this is done, fibers are bonded on their top surfaces only.

CONFIGURATIONS

The nature of the spray process is such that almost any simple configuration can be produced. The easiest to form are flat plates and cylinders, although cones and even spheres (with a hole for substrate removal) are possible by suitable movement of the work and/or the gun during the spraying operation. Because of spray-angle effects, the deposit does not form at the same rate in recesses and on edges as it does on other surfaces. The highest density is always achieved when the spray strikes normal to the surface, and angles more oblique than 45° appear to be impractical.

SIZE LIMITATIONS AND DIMENSIONAL CONTROL

Close tolerances are possible with particle-sprayed parts through close control and mechanization of the spraying process. When these precautions are taken, part dimensions can be controlled to ±0.001 in. on cylindrical surfaces and to ±0.002 in. on flat surfaces. Also, most sprayed materials can be surface-ground if closer tolerances (or better surface finishes) are required.

There is no inherent size limitation in coating parts by the spray processes. However, when spraying large free-standing shapes on a removable substrate, some difficulties might be expected from cracking due to internal stresses. These difficulties are not insurmountable, however, and the production of alumina or zirconia parts several feet long with up to 1/2 in.-thick walls seems well within the range of possibility.

STRUCTURE OF DEPOSITS

When examining polished sections of sprayed structures, lines of demarcation between flattened particles are usually observed. In some deposits these boundaries can be detected without etching; in others, a severe etch is required before they become visible. These are not grain boundaries in the usual sense. The crystals, because of rapid quenching, are normally too small to be seen with a microscope.

In addition to the flattened particle boundaries, striations or lamination boundaries can often be detected. These appear to be associated with the application of successive layers during the spraying.

In general, the higher the particle velocity, the less distinct the flattened-particle boundaries. In fact, in flame-plate deposits, which are prepared with particle velocities up to 2,500 ft per second, the boundaries are usually undetectable in the polished sections. Particle size can also affect the distinctness of the boundaries.

Pores in the deposits are normally small and uniformly distributed. Occasionally, in some of the powder processes, a few unmelted grains are present.

X-ray diffraction patterns of deposits will show line broadening typical of a very fine crystal size. This is to be expected in view of the extremely high quenching rates on impact. The occurrence of metastable and defect crystal structures is common. For example, the rapid quench rate in the case of alumina prevents the formation of the stable alpha phase. Instead, metastable phases form. The phase may be gamma, eta, or delta, depending on the cooling rate. It has been shown that monoclinic zirconia converts to the cubic form on spraying. Also, hafnia and some other oxides are difficult to spray without loss of stoichiometry. Zirconium silicate (zircon) dissociates on spraying to cubic zirconium oxide and silica.

PROPERTIES OF DEPOSITS

So far as is known, no molten-particle spray deposit has ever been prepared that has strength properties in the as-sprayed condition approaching those of its sintered or hot-pressed counterpart. The modulus of rupture of alumina sprayed with a rod gun is about one-fifth that of pressed and sintered alumina. This may be due partly to the different crystalline phases that are present, but the major factor is probably the lack of strong cohesive bonding among the flattened particles in the sprayed deposit. The particles remain molten only for a few milliseconds after impacting the cold layers deposited earlier, and this is probably an insufficient time for the strongest type of cohesion to develop. From the microstructures, considerably stronger cohesion may be expected for the flame-plate and best plasma-sprayed deposits than for the deposits formed by the lower-velocity processes. This is borne out by modulus of rupture values for flame-plated alumina, which are reported to be in the range 20×10^6 to 24×10^6 psi.

Moduli of elasticity are also lower for the sprayed deposits than for their pressed and sintered counterparts. The modulus for rod-sprayed alumina, for example, has been reported to be only 6.5×10^6 psi as against 30×10^6 to 40×10^6 psi for pressed and sintered alumina. The elastic modulus of flame-plated alumina is approximately 12×10^6 psi.

The usual porosities of sprayed deposits formed by the different processes are included in Table 5. These are the porosity ranges normally achieved when spraying alumina or zirconia. With other materials, the porosity could be higher or lower than those listed. The spraying of largely nonporous deposits is theoretically possible on hot substrates, since quenching rates are lower and the molten particles have longer flow times after impact.

All normally formed sprayed deposits are permeable. Even the flame-plate product, which appears from the microstructure to be completely free of connecting pores, will permit some penetration of fluids. This behavior suggests the presence of micro-sized capillaries, possibly caused by occasional poor cohesion between particles.

In molten-particle spraying, the small particles strike the cold substrate and solidify, particle by particle, in successive layers. Each particle shrinks on solidification and then shrinks further by thermal contraction as it cools. This deposit mechanism generates internal stress gradients in the system, with the initially formed layers in compression and the outer layers in tension. Such stresses can be relieved by a suitable heat treatment, or they could be reduced to insignificant levels by spraying onto a substrate maintained at high temperature.

UNIFORMITY AND REPRODUCIBILITY

The principal current use for molten-particle spraying processes is the application of protective coatings to metal substrates to provide wear resistance, thermal insulation, thermal control, or electrical insulation. There is presently a sizable commercial production of alumina and zirconia coatings on metals and alloys, and this market is expanding. The continued commercial use of the coatings at least implies that uniform and reproducible applications are possible. The most uniform applications demand close control of all spraying parameters by the manufacturer. In the case of the flame-plate process, the coatings are always applied by the manufacturer of the equipment, to ensure that optimum control is achieved for each application.

The same type of process control could be achieved in the forming of free-standing shapes. Reproducible deposits should be achievable with practically no limitation of size. However, without more research, some nonuniformity could be expected on a micro basis.

FABRICATION COSTS

Classification of fabrication costs by the molten-spraying processes is included in Table 5. These costs do not include capital outlay for the equipment, which varies from a few hundred dollars for an oxyacetylene gun to several thousands of dollars for plasma spray guns or flame-plating equipment. Where power costs are low, the plasma gun is perhaps the most economical method of application. A cost of $9.35 per pound of deposited zirconia was reported in 1964. Still more economical applications might be achieved with the liquid-fueled deposition gun now under development.

PARTICULATES

The molten-particle spraying processes lend themselves readily, by simply omitting the target and spraying into a large chamber, to the preparation of small spherical particles. These particles have high density, are free-flowing, and can be made with high purity. However, with few exceptions they have been laboratory curiosities because of high cost, which may be four to five times that of irregular-shaped powder. One current use of particles made in this way is that of aluminum particulates used for certain solid-fuel propellants. Ceramic materials that have been spheroidized for special purposes (usually in a plasma flame) include alumina, zirconia, boron carbide, uranium dioxide, uranium carbide, and mullite. A more interesting technique for present purposes is to spray particles of high-purity metals into oxygen, thus burning them to yield a high-purity oxide "smoke." Efforts have previously resulted in incomplete burning, but this should be surmountable.

OPPORTUNITIES FOR RESEARCH AND DEVELOPMENT

Certain features of molten-particle spraying processes make them attractive for a number of structural-ceramic applications. A brief summary of both the advantages and present limitations of the spraying processes is given in Table 6.

The advantages listed are very important ones. With the advent of high-velocity spraying methods, molten-particle spray processes have now demonstrated an excellent potential for the fabrication of high-performance ceramic bodies. Partly because of the listed disadvantages (including cost), and partly because spraying development has largely been conducted by commercial technologists, this potential has not been adequately recognized. The important limitations can be overcome by systematic research, while the great variety of circumstances under which spraying seems attractive require verification and development work.

Of all the types of fluid processes studied, the molten-particle spray process is among those capable of the most rapid and significant advancement through research. It promises a wide variety of product configurations of superior quality for structural applications. A great deal of work needs to be done, however, before this capability can be realized.

The procedure of spraying onto a cold substrate holds little promise for forming highly uniform and reliable free-standing structural ceramics. The improvements in character that might be achieved by spraying onto a hot substrate, however, are sufficiently attractive to justify considerable research in this area. Such research should be directed to the following: flow properties of molten droplets as a function of substrate temperature, effect of size range and velocity of particles on structure, effect of substrate temperature on particle cohesion, effect of substrate temperature on internal stresses, and effect of postdeposition heat treatment on microstructure.

Systematic studies of all the process variables are recommended for the

Table 6.   Advantages and Limitations of Molten-Particle Spray Processes

Advantages	Limitations
Versatility in configuration, size, shape, and structure	Due to inadequate bonding between deposited particles (at present), strength is typically low, thermal conductivity may be directional, and density is usually less than theoretical.
No furnace facility is needed for cold substrate, only moderate temperature for hot substrate modifications.	While deposition rates are adequate, over-all costs are high.
Mixed compositions can be sprayed.	
Spraying is applicable to ceramic finishing, surface prestressing, patching and repairing.	The residual-stress problem currently limits thickness, but should be surmountable.
Parts can be sprayed with good dimensional control.	The gas environment is a limitation of the fluid-spray processes for those ceramics that are sensitive to reaction with the hot gases (in some cases combustion products). In addition, oxides may spray anion deficient; and the structures of some oxides after spraying show the presence of metastable phases.
Ultrafine crystal sizes are characteristic of the molten-spray process because of the rapid quenching. Hence, if good cohesion between individual particles could be achieved, the ultrafine grain size might well result in a structural ceramic with exceptional strength properties. With the possible exception of glass ceramics, the molten-spray process produces smaller crystal size than any other currently used ceramic-processing method.	

plasma methods and for the newest liquid-fuel method. These should include feed sizing and flow, the flame and plasma variables, gases present, and substrate distance and temperature, for example, and should be correlated with the resultant material properties and character.

Inexpensive removable substrates or forms, and investigations of parting agents, are needed for spraying free-standing shapes.

Spraying of various novel compositions needs to be assessed. Some examples are glass and crystallizable glass, and oxides together with metals, carbides, or carbon by codeposition.

Burning of pure metals sprayed into air or oxygen should be investigated further, as a possible means of preparing very-high-purity reactive oxide particles as feed for solids processing.

Spraying as a means of welding ceramics together needs to be investigated. Here, perhaps more than in any other case, the problem of interfacial strength and bonding must be solved.

Other research needs include more and better data on volume changes of ceramics on solidification from the melt, improved methods and tools for characterizing fluid-sprayed structures, and additional data on the viscosities, surface tensions, and wetting properties of molten ceramics.

DEVELOPMENT OF RECOMMENDATIONS

A thorough understanding of the ultimate capabilities and limitations of a particular process, an appreciation both of its present technological status and of the status and depth of the physical science and engineering on which it depends, and the weighing of the purposes of pertinent research and of the likelihood of achievement of these purposes, are all requisite to the intelligent framing of approaches to any particular new processing research project. It is hoped that the foregoing status reports will furnish guidance in this regard. To provide for greater penetration of any of these subjects there is a Bibliography at the end of this chapter. Consulting these resources should lead, through their own references, directly into the original literature, from which additional information in any limited segment of these subjects can be obtained.

The first purpose to be served by the present study and recommendations is, however, to point out in somewhat general terms where the needs and opportunities for research lie within a total context. Much of research, especially "basic" research, produces information that is general in nature. It is important, therefore, to identify areas of basic research that will benefit all (or large fractions) of fluid-processing technology. With respect to applied research and engineering development, the pursuit of which usually leads to more specific technological advancements of limited breadth, it is important to delineate all the areas of opportunity together so that selections of research objectives can be made from a balanced view of the entire front and the entire need rather than from one sector only.

One of the goals of this section, therefore, is to summarize and digest the content of the status reports to give an over-all view of:

1. The important characteristics, capabilities, and limitations of the various types of fluid processes relative to each other and to solids processes.

2. The areas of basic science in which progress is required to further the foundations of fluid processing in scientific principles and knowledge.

3. The areas of applied research and engineering development in which progress is needed or in which opportunities lie for significant and timely advancement of performance, uniformity, and reproducibility in the structural qualities of oxide ceramics through improved fluid processing.

It is recognized, however, that advances in the science and art of fluid processing, across the whole front, cannot all be expected to be accomplished (or even needed) at the same time or at the same pace within the framework of ceramic applications needs of the Department of Defense or of the ability of the Government to fund research and development work. Consequently the final object of this section is to evaluate the many areas of desirable R&D in the light of DOD needs, and, based on this evaluation, to recommend a smaller list of R&D objectives as being of highest pertinence. If possible, this list should retain a "programmatic" quality: i.e., the work recommended should be mutually reinforcing or complementary, and should comprise an efficient, combined "series-parallel" program providing a high likelihood of achievement of a limited number of important technological goals.

1. Summary of Characteristics of Fluid Processes

COMPOSITION AND PURITY

Table 7 is a digest of the Panel's assessments of the broad types of fluid processes recognized in this report, with respect to their important characteristics and capabilities. Elaborations are given in the following paragraphs in terms of the inherent capabilities of fluid processes for accomplishing certain elements of character in oxide ceramics. The elements of character selected are those considered as pertinent to structural applications, including those considered to be important for maximizing strength and for minimizing the scatter of strength.

Control of composition and its variability has been advanced to a refined art in glassmaking, where in addition the molecular state of dispersal of impurities usually minimizes their effect on mechanical properties. While in general for all processes the avoidance of impurities depends first on feed-material specification and second on engineering aspects of containment (with difficulties rising rapidly with increasing temperature of processing), some fluid processes can be contrived to avoid deleterious contact between the feed material and any foreign solid container. "Skull" melting, PVD, CVD, molten-particle spraying, and crucibleless crystal growth are examples. The classical single-crystal growth processes and the zone-melting techniques tend to sweep many impurities away from the bulk of the product, requiring only that end sections be cropped.

Conversely, the very mobility of the constituents of fluid media and the partition that occurs on crystallization lend difficulties to fluid processing which in some cases are more aggravated than in solids processing. The familar change from large columnar grains to finer equiaxed grains at the conclusion of bulk freezing is largely due to a change in nucleation accompanying the buildup of impurities in the residual liquid as freezing progresses. The residue of intergranular glass in crystallized-glass products, while it can be very uniformly distributed on a gross scale, has an evident effect on the high-temperature yield stress and strength. The distribution of solutes in "doped" single crystals is rarely uniform and may affect substructure, while the effects of impurities in the melt or flux on crystal growth rate, and even habit, are often marked. It is known that various impurities may be swept forward or backward or left stationary in zone refining, the direction and efficiency depending on each individual partition coefficient. Liquid-liquid phase separation in glass forming is becoming more generally recognized. Boundary-layer effects in CVD processes can have a striking influence on impurity distribution.

In general it is desirable that the composition of the fluid phase at the fluid-solid interface remain constant with the progress of "solidification." This condition is best met by the establishment of a uniform environment of the melt and vapor, for example (poorly approached by the melting of large batches of refractory materials, but well illustrated by specialty-glass melting operations, the best-controlled PVD and CVD processes, the best single-crystal growth processes, and electrolytic processes), and by vigorous agitation (again poorly approached in bulk freezing, adequate to excellent in glassmaking, excellent in fluidized-bed CVD, usually poor in crystal growth processes, and adequate to excellent in electrolytic processes).

Rapid, nonequilibrium conversion to the final product promotes the incorporation of impurities in uniform distribution, on both a gross and a fine scale. In this regard bulk freezing of oxides rates poorly, especially in large masses, owing to the low thermal diffusivity. The effectiveness of the chilling of glass melts is also size-dependent, although the high viscosity of glass compositions is an aid in preserving uniformity, and the absence of crystallization removes much of the driving force for segregation (i.e., in the ideal case there is no interface). Spraying of uniform molten particles can yield extreme compositional uniformity on a gross scale under adequate process control, and owing to the very rapid chilling, this uniformity can extend to the scale of angstroms if the particles themselves are alike.

Within the practical range of evaporation rates, PVD composition control is, in principle, independent of deposition conditions, and is excellent. However, CVD processes tend to incorporate more impurities with increasing departure from equilibrium because of the boundary-layer effect. Electrolytic processes similarly suffer increased impurity pickup in the product and increased variability with departure from equilibrium conditions. Anodic-sparking compositions are not yet entirely predictable. Single-crystal growth processes tend to be operated near equilibrium, but here as well (especially in solute crystallization) the impurity pickup and its variation generally increase with increasing rates. In the boule method, which has some similarity to molten-particle spraying, the scale of compositional uniformity is refined by increasing the rapidity of crystallization, although crystal perfection may suffer in consequence.

In addition to reacting with containing vessels as previously noted, liquid or vapor feed materials at very high temperatures are susceptible to inter-

Table 7. Summary of Fluid-Process Characteristics

	Bulk Freezing	Bulk-Glass Processes		Incremental Gas-Phase Molecular Transport		Molten-Particle Spraying			Incremental Liquid-Phase Molecular Transport					
									Melt-Freezing			Solute Crystallization		
	Bulk Freezing	Glass Forming	Glass Crystallization	PVD	CVD	Detonation Gun	Chemical Flame	Electrical Flame	Crucible	Withdrawal	Boule	Ambient P	Hydrothermal	Electrolytic
COMPOSITIONS FOR WHICH SUITABLE														
Oxides	III (II)	I	I	III (II)	I	I	I	I	I	I	I	I	I	I
Carbides, nitrides	II (I)	N	N	N	I	II (I)	II	II (I)	II	II	II	N	N	N
Borides, beryllides	II (I)	N	N	N	III	III (II)	III (II)	II (I)	N	II	II	II	N	N
Elements (C, B)	N	N	N	N	I	N	N	(II)	I	I	I	I	N	II (I)
Composition control	II (I)	I	I	I	II (I)	II (I)	II (I)	II(I)	I	I	I	I	I	I
Uniformity control	III (II)	I	I	I	II (I)	I	I	I	I	I	II (I)	I	II	
High-purity capability	II (I)	I	I	I	II (I)	I	II (I)	I	I	I	II (I)	II	II	II (I)
EVALUATIONS FOR OXIDIC MATERIALS														
Configurations														
Shell, sheet, tube	III (II)	I	I	I	I	II	I	I	II	N	(II)	N	N	II
Block, bar	I	I	I	III	III	III	II (I)	II (I)	I	I	I	N	II	N
Matrix for reinforcing	III	II	II	(II)	II (I)	II (I)	II (I)	II (I)	N	N	N	N	N	N
Coating, patching, joining	III	I	II	(II)	I	I	I	I	N	N	N	N	N	II (I)
Reinforcing, fibers, filaments	N	I	III (II-I)	III	I	N	N	N	N	II (I)	N	II	N	N
Particulate feed	II	II	II	II	I	III	II	II	N	N	N	I	N	N
Max lateral dim (in.)	>12	10^3	10^2	10^2	10^2	10^2	10^3	10^2	12	12 (10^2)	12 (10^2)	(1)	2 (12)	10^2
Max thickness (in.)	>12	12	6	2	2 (6)	1	4 (12)	4	12	2 (4)	2 (10)	(1)	2 (12)	0.1
Dimensional control	III (II)	I	I	II (I)	I	I	I	I	I	II	II	III	III (II)	I
Surface finish	II (I)	I	I	II – I	II – I	I	II – I	II – I	I	I	I	I	I	I

114

Table 7 (continued)

| | Bulk Freezing | Bulk-Glass Processes | | Incremental Gas-Phase Molecular Transport | | Molten-Particle Spraying | | | Incremental Liquid-Phase Molecular Transport | | | | | Electrolytic |
| | | Glass Forming | Glass Crystallization | PVD | CVD | Detonation Gun | Chemical Flame | Electrical Flame | Melt-Freezing | | | Solute Crystallization | | |
									Crucible	Withdrawal	Boule	Ambient P	Hydrothermal	
Internal structures														
Polycrystal (1 phase)	I	N	N	I	I	I	I	I	N	N	N	N	N	II (I)
Glass crystal	N	↑	I	N	N	(I)	(I)	(I)	N	N	N	N	N	N
Multiphase crystal	II (I)	↑	III (II - I)	(I)	(I)	I	I	I	N	N	III	N	N	III (II)
Glass and SRO	N	I	N	N	I	(I)	(I)	(I)	I	I	I	I	I	(II - I)
Single crystal	N	N	N	(II)	I	N	N	N	I	I	I	I	I	III (II)
Phase distr control	III (II)	↑	I	(I)	(I)	I	I	I	N	N	II	N	N	(II)
Polycrystal structures														
Min grain size (μ)	>100 (10)	N	<0.1 (<.01)	0.1	<0.01	<0.01	<0.01	<0.01	N	N	N	N	N	1. (<0.01)
Size control	III (II)	N	I	(I)	I	I	I	I	N	N	N	N	N	(II)
Uniformity control	III (II)	N	I	(I)	II (I)	I	I	I	N	N	N	N	N	(II)
Grain shape, typical	C, E	N	E, F, P	C, E	C, E	E	E	E	N	N	N	N	N	C, E
Orientation, typical	O, R	N	R	O, R	O, R	R	R	R	N	N	N	N	N	O, R
Orientation control	III (II)	N	I	(II)	I	I	I	I	N	N	N	N	N	(II)
Min porosity (%)	0.0 - 0.2	0.0	0.0	0.1	0.1	0.5 (0.1)	2 (0.2)	0.5 (0.1)	0.0	0.0	0.0	0.0	0.0	1. (<0.1)
Max forming rate (lb/hr)	10^2	10^4	10^2	0.1	0.1 (1.)	1.	10 (10^3)	10.	1.	1.	1.	10^{-4}-10^{-2}	10^{-3}	0.1
Uniformity*	III (II)	I	I	(I)	I	III (I)	III (I)	III (I)	I	I	II	II (I)	II (I)	I
Reproducibility*	II	I	I	(I)	I	I	I	I	I	I	II	II (I)	II (I)	I

Open Entries, present capability; bracketed entries, future potential. Evaluations: I, superior; II, average; III, inferior; N, not applicable. Numerical Values: units in left column. Grain Shape: E, equi-axial; C, columnar; F, fibrous, filamentary; P, platelet. Grain Orientation: R, random; O, oriented. *, overall assessment.

115

actions with other components of the environment. Effects on composition and its variability are evident. Simple gas-solution and exsolution phenomena are discussed later, under Porosity. Electrode materials are incorporated into the charge in arc or resistance heating, and interactions with flame constituents occur in glass-forming and in other chemical fuel-fired processes: molten-particle spraying and Verneuil crystal growth (although in most cases alternate and cleaner heating methods are available). Reactions with atmospheric leaks are possible in PVD and CVD processes, and in the latter as well as in elec-trolytic processes and hydrothermal crystal growth, corrosive feed materials or byproducts may attack all materials of construction. Many oxides are anion-deficient at the melting-point under nonoxidizing conditions, and this condition may persist on freezing and cooling to room temperature (especially in spray processes where chilling is rapid, and in large masses through bulk casting).

Although these problems may require more detailed attention in fluid than in solids processing, in most cases the principles governing compositional uni-formity are understood, and engineering methods for achieving adequate control are available. There is no inherent characteristic of most fluid processes that renders compositional variability inescapable, as this affects product unifor-mity or reproducibility. Furthermore, the deliberate gradation of composition is a peculiar capability of a number of these processes, viz., glass forming and most of the incremental methods.

POROSITY

Porosity approaching zero is achievable in principle by all variants of bulk fusion, crystallization, and other molecular transport processes. In general, trade-offs must be struck between processing under near-equilibrium conditions that favor the rejection of pores as well as other structural flaws but may be impractically slow or may favor large grains, and processing rapidly for eco-nomic or other microstructural ends, but risking imperfections. Voids or "blebs" due to shrinkage in bulk-fusion casting appear to present a difficult engineering problem, but this cannot be judged realistically until compositions and procedures suitable to the solution of the grain-size control problem are selected and a specific configuration is approached. Pores resulting from gas exsolution (e.g., in fusion casting, glassmaking, and single-crystal growth) are in principle always avoidable; but economic penalties may attend the re-quirement of vacuum or controlled atmosphere and the restrictions these may place on modes of heating and containment. Porosity resulting from decom-position of impurities in the feed material (e.g., during melting) or from side reactions (e.g., in electrolytic processes) is always in principle avoidable by purity specification, "fining," vacuum degassing, or careful control of proces-sing parameters, for example, as each case warrants. Pores in PVD or CVD processes are usually the result of inadequate process control or of sacrifice to another microstructural end or to economically favorable deposition rates.

The porosity occurring in high-velocity spraying processes is a special problem. Insufficient effort has been spent on defining the variation in tempera-ture and velocity of particles as functions of particle-size variation, location in the flame, and other process variables. Consequently, the ingenuity required to overcome these possible causes cannot yet be accurately judged. Decomposi-tion and dissolved-gas exsolution are also possible contributors. Finally, the impingement and rapid freezing of particles on the substrate (including depen-dence on variations in particle temperature and velocity) are known sources of porosity. There are reasons for confidence that pores and other structural deficiencies of spray-processed materials can be eliminated by systematic research.

Thus, with few exceptions, porosity either as a source of general weakness (performance and uniformity considerations) or as an occasional flaw (reli-ability and reproducibility considerations) appears subject to technical means of elimination or at least reduction to secondary importance through fluid processing. The deliberate creation of a highly porous, even foamed, structure has not been encompassed in this study; however, capabilities exist in many fluid processes, viz., in glass forming, CVD, molten-particle spraying, and electrolytic process variants.

INTERNAL STRUCTURE

Internal-structure capabilities of fluid processes are varied, frequently unique, and in many cases characteristically highly uniform. The vitreous state and the single crystal are achieved only through fluid processing and can be extremely uniform on a gross or fine scale. Short-range-order (SRO) structures have been achieved via CVD (e.g., boron, carbon, and Al_2O_3). Structures ranging from SRO to hyperfine polycrystals are achievable by other CVD variants, by glass crystallization, by molten-particle spray processes, and by electrolysis. In the range from SRO to 0.1 μ grain size, there have been very few investigations of crystal size variability. Consequently, it is difficult to judge the ultimate characteristics of these processes as regards the scatter of strength due to this cause. However, their promise is exceedingly high, especially when codeposits for nucleation control are factored in. There are few records of attempts at codepositing, but the meager results are encouraging. The hyperfine grain structure of spray deposits has never been exploited, owing to their (probably curable) deficiency in interparticle bonding, discussed below. The nucleation techniques of the glass industry apparently have not been assessed for applicability to nonglassy materials, and should be investigated.

Considering the immense array of complex oxidic compositions available, experimental work leading to multiphase structures has barely been begun. Eutectics, peritectics, and subsolidus multiphase phenomena as well as other heterogeneous systems remain the largely untested hope for bulk-fusion casting, in producing fine grains. Refractory (in many cases, nonsilicate) glass and crystallizable glass compositions provide a large area for future advances into both vitreous and multiphase crystalline materials. Although glass-crystallization processes can yield angstrom-scale crystals, this size range has not been characteristic of exhaustively devitrified materials. However, there appears to be no inherent limitation in the process. Multiphase compositions via spray processes, and utilization of spraying to preserve the vitreous state for subsequent crystallization, have been little examined. Again, the potential seems evident. The CVD approach to multiphase materials presents some anticipated difficulties, but these will not be insurmountable in all situations.

As regards freedom from the occasional large grain or flaw, and reproducibility (part-to-part structure variation), fluid processes are often inherently superior. This characteristic derives from the ability to mix large batches of feed material, from the disappearance of individual particulate character in the fluid state, and from the incremental quality of many of the processes and their ability to be automated and continuous. Glass and glass-crystallization processes are excellent in this regard. The tendency of PVD and CVD processes to accentuate nonuniform structural features with increasing thickness can in principle be overcome by continuously buffing off the high points. Spray processes are inherently uniform on a gross scale. Electrolytic processes present a relative unknown in this matter, needing exploration; fusion casting is presently inferior.

Deliberate gradation in grain size through the use of incremental fluid processes as finishing operations appears particularly hopeful, since these methods, while capable of fine-grain structure, are costly on a mass basis. The principal problems (bonding and internal stress) are discussed below.

Intergranular or interparticle bonding varies widely from process to process. In general, melt processes and molecular-transport processes can be excellent in this regard, but there are significant exceptions.

Inter- or intragranular flaws can result from differential contraction on cooling, which occurs at increasing frequency with increasing grain size. Consequently, bulk fusion casting as presently practiced is inferior. Other fluid processes (e.g., CVD), when conducted so as to yield large grains, are also susceptible. Glass crystallization yielding fine grains is excellent up to the point of complete devitrification.

Any process yielding a high-melting solid at low temperatures, when conducted at a high deposition rate, risks poor bonding. Thus PVD and CVD processes, conducted at incipient "snowing out" (conditions favoring hyperfine grain size), can be subject to either occasional or general weak bonding. Electrolytic processes must similarly be controlled between slow but atomic deposition which is economically unfavorable, and more rapid rates which risk loss of bonding integrity with a sacrifice in strength. Further detailed investigations of subsequent sintering or pressure sintering to heal such flaws are indicated.

The high-velocity molten-particle spray processes have been notoriously poor in regard to bonding, yet there seems no inherent necessity for this. Variations of particle temperature and velocity must of course be controlled; but beyond this the use of a hot substrate seems an obvious approach, with little record of actual trial and no apparent record of definitive research. The dwell time of each particle in the liquid state could stand considerable extending before grain growth would become troublesome, and the interdiffusion of the particle with the solid base should consequently be markedly improved. Elimination of much of the presently characteristic porosity would be an expected byproduct, as well as elimination of residual stress. This approach should be vastly superior to a subsequent sintering step.

The role of gas films in preventing bonding requires exploration for fluid processing as well as solids processing. Both CVD and spray processes may be susceptible to this source of trouble, particularly the latter. Electrolytic processes may be similarly troubled at high-deposition rates.

Residual stresses and cracking are phenomena evidenced from nil to extreme by various fluid processes. Bulk fusion casting is presently quite inferior in this regard, the effect becoming more serious with increasing process temperature, grain size, and size of artifact. Glass forming is comparably susceptible at large sizes, and some of the single-crystal growth processes are also size-limited on this account. Auxiliary heating or heat-flow control during processing, and subsequent annealing, are presently practiced with dramatic success for glasses and single crystals.

Given a reasonably isotropic material and not-unreasonable configurations, the incremental processes hold great promise for avoiding this type of general or occasional defect. When conducted to yield very fine grains, either low-temperature processes (e.g., PVD) followed by annealing, or high-temperature processes (CVD, spraying, electrolytic) utilizing a hot substrate and subsequent annealing, should be practically size-unlimited in consequence of differential shrinkage.

SURFACE CHARACTER

The surface character of fluid-processed ceramics is not, on the whole, perceivably different from that of the immediately underlying bulk. Large-grained CVD and PVD products show an appreciable change in character with increasing thickness of deposit, but this can be minimized or nullified if there is adequate new nucleation leading to very fine grain size or SRO structure. The character of electrolytic deposits tends to change continuously with thickness, owing to the increasing electrical resistance. This can be overcome to a substantial degree by a carefully programmed increase in potential aimed at constant current. A peculiar and advantageous quality of some fluid processes (viz., glassmaking and glass crystallization and the incremental deposition processes generally) is that the surface character is not appreciably altered by increasing the dimensions of the artifact in the plane of the surface.

Present practice in melt-freezing produces a compressive surface stress, while present molten-particle-spraying practice leads to tensile stresses in the growing surface. Means of overcoming the latter are mentioned above. Control of the surface stress state in glasses and crystallized glasses by subsequent finishing operations has been notably successful. Also, in these materials the introduction of a large density of mild surface flaws (by hyperfine etching) has been shown to decrease the concentration of stress at the occasional accidental surface flaw and consequently to reduce the scatter of strength values by an impressive amount. Although some of these techniques have recently been attempted on polycrystalline materials, the bodies utilized were relatively large grained and relatively porous. Where nonporous, hyperfine-grained or SRO bodies (or surface layers) of good integrity can be produced by fluid processes, these products should be capable of still more marked improvement in strength and in reduced scatter of strength by finishing operations analogous to those used with glass.

The faithfulness of some fluid-processed artifacts to useful shapes and to useful dimensional tolerances can be superb. Although fusion casting may be persistently inferior in this regard, the precision achievable in glassmaking is by contrast excellent. Little research appears to have been invested to date in making single crystals of predetermined useful shapes and dimensions; but the potential of such variants as shaped crucibles, "float" modifications, and elegant withdrawal and boule techniques appears exciting.

Incremental polycrystal and SRO deposition processes employing a removable form can be quite faithful to both its shape and its surface finish. Elastic relaxation on removal of the form, due to residual stress, should be minimized or eliminated by proper annealing. The growth surface, however, would ordinarily require some machining if dimensional or finish tolerances are demanding. Because of the heavy emphasis to date on the use of incremental processes for coating, efforts to prepare free-standing objects by these means will probably require innovations in the area of removable, reusable forms and of parting agents.

CONFIGURATIONS

The configurations achievable by selected fluid processes include numerous unique or superior contributions to ceramic technology. The immense flexibility of fluid molding or casting methods, utilized in the fields of metallurgy and organic polymers, has not been equally exploited in polycrystalline oxide ceramics because of their unfortunate resultant microstructural characteristics. But present practice in glass casting and molding evidences a sophistication and a range of applicability comparable to that in plastics and superior to that in metals. It can be anticipated that casting and molding methods for polycrystalline ceramics will partially close this gap if compositions can be found that yield satisfactory microstructures, uniformity, and avoidance of flaws.

The range of configurations achievable in glasses and crystallized glasses by forming methods other than casting is relatively familiar and is vast. Although there are size limitations imposed on castings, on sheets, and on extrusions, for example, by the nature of glass, these limitations obviate very few potential applications of this material. With the advent of photosensitive crystallizable glasses, details of configuration such as embossing and perforations of a wide and complex variety can be accomplished without machining and with remarkably precise dimensional control.

A very few oxide compositions (notably Al_2O_3) have been developed in large bulk single-crystal form. Size limits are inherently technological and consequently not permanently fixed. The spur given recently to sapphire-growth technology by laser needs illustrates that the same advances can be made in numerous other oxides under suitable incentive, and it may be predicted that a small arsenal of bulk single-crystal materials will emerge, like sapphire, from the domain or rare gems into that of economically attainable, technically useful components. In one area, of transparencies, these will complement glasses and probably remain superior to the best polycrystalline transmitting materials of the same compositions. Methods of growing refractory oxide single crystals in "window" configurations of large size should accordingly be advanced.

Single-crystal materials are capable of exhibiting near-theoretical strength and retaining useful strength and creep properties to temperatures far higher than is the case for glasses and glass crystals. Many new mechanical applications will be called forth. It can be anticipated that cubic crystal structures will be superior to the hexagonal structure of Al_2O_3 for numerous of these, and consequently cubic refractory oxides (such as spinel and yttrium aluminum garnet) should be developed as large single crystals of reasonable cost. At the same time, the technical and cost obstacles to "hogging" useful shapes out of shapeless blanks will become increasingly important. Methods will be needed for growing single crystals economically in shapes closely approximating finished artifacts, within the size range of current technology. Concepts of such methods presently exist.

Sheets, tiles, and thin-walled bodies of revolution (hemispheres, cones, ogives, cylinders) of greatly extended lateral dimensions are achievable by glass-forming methods and by incremental deposition processes. As has been noted, such elements of character as the bulk and surface microstructure, the residual stress, the occurrence of occasional flaws, and dimensional fidelity do not present unusual difficulties with increasing size when appropriate fluid processes are used. Furthermore, if the very high strengths of which these processes appear capable can actually be realized, wall thicknesses can be reduced and elastic accommodation to small mismatches in attachment will give rise to lower stresses.

Many superior materials of construction are composites, and the design problems associated with the brittleness of ceramics can be substantially relieved by their incorporation also into composite materials. Two approaches are apparent: (a) the use of fiber or filamentary forms of oxides within matrices of plastics, metals, or even other ceramics, in which the high elastic modulus and high strength of the reinforcement are coupled with a flexibility or compliance that minimizes local stress concentration; and (b) the use of oxides as matrices in which are embedded metal or other fibers, wires, or filaments, wherein the reinforcing medium is utilized primarily for compressive prestressing.

Filamentary materials are excessively strong when their internal structure is without boundaries (e.g., glasses; "amorphous" B or C; single-crystal graphite, SiC, B_4C, or sapphire). The potential of hyperfine-grained polycrystal filaments for high strength is still indistinct. Oxides of such structure and ranging down to SRO structure need to be developed as filaments and evaluated. For such purposes, fluid processes are the only available resources. Adaptation of the withdrawal method to the forming of filamentary sapphire has been begun with encouraging results. Deposition of aluminum oxide in SRO form on a metal wire by CVD appears feasible, and electrolytic methods hold some promise for making filaments of SRO or hyperfine grain structure. The need in glass filaments is for greater refractoriness, higher modulus, and higher strength, achievable through a search for new compositions. Glass crystals of hyperfine grain size need to be made in filamentary form and evaluated. Short fibers are currently made by CVD and by crystal-growing processes from the melt or from flux.

For building an oxide matrix around a fibrous reinforcing medium, again fluid processes appear attractive. Low temperatures are desirable to eliminate interaction between oxide and wire, the result of which would be to deteriorate the strength of the wire. Low-temperature buildup and bonding of matrix layers to wire is possible by CVD and by spraying—from both sides if necessary. Multiple composite layers can be built up by diffusion bonding of single composite layers. The potential of electrolysis is essentially unknown.

Incremental fluid processes are uniquely capable of finishing operations—coating, material addition, patching, and joining—without requiring reheat of the base materials to sintering temperatures. The need to reach only annealing temperature allows for the potential preservation of complex assemblages through such operations, in which less refractory components might otherwise be ruined. Emphasis should be on CVD and on spraying.

Finally, particulates for solids processing feed can be prepared with unique characteristics, including purity, particle surface and internal structure, density, and sinterability, by variants of CVD, the sol-gel reaction, and spraying. Thus fluid processing means are available for increasing the arsenal of raw materials for more conventional ceramic fabrication.

2. Basic Science Areas

In consideration of the general importance of condensation to the solid state from the liquid or gaseous state, and of the general paucity of basic information on oxides or their precursors near their transition temperatures as well as of information on the transitions (or reactions) themselves, a number of areas of basic science and of basic material-property data are evident in which progress in research will be of quite general benefit to fluid processing.

This list is presented in Table 8. At this stage the list is deliberately kept broad. No specifications are given as to what material should be studied, what phenomena or properties are most important, what data are most urgently needed, or to which fluid processes they relate. The reason for this mode of presentation lies in the quality of basic research that results and interpretations are generalizable and often produce understanding in unforeseen directions. The list is reconciled with more specific objectives in Section 5.

3. Areas of Applied Research and Engineering Development

R&D objectives that are more or less specific to the individual types of fluid processes are compiled from the observations of the characteristics, needs, and opportunities made in Section 1 (p. 112) and detailed in the status reports. There are presented in Table 9.

This list is intended to be comprehensive, and is oriented toward the opportunities for fullfillment of the technological potential of the various fluid-processing methods. It is reconciled with DOD needs in Section 6.

4. Establishment of "Priority" Fluid Processes and Their Material Objectives

The condensing of the long lists of desirable R&D given in Sections 2 and 3 into a manageable "Priority Program," without sacrificing the detachment of the objectives from specific end-items, was accomplished in the following way:

First, the broad needs of the Department of Defense were examined for the existence of groupings of oxide ceramic components or applications that have similar qualitative performance requirements and configurations (quantitative differences were ignored). To these groups, based on needs, were added some considerations of the unique or special opportunities of fluid processes to perform certain functions also important to the DOD.

The result is a set of eight "Model Objectives" of ceramic processing, each related to DOD structural applications of oxide ceramics, and to each of which at least one fluid process merits an attractive rating (see Table 7) for a preferred composition, general configuration class, suitable internal structure, polycrystal character (where appropriate), and in the over-all uniformity and

Table 8. Areas of Basic Science and Basic Data Important to Fluid Processing of Oxide Ceramics

---

High-temperature structures, properties, and phenomena related to oxidic compounds, solutions, and related materials

---

SOLIDS

Structure and physical properties near the melting point
Defects and transport properties near the melting point
Surface structure and composition (vis-à-vis bulk), surface energies
High-temperature phase relations, solubilities, homogeneity ranges, and thermodynamic quantities
Internal stress and plastic-deformation phenomena

LIQUIDS, INCLUDING GLASSES

Structure and theory of structure; influence of flow, composition, and temperature
Physical properties: density, thermal expansion, compressibility, surface tension; relations to structure and composition
Transport properties: electrical conductivity and solute transport, diffusion, viscosity, flow characteristics; relations to structure, composition, temperature, and gradients
Phase relations, solubilities, and thermodynamic quantities
Surface structure and properties (vis-à-vis bulk)
Properties of supercritical liquids

GASES

High-temperature thermodynamic quantities
Equilibria with condensed phases

INTERPHASE PHENOMENA

Interfacial structures, energies and transport kinetics; interphase impurity distribution
Nucleation and crystallization mechanisms and kinetics; undercooling; impurity dynamic behavior; electrolytic and anodic phenomena
Physics and thermodynamics of epitaxy; structural relations (including films) at interfaces and in interphase transitions (e.g., melting and freezing)
Surface changes and interactions with environment
Volume and other physical (e.g., viscosity) changes with melting, freezing, and undercooling
Accommodation and condensation coefficients
Molten-particle flow and substrate interaction on high-velocity impact; high-speed freezing phenomena
Particle-gas exchange phenomena: kinetic and thermal

---

reproducibility evaluations. The rating may represent either present capability or future potential. The cost element was then invoked in a few cases to reduce the number of candidate processes. These eight objectives are presented in Table 10.

The fluid processes included in Table 10 as candidates for achievement of these eight Model Objectives follow, together with the kinds of oxide configurations which are to be sought, or are needed, through their development and exploitation. The numbers in parentheses reference the identification of the corresponding Model Objectives in Table 10. These may be taken as indicating those fluid processes and their material objectives deemed by the Panel to be worthy of "priority" status for research and development:

Glass and glass-crystallization processes: bulk forms (1, 2) and filament (5).

Chemical-vapor deposition: bulk forms (1, 2), filament-reinforced sheet, (3), coaxial filament (5), surface finishing (7), particulates (8).

Incremental freezing single-crystal processes: large crystals (4), filaments (5), short fibers (6).

Incremental flux single-crystal processes: filaments (5), short fibers (6).

Table 9. Areas of Applied Research and Engineering Development Important to Fluid Processing of Oxide Ceramics

FUSION AND FREEZING

Investigate electron-beam heating of oxide melts for improved control of composition and purity.

Investigate programmed cooling of molds for improved control of grain size and habit

Investigate the use of applied isostatic pressure on the melt instead of temperature reduction to cause freezing, i.e., use of $\Delta(PV)$ to replace ΔE as driving force, as means of controlling crystallization

Investigate the following to control crystal size, morphology, and orientation in the solid product:

Eutectic or peritectic oxide compositions

Solid solutions with a large temperature coefficient of solubility of one component

Compositions containing an insoluble and inert particulate foreign phase

"Metallurgical" heat treatments, following freezing, of compositions having appropriate subsolidus phase changes

GLASS AND GLASS CRYSTALLIZATION PROCESSES

Investigate means of forming glass objects economically in small numbers

Investigate refractory and high-modulus glass compositions (probably nonsilicate) for preparation as filament

Investigate refractory and high-modulus crystallizable glasses (probably non-silicate)

Investigate methods (and appropriate compositions) for nucleation and crystallization of refractory glasses yielding extremely fine ($\leq 0.01\ \mu$) grain size upon complete crystallization

Investigate new methods and materials for melting and forming of refractory-

glass compositions, e.g., molten-particle spraying

INCREMENTAL GAS-PHASE MOLECULAR TRANSPORT

Investigate new and inexpensive methods and materials for removable molds and mandrels, including parting agents

Investigate CVD or combined PVD/CVD methods for depositing oxides (e.g., Al_2O_3, ThO_2, ZrO_2, TiO_2) and for co-depositing these with inert insoluble foreign atoms (e.g., C, Pt metals, refractory metals) to yield 1/4 in.- to 1/2-in.-thick freestanding ceramics of high density and extremely fine grain size

Investigate new CVD approaches to form coatings of Al_2O_3 or BeO on metal wire (after the method of depositing B on W); objective is short-range-order oxide

Investigate and evaluate CVD methods of preparing very-high-purity sinterable particulate oxides by gas-phase oxidation, reduction, or hydrolysis and by "snowing out"

MOLTEN-PARTICLE-SPRAY PROCESSES

Investigate the use of programmed heating of substrates during deposition to relieve stress by high-velocity processes to improve interparticle bonding, leading to freestanding shapes

Investigate systematically the process variables of arc or RF plasma deposition of an oxide, relative to complete characterization and mechanical evaluation of the product

Develop the liquid-fuel-spray method for optimum mechanical performance of an oxide product, using the systematic approach outlined above, and maintaining high deposition rates

Investigate the postfabrication heat treatment (including use of pressure) of freestanding spray-deposited oxides to im-

prove interparticle bonding and mechanical strength and to convert metastable phases; with and without hot-substrate spraying

Develop methods and materials for inexpensive removable forms and mandrels for spraying oxides, including parting agents

Investigate and evaluate methods of spraying oxides over a pattern of reinforcing fibers (e.g., metal, carbon, or boron), sequentially from both sides to yield a reinforced or prestressed sheet configuration; ultimate object will be multilayering of these by pressure bonding

Investigate spraying of complex ceramic compositions, including:

Refractory-glass and crystallizable-glass compositions

Mixtures of oxide and metal to yield microcomposites analogous to Co-WC

Develop and evaluate techniques for high-strength seam welding of ceramic sheets by high-velocity spray methods

Investigate and evaluate the preparation of very-high-purity sinterable particulate oxides by spraying of decomposible or combustible particles into an appropriate atmosphere (e.g., high-purity Al in O_2) and "snowing out"

INCREMENTAL LIQUID-PHASE MOLECULAR TRANSPORT

Develop shaped-crucible method of growing single-crystal Al_2O_3 directly in useful form and nearly to tolerance, e.g., for turbine buckets, nozzle inserts, leading edges; object includes easy removal and some reuse of molds

Investigate modified crucible method of growing single crystals of Al_2O_3, yttrium aluminum garnet, or spinel in disk or sheet form by floating the melt on top of a denser liquid

Investigate "floating-orifice" technique

for growing very long Al_2O_3 or BeO whiskers from melt or from flux

Develop improved heating devices and methods for float-zone melting of oxides

Evaluate the "sol-gel" process for making possible bulk oxides with superior mechanical performance, through improved particulates for solids processing; investigate modification of the "sol-gel" process to yield ceramic microcomposites (containing C, Pt metals, or refractory metals) of extremely fine grain size

Develop superior and larger autoclaves and closures for hydrothermal crystal growth

Investigate means of improving uniformity of distribution of dopants in large oxide single crystals, either in the course of growth or by subsequent zone leveling

Investigate and evaluate anodic sparking for forming freestanding sheet, shell, and tube configurations

Investigate complete anodizing of other metals than aluminum, followed by heat-curing, to yield sheet or wire configurations of oxide in SRO or very-fine-grained polycrystal form

Investigate and evaluate methods of electrolytic deposition of oxides from molten electrolytes, followed by heat-curing, to yield either freestanding dense material or dense coatings on wire or sheet

Table 10. Model Objectives: Fluid Processing for DOD Structural Applications

	1. Oxide (or Microcomposite) Nonrefractory Shapes	2. Oxide (or Microcomposite) Refractory Shapes	3. Oxide Shapes with Filament Reinforcing
	DOD needs: Pressure vessels, low-temperature structural members, armor, transparent armor Configurations: Sheet, shell, tube, bar	DOD needs: Radomes, turbines, hot structures Configurations: Sheet, shell, tube, bar	DOD needs: Reentry and leading-edge surfaces, rocket-engine liners, throats, plus low-temperature uses Configurations: Shell, sheet, tube, and variations
PRESENT DEFICIENCIES	Glasses are generally reliable but relatively low in elastic modulus and strength; polycrystals exhibit adequate elastic properties and the best compressive strengths are sufficient, but strength properties are variable and toughness is absent	Nonoxides are generally brittle, lacking in corrosion resistance, and of unfavorable electromagnetic characteristics; oxides are brittle, susceptible to thermal shock, and lacking in uniformity and reliability; glass-base materials lack refractoriness for some applications	Nonoxides and metals generally lack high-temperature corrosion resistance; oxides lack thermal-shock resistance, uniformity and reliability
REQUIRE-MENTS	Very high modulus, hardness, and strength; very high uniformity and reliability; some toughness to withstand stress concentrations, especially due to joining and thermal shock; moderate cost	High modulus, hardness, and strength to high temperatures; high thermal shock resistance; toughness, spalling resistance; moderate cost	High tensile and shear strength to high temperatures; high uniformity; bonding to monofilament
APPROACH	Very-fine-grained uniform dense microstructure; for toughness, second phase or reinforcing	Very-fine-grained uniform dense microstructure in refractory compositions; for toughness, second phase or reinforcing	Very-fine-grained uniform dense microstructure in refractory compositions; possibly microcomposite; dimensional uniformity; (for use with high modulus, high strength filament)
PROCESSES	Glass, glass crystallization, spraying, CVD	Spraying, refractory-glass crystallization, CVD	CVD, spraying: adapted to cover filaments from both sides
CANDIDATE COMPOSITIONS	Al_2O_3, $MgAl_2O_4$, SiO_2, high-modulus glasses, crystallized glasses	Al_2O_3, BeO, ZrO_2, spinel, SiO_2, refractory crystallized glasses	Al_2O_3, BeO, ZrO_2, spinel, SiO_2

4. Large Oxide Single Crystals	5. Oxide Monofilament and Long Fibers	6. Oxide Single Crystal Short Fibers	7. Joining, Material Addition, and Patching	8. Oxide Particulates
DOD needs: Windows (radar, infrared, visible), transparent armor, structures, bearings, turbines, leading edges Configurations: Sheet, shell, tube, rod, sphere, and variations	**DOD needs:** Reinforced composites for service to moderately high temperatures: structural members, reentry surfaces, vehicular stressed skin, armor Configurations: Monofilament, long fibers	**DOD needs:** Reinforcing for metal, glass, plastic, and ceramic matrices Configurations: Short fiber or platelet crystals	**DOD needs:** Especially for joining segments of ceramic sheet (etc.) into larger assemblages; potential also exists for surface finishing Configurations: Deposition on surfaces, and (for joining) linear buildup	**DOD needs:** Improved raw feed for solids processing Configurations: High-purity ultrafine powders
Size and shape limitations; cost	Glass filaments lack maximum elastic properties and refractoriness; there is yet no proven means of producing monofilament single crystals	Low yields, high costs, tedious harvesting and classification	No reliable means of welding or joining ceramics (other than glass) exists; means are also desired for patching minor surface damage, increasing thickness, or modifying surface composition, microstructure, or stress state	The combination of purity, reactivity, density and uniformity needed is often lacking in conventional powders
Up to 8 in. in two dimensions, controlled surface character; reasonable cost; forming in shapes	Short-range-order oxide or refractory glass filament, or single-crystal filament; $E \gtrsim 30 \times 10^6$ psi, $\sigma \gtrsim 150 \times 10^3$ psi	Short single-crystal fibers, platelets, etc., of high modulus and strength at moderate cost	Means of adding ceramic material to a surface (of the same or different composition), with excellent bonding and without damaging the underlying material	Reactive pure uniform powders at moderate cost
Advance engineering processes holding maximum promise: especially, shaped-crucible and "float" methods	Explore and advance processes holding maximum promise	Advance processes holding maximum promise	Dense fine-grained surface layer of controlled thickness and extent; moderate cost	Modify and develop fluid processes to yield particulates of superior properties for solids processing
Incremental freezing	Refractory glass and glass crystallization; single-crystal fiber withdrawal; coaxial CVD, anodizing, or electrolysis	Melt- or flux-growth, using crystal fiber withdrawal: "floating orifice"	Spraying, and (for finishing only) CVD	CVD, spraying, sol-gel
Al_2O_3, MgO, spinel, yttrium aluminum garnet	High-Al_2O_3 or BeO-base glasses; Al_2O_3 crystal fibers; coaxial Al_2O_3, ZrO_2, spinel	Al_2O_3	Al_2O_3, MgO, spinel, ZrO_2, glasses	Al_2O_3, MgO, spinel, ZrO_2, refractory and crystallizable glasses

<u>Sol-gel process</u>: particulates (8).
<u>Anodizing</u>: coaxial filament (5).
<u>Fused-salt electrolysis</u>: coaxial filament (5).
<u>High-velocity spray process</u>: bulk forms (1, 2), filament-reinforced sheet (3), joining and surface finishing (7), particulates (8).

5. Derivation of Abbreviated List of Pertinent Areas of Basic Science

The purpose of this section is to reduce the number of Areas of Basic Science listed in Table 8, by reference to the foregoing list of priority processes, their material objectives, and their candidate compositions. Since aluminum oxide is a prominent candidate in many cases, and a large number of the material objectives involve refractory-crystallizable glasses (see Table 10), basic scientific investigations that employ Al_2O_3 or refractory-crystallizable glass compositions as vehicles would be considered most pertinent to the advancement of these priority processes.

A further criterion was used to reduce the Basic Science Areas list to manageable size. Even though Table 8 may be regarded as containing "basic" research objectives, many of the measurements listed are required in order to determine process parameters in any sophisticated "applied" study of processes. Such measurements were removed. The residuum of Basic Science Areas accordingly comprises those studies that should result in greater understanding of the nature of materials and of phenomena pertaining to those fluid processes of highest priority for advancement, but which would not be called for automatically in the process investigations themselves. This reduced list is given in Table 11.

The performance of government-supported basic research is rarely on a solicited basis, hence it is not suggested that such work can or should be organized as a "program." There are not too many scientists in the United States who qualify and are interested in these areas, which compounds the difficulty

Table 11. Abbreviated List of Basic Science Areas Pertinent to the Fluid Processing of Alumina and Refractory Glass Ceramics

---

High-temperature structures, properties, and phenomena pertaining to Al_2O_3, and to refractory-crystallizible glasses where appropriate

---

SOLID Al_2O_3

Structure and physical properties (specific volume, thermal expansion, elastic properties, compressibility, and optical properties) near the melting point
Defects and transport properties (thermal conductivity, electrical conductivity, diffusion, and deformation) near the melting point

LIQUID Al_2O_3 AND GLASSES

Structure and theory of structure; physical properties (specific volume, thermal expansion, compressibility, surface tension, and optical properties)
Transport properties (thermal conductivity, electrical conductivity, diffusion, viscosity, and flow)
Liquid-liquid phase relations in glasses; surface structure of molten glasses

INTERPHASE PHENOMENA IN Al_2O_3 AND GLASS CRYSTALS

Solubilities of common gases in Al_2O_3 and in glass compositions as functions of pressure and temperature, above and below the mp (or liquidus)
Interfacial structures and energies; supersaturation phenomena; positive and negative catalysis mechanisms; physics and thermodynamics of epitaxy
Nucleation and crystallization mechanisms and theory
Changes in bulk structure and physical properties occurring with isothermal (equilibrium and nonequilibrium) change of phase

of the science itself with an extreme difficulty of performing good experimental work at temperatures ranging from about 1,000 to 2,300° C or higher with corrosive materials and under rigorous environmental control. Therefore the work outlined must be regarded as having a very long-range purpose: A major contribution to the practical advancement of processing is not likely to occur in less than five years. Nevertheless, it is important that an incentive be provided by the government by expression of interest in these areas of work (some of which are indeed already funded and in progress), in order that opportunities for advancement of fluid-processing technology through basic understanding will not be overlooked.

6. Derivation of a Priority Program of Applied Research and Engineering Development

The most urgent applied R&D objectives for DOD consideration in the advancement of fluid processing are logically derived from Table 9 by reference to Table 10 and the corresponding list of priority processes on page 122. For purposes of obtaining and demonstrating the maximum potential achievement of these processes, it will generally be perfectly satisfactory to perform the processing investigations using only aluminum oxide, refractory glasses and glass crystals, and minor (e.g., composite) modifications of these as product compositions. Exceptions will be noted. Two important virtues of concentrating most of the work in the Priority Program on only two basic types of compositions are that the work will be more mutually reinforcing, and that a better intercomparison of accomplishments will be possible among fluid processes and between fluid and solids processes. This nominal restriction was therefore adopted, in the interests of research economy.

In order to condense still further, those R&D objectives that are concerned purely with engineering and cost tactics (e.g., removable mandrels) were omitted. It was felt that a search for elegant engineering, while important to the advancement of technology, should be subordinated in this Program to the central theme of deriving maximum performance from fluid processing products by investigating the essentials of processing operations themselves. The condensed list of recommended R&D work is described in Table 12.

Within this Priority Program, the tasks may be advantageously grouped according to the configurations to which each is addressed. Two groups of four task areas result, which are indicated in the footnote of Table 12 and repeated in full on pages 69 and 70.

7. General Recommendations

In the preceding derivation of recommended areas for research and development, listings have been included of many basic science objectives that pertain to fluid processing (Table 8), and of many applied-research and engineering-development objectives that offer important opportunities for exploiting fluid processes and their ultimate capabilities (Table 9). Numerous oxidic compositions are included among candidates for processing by one or another of these means, which offer excellent possibilities for achievement of improved performance in the kinds of advanced DOD applications described.

In reducing these listings to what has been termed a Priority Program of Applied Research and Engineering Development (Table 12), and a supporting Abbreviated List of Pertinent Basic Science Areas (Table 11), arbitrary criteria as well as considered judgment have been employed to achieve a small and manageable number of objectives. In some cases (e.g., fusion and freezing and anode-sparking processes), eliminations or priorities have been determined with the knowledge and comfort that government-supported programs are currently in progress, and in the expectation that these will continue. It is the

Table 12. A Priority Program of Applied Research and Engineering Development for Fluid Processing of Alumina and Refractory-Glass Ceramics

A. BULK GLASS AND GLASS-CRYSTALLIZATION PROCESSES

1. Conduct a combined investigation and exploration of
   a. Techniques for nucleation and crystallization of refractory-glass compositions to yield extremely fine gran size ($\leq 0.01\ \mu$) upon complete crystallization, together with
   b. New refractory and high-modulus glass and crystallizable-glass compositions (probably nonsilicate)

   Ultimate objective is either or both of bulk and filament configurations: high modulus and high strength

B. INCREMENTAL GAS-PHASE MOLECULAR TRANSPORT

1. Investigate CVD or combined PVD/CVD methods for depositing Al_2O_3, or for codepositing Al_2O_3 with inert, insoluble foreign atoms (e.g., C, Pt metals, refractory metals) to yield 1/4-in.- to 1/2-in.-thick freestanding bodies of high density and extremely fine grain size, high modulus, and high strength

2. Investigate CVD methods for depositing Al_2O_3, or codepositing Al_2O_3 with inert, insoluble foreign atoms (C, Pt metals, refractory metals) on refractory-metal wire, to yield a coaxial coating of extremely fine grain size or short-range-order structure and full density, high modulus, and high strength

3. Investigate CVD methods of depositing dense fine-grained Al_2O_3 (or codeposits) as a sheet on both sides of an array of refractory metal, boron-, or carbon-reinforcing filaments; for good bonding and high strength

4. Investigate CVD methods of preparing very-high-purity sinterable Al_2O_3 powders by "snowing out," from halides, metal-organics, etc.

C. INCREMENTAL LIQUID-PHASE MOLECULAR TRANSPORT

1. Develop shaped-crystal methods of growing single-crystal Al_2O_3, spinel or yttrium aluminum garnet, etc., directly in useful form and nearly to tolerance, e.g., shaped-crucible method for turbine buckets, leading edges, or float method for windows, transparent armor, and other articles requiring disc or sheet forms; high strength is required in both examples, high transparency as well in the second

2. Investigate withdrawal techniques, using freezing or flux method, to grow single-crystal Al_2O_3 in filament or long-fiber configurations of high modulus and high strength

3. Investigate anodizing or fused-salt electrolysis of appropriate chemical systems, followed by heat-curing as necessary, to yield oxides of extremely fine grain size or short-range-order structure and full density, high strength; intended ultimately for coaxial filament

4. Investigate the sol-gel process for preparing pure, dense, sinterable powders of Al_2O_3 or Al_2O_3 admixed with an extremely finely subdivided foreign phase (C, Pt metals, refractory metals, or carbides)

D. INCREMENTAL MOLTEN-PARTICLE-SPRAY PROCESSES

1. Investigate systematically all the process variables of electric flame and liquid-fuel-fired spray deposition of Al_2O_3, including the use of programmed heating of the substrate and postfabrication annealing, for optimum mechanical performance and deposition rate; intended for bulk configurations of high modulus and high strength

2. Investigate spraying of complex ceramic compositions, including: refractory glass and crystallizable-glass compositions, and admixtures of Al_2O_3 with an extremely finely subdivided foreign phase (C, Pt metals, refractory metals, or carbides); intended for bulk configurations of high modulus and high strength

3. Develop techniques for high-strength butt welding of Al_2O_3 sheets by high-velocity spray methods; evaluate relative to the base material

4. Investigate methods of spraying dense fine-grained Al_2O_3 (or codeposits) as a sheet on both sides of an array of refractory-metal or boron-reinforcing wires, for good bonding and high strength

5. Investigate the preparation of very-high-purity sinterable Al_2O_3 powder by arc or RF plasma spraying of decomposible or combustible particles into an appropriate atmosphere and "snowing out"

Group I. Bulk Configurations: A-1, glass and glass-crystallization approaches; C-1, shaped single-crystal approaches; D-1, molten-particle-spraying approaches; D-2, logical follow-on to D-1; B-1, chemical-vapor-deposition approaches.

Group II. Special Configurations: joining: D-3; filaments: C-2, B-2, C-3, A-1; matrices: D-4, B-3; powders: C-4, B-4, D-5.

intent of the Panel that no current work falling within the scope of Tables 8 and 9 should be set aside, but rather that the objectives listed in Tables 11 and 12 represent areas where greater effort is needed than is currently in progress under either government or private funding.

It is implicit in these recommendations that, in the opinion of this Panel, the fluid processes included in Table 10 (and in the Priority Program) show relatively good prospects of achieving the general objectives for oxide ceramics with which each is identified—relative, that is, to other fluid processes and to solids-processing approaches. It is not implied, however, that other processes or other compositions will not satisfy selected specific hardware needs falling within the scope of the eight Model Objectives of Table 10. Nor can it be guaranteed in advance that all the research recommended here will meet with success. Risks are inherent, and redundancy has been built in where the present base of knowledge is tenuous.

Thus, the recommended Priority Program is not intended to displace worthy basic or applied research relevant to other than fluid-processing methods or to other compositions than oxides. Indeed, if there is any supported effort which should be sacrificed to enable increased systematic research in oxidic-ceramic processing, it is the wasteful, hurried, and unreported search for a satisfactory material or fabrication method that so often accompanies scheduled hardware-development work.

This Panel Report also recognizes the need for a "new" methodology in ceramic processing and in processing research and development. There have been numerous Materials Advisory Board expressions of this need and of a rational philosophy to fill it: for example, by the Ad Hoc Committee on Processing of Ceramic Materials, in Report MAB-195-M; by the Ad Hoc Committee on Characterization of Materials, in Report MAB-229-M; and by the parent Committee of this Panel. The Fluid Processing Panel supports and concurs in the general conclusions of the above bodies, in respect to the needs: for furtherance of a science of materials (ceramics); for furtherance of a science of processing (of ceramics); for the experimental foundation of both in the adequate characterization of materials; for interpretations of the process ⟶ character relationship and the character ⟶ property (or, behavior) relationship in terms of the fundamentals of chemistry, physics, and mechanics as their scientific foundation; and for materials-related R&D to be conducted increasingly upon these experimental and scientific foundations.

In particular it is absolutely necessary, for the purpose of achieving the inherent potential mechanical qualities of ceramic materials, to increase the amount of processing research and development work that is scientific in the above sense; and to decrease the amount of work that is founded on the short-cut fiction of "process ⟶ properties," or on the identification of accomplishment with a piece of hardware (however useful it may be), unless accompanied by published descriptive and performance information.

This Panel therefore recommends that research programs such as developed in this Report be held aloof from immediate and specific hardware objectives, and that any processing R&D tasks be so specified and funded as to ensure their conduct in accordance with the above principles of a science of ceramic processing.

Several detailed recommendations for the execution of such a program follow:

1. Work conducted under the task objectives listed in the Program must be performed with an extreme regard for sophisticated characterization of raw and in-process and product materials, and for systematic coverage and where possible, isolation, of the processing variables. Methods of characterization must be described. Correlation of processing with features of character and explanation of behavior in terms of the atomistic mechanics of brittle materials are of paramount importance. In no part of the Program should processing be correlated with indices of mechanical performance without diligent

130

effort being made to interpose character, coupling to it from both sides. Contract funding must be provided for this essentially scientific aspect of the work.

2. Knowledge is desired, in consequence of performance of these tasks, of how processing parameters influence the mean or modal mechanical behavior (i.e., "performance") of products, and through what features of character. Also important is determining how the scatter of mechanical properties is influenced by processing parameters, and through the variations of what features of character, especially as a function of location within a part (i.e., "uniformity"). A search for the rare flaw or variation and its sources in processing must also be included. Piece-to-piece variation in processing (i.e., "reproducibility"), its origin and control, should be investigated. The development and exploitation of continuous in-process control instrumentation should follow the determination of quantitative process-parameter ⟶ character relationships of importance, and should be an additional objective as tasks mature toward defined engineering processes. Again, these objectives will have to be explicitly specified and funded in R&D contracts.

3. Because each task objective should be framed in terms of the couplings: processing ⟶ character ⟶ behavior, there is a need for uniform and reliable test methods in each task. Even though the science of physical ceramics is yet naive and imperfect, the risk in a haphazard and piecemeal approach to testing is far greater than the risk in using uniform and standardized test procedures. Ways of qualifying participants for performing their own testing should be considered. Alternatively, consideration should be given to the concept of having a single laboratory perform a few well-understood and valid tests for all participants in the Program.

4. It is recommended that research participants be selected on the primary basis of their competence in materials science, as exemplified by past history of intense concern for characterization, experimental rigor, and a scientifically sound and methodical approach to materials problem-solving, and by the scientific quality of the proposed work and interpretation.

5. It is recommended that, as far as feasible, the applied research and development of Table 12 be conducted as a Program, with all participating researchers meeting periodically in workshop sessions for mutual aid and stimulation. A means of administration of the work as a coherent whole rather than as disjointed individual projects should be considered. Such a treatment seems especially necessary in view of the extreme variation in difficulty among individual projects, and in the likelihood of early hardware achievement that attaches to the several tasks. Under ordinary procurement policies, the less certain tasks will be badly delayed or omitted, whereas their timely inclusion and the corresponding provision of reliable information (even if sometimes negative in the hardware sense) is required if the DOD is to attain its desired goal.

Finally, it is recommended that periodic reviews be made of the course and accomplishments of such a Program, in the light of the amount of funding actually expended and the tasks actually mounted, pursued, and concluded. Follow-on efforts in a number of cases will be obvious; but more difficult decisions will also need to be made, between the continuing of efforts that have not yet proved successful and discontinuing them in favor of untried alternatives. New information and new inventions to meet or circumvent problems will appear, none of which is visible at the present time. These will call for changes of approach or of emphasis.

Reviews made under a program philosophy and commitment should, moreover, ensure continuing attention to the gaps in progress rather than encourage "bandwagon" rushes to the areas of success. The former is the role of research, which should be neither shut off by discouragement nor suffocated by the pressure to exploit other accomplishments. To the extent the material objectives described in this Report remain valid with time, the means to the achievement of each of them should continue to be explored and developed. If this philosophy is preserved, the maximum benefits of scientific advancement and engineering ingenuity across the whole area of structural ceramics applications can be assured.

ACKNOWLEDGMENTS

In addition to the appointed liaison representatives from the Government agencies, other persons have served from time to time in this same capacity. These include Charles F. Bersch, Navy, and Samuel W. Bradstreet, Air Force.

Two recognized authorities in two of the processing areas were invited to address the Committee. Their support of this study and their contribution of valuable information and time are acknowledged with thanks: David Duke, Corning Glass Works; and John F. Pelton, Union Carbide Corporation.

The Panel members, together and severally, also owe appreciation to the many colleagues, advisors, and MAB and DOD representatives with whom they discussed related matters in the course of the study.

BIBLIOGRAPHY

Selected readings pertaining to each of the five major groupings of Fluid Processes are listed below:

Bulk Fusion and Freezing

W. H. Bauer, "Fusion Casting of Ceramics," 1st Annual Report, USN Contract No. Now 65-0294-d, April 1966.
Bruce Chalmers, Principles of Solidification, John Wiley & Sons, Inc., New York, 1964.
A. R. Cooper, "Melt Forming of Ceramics," USAF Report AF33(657)-10574, June 1964.
D. T. J. Hurle, Mechanisms of Growth of Single Crystals from the Melt, Pergamon Press, New York, 1962.
A. A. Litvakovskii, "Fused Cast Refractories," National Science Foundation, Washington, D.C., 1961 (Trans. from Russian).

Bulk Glass and Glass-Crystallization Processes

B. R. Emrich, "Technology of New Devitrified Ceramics - A Literature Review," Air Force Materials Laboratory, AFSC, Wright-Patterson AFB, Ohio, 1964.
P. W. McMillan, Glass-Ceramics, Academic Press, London, 1964.
S. D. Stookey and R. D. Maurer, Progress in Ceramic Science, Vol. 2, Pergamon Press, New York, 1961.
The Structure of Glass: Catalyzed Crystallization of Glass, Vol. 3, Consultants Bureau, New York, 1964.

Incremental Gas-Phase Molecular Transport

M. Basche and D. Schiff, Mater. Design Eng., 59 (2), 78, New York, February 1964.
B. Becker, USAF Report AD-274040, April 1962.
M. R. Browning, Quarterly Reports, USAF Contract AF33(616)-7016, September 1961, et seq.
R. J. Diefendorf, J. Chim. Phys., 57, 815, Paris, 1960.
J. Glasser and W. E. Few, USAF Report ASD-TDR-62-999, September 1962.
L. Holland, The Vacuum Deposition of Thin Films, John Wiley & Sons, New York, 1956.
D. M. Mattox, "Film Deposition Using Accelerated Ions," Electrochem. Technol., 2 [9-10], 295-8, New York, 1964.
C. F. Powell, J. H. Oxley, and J. M. Blocher, Jr., Vapor Deposition, John Wiley & Sons, New York, 1966.

132

H. Schäfer, Chemical Transport Reactions, Academic Press, New York, 1964.
Wright Air Development Center, "Proceedings of Conference on Structural Plastics, Adhesives, and Filament-Wound Composites," Vol. III, Wright-Patterson AFB, Ohio, December 11-13, 1962.

Incremental Liquid-Phase Molecular Transport

R. H. Arlett, M. Robbins, and P. G. Herkart, "Growth of Large Sapphire Crystals from Cryolite," J. Am. Ceram. Soc., 50, 58, Ohio, 1967.
S. B. Austerman, "Growth and Properties of Beryllium Oxide Single Crystals," J. Nucl. Mat., 14, 225, Netherlands, 1964.
D. J. Frosch and L. Derick, "The Preparation and Floating Zone Processing of Gallium Phosphide," J. Electrochem. Soc., 108, 251, New York, 1961.
L. L. Gruss and W. McNeill, "Anodic Spark Reaction Products in Aluminate, Tungstate, and Silicate Solutions," Electrochem. Technol., 1, 283, New York, 1963.
R. C. Johnson and J. A. Kelley, "Growth and Properties of Zirconia and Titania Whiskers from Fused Salt Baths," U.S. Bureau Mines Rept. Invest., No. 6667, 15, 1965.
H. LaBelle, Jr. and A. I. Mlavsky, "Exploratory Investigation of Novel Filament Formation Techniques for Continuous Crystalline Alumina," Tech. USAF Report AFML-TR-66-246, August, 1966.
R. A. Laudise, "Hydrothermal Synthesis of Single Crystals," Progr. Inorg. Chem., 3, 1, New York, 1962.
R. A. Laudise and J. W. Nielsen, "Hydrothermal Crystal Growth," Solid State Phys. 12, 149, London, 1961.
E. S. Peiser, Crystal Growth, Pergamon Press, New York, 1967.
W. G. Pfann, Zone Melting, 2nd Edition, John Wiley & Sons, New York, 1958.
F. A. Scott, "The Electrolytic Growth of Dense Self-Supported Uranium Dioxide Shapes," Final Status Report (10/5/62) USAEC Contract AT(45-1)-1350, Nucl. Sci. Abstr., 3, 846, Washington, D.C., 1963.

Molten-Particle Spray Processes

Neil M. Ault, "Characteristics of Refractory Oxide Coatings Produced by Flame Spraying," J. Am. Ceram. Soc., 40, 69, Ohio, 1957.
P. R. Dennis, C. R. Smith, D. W. Gates, and J. B. Bond, "Plasma Jet Technology," NASA Report SP-5033, National Aeronautics and Space Administration, Washington, D.C., October 1965.
H. S. Ingham and A. P. Shepard, Metallizing Handbook, Metallizing Engineering Co., Inc., Westbury, L. I., New York, 1959.
B. E. Kramer, M. A. Levinstein, and J. W. Grenier, "Effect of Arc Plasma Deposition on Stability of Non-Metallic Materials," Final Report on USN Contract NOas60-6076-C, May 1961.
H. Meyer, "On The Flame Spraying of Aluminum Oxide," Werkstoffe Korrosion, 11, 601-616, 1960.
D. G. Moore, A. G. Eubanks, H. R. Thornton, and W. D. Hayes, Jr., "Studies of the Particle-Impact Process of Applying Ceramic and Cermet Coatings," ARL Report 59, Aero. Res. Lab., USAF, August 1959, also ASTIA Report AD266-381.

General

S. D. Brown et al., "Critical Evaluation of Ceramic Processing at Subconventional Temperatures," USAF Report AFML-TR-67-194, June 1967.

PANEL ON FLUID PROCESSING

STEPHEN C. CARNIGLIA, <u>Chairman</u>
Section Chief, Materials Section
Atomics International, Division of
    North American Aviation, Inc.

Members

JOHN M. BLOCHER, JR.
Division Chief
Battelle Memorial Institute

SHERMAN D. BROWN
Principal Scientist
Materials Research
Rocketdyne, Division of
    North American Aviation, Inc.

F. R. CHARVAT
Supervisor, Crystal Development
    Laboratories
Union Carbide Corporation
Linde Division
Speedway Laboratories

JOHN F. MACDOWELL
Manager, Glass Ceramics Research
    Department
Corning Glass Works

DWIGHT G. MOORE
Head, Coatings and Composites Group
Metallurgy Division
Denver Research Institute

LIAISON REPRESENTATIVES

SAMUEL W. BRADSTREET
(Air Force Representative from
March 8, 1965 to September 6, 1966)

IRVING MACHLIN
Materials Engineer
Naval Air Systems Command
Materials and Processes Branch
U.S. Department of the Navy

WILLIAM MCNEILL
Pitman-Dunn Institute for Research
U.S. Department of the Army

CLARENCE A. PRATT
Air Force Materials Laboratory
U.S. Department of the Air Force
Wright-Patterson Air Force Base

VAUGHN E. SEITZINGER
National Aeronautics and Space
    Administration
George C. Marshall Space Flight Center

PROFESSIONAL STAFF

DONALD G. GROVES
Staff Engineer
Materials Advisory Board

CHAPTER 4

Report of the Panel on Finishing

ABSTRACT

Finishing processes are used in the manufacture of ceramic products to obtain a specified shape, size, and surface finish and to achieve improved or new properties different from the original fired ware. These processes change the character and properties of the product, and therefore the proper selection and control of these finishing operations are imperative for obtaining product reliability and reproducibility.

To control finishing processes properly, it is necessary to determine the effect of the processes on the character of the surface and body and hence the final properties of the finished product. Methods of characterization are discussed and the needs of further development are recommended.

The finishing processes considered are discussed under four major headings: Material Removal, Surface Treatment, Body Treatment, and Joining and Assembly. Each is further subdivided into separate specific processes. The present state of the art for each specific process as developed in the study is presented. This is followed by recommendations for further research and development in each area. In many cases, the recommendations were scaled to the initial research effort. The extension of this work will depend upon the success of the initial investigation.

New and improved finishing processes, focused on the enhancement or extension of the properties of present ceramic products, were also studied. These processes are discussed under their proper process categories, and recommendations are included for further research and development.

SUMMARY OF RECOMMENDATIONS

Finishing processes on ceramic products usually change the character or properties of the original body. The control of these processes is therefore critical in contributing to the reliability and reproducibility of the product. To better understand and to establish improved processes, the following recommendations are made for future research and development in ceramic-finishing processes.

Characterization

1. Develop methods for characterizing surfaces
2. Analysis and measurement of stresses
   a. Mathematical model of local stresses in a polycrystalline body
   b. Develop a method of measuring local stresses
   c. Develop a method of measuring large-scale stresses

Material Removal

1. Abrasive machining
   a. Engineering study of techniques and their effects on surface character and properties
   b. Basic study of mechanism of abrasive material removal
   c. Coolants and lubricants
   d. Ultrasonic material removal
2. Chemical methods of material removal
   a. Research on chemical methods
   b. Continue development of leaching and machining process
3. Evaluate energy-beam methods of material removal

Surface Treatment

1. Strengthening processes
   a. Chemical strengthening by developing a compressive surface layer
      (1) by changing thermal expansion
      (2) by causing phase transformation
      (3) by chemical reaction and stuffing
      (4) by developing preferred orientation
      (5) by studying the effects of compressive surface layers on the resistance of ceramics to environmental factors and on reliability
   b. Physical strengthening by developing compressive surface layer
   c. Methods of chemical strengthening that do not produce a compressive layer

Body Treatment

1. Precipitate secondary phases in a body by special composition additions and/or heat treatment to give new properties

Joining and Assembly

1. Develop study techniques and establish essential criteria for ceramic joining
   a. Organic adhesive bonding
   b. Ceramic adhesive bonding
   c. Sintered joining
   d. Ceramic welding
   e. High-temperature brazing
2. Engineering study to generate design guidance information for good ceramic joining
   a. Mechanical joints
   b. Bonded joints

INTRODUCTION

Many ceramic products require some type of finishing operation to obtain the specified shape, size, surface finish, or other new or improved property different from that of the original fired ware. Since the finishing process usually changes some character or property of the original body, the degree of understanding and control of the processes will have a major influence on the reliability and reproducibility of the product.

A Panel on Finishing was appointed to study the ceramic-finishing area, evaluate the state of the art and recommend future actions. Specific objectives of this panel were defined as:

1. Evaluate the capabilities and limitations of ceramic-finishing processes

2. Outline the factors that relate the character of the finished product to the selection and performance of the finishing process

3. Recommend scientific or engineering research to improve the understanding of the ceramic-finishing processes and to determine the effect of these processes on the surface properties and total character of the product

4. Survey new finishing processes for enhancing the properties of ceramic products and recommend research to achieve controlled property improvement by these processes.

Ceramic finishing is any process or treatment accomplished on the material subsequent to the final firing treatment by the producer. It often consists of some type of mechanical material removal or abrasive process such as sawing, drilling, contouring, grinding, or polishing. There exist in the ceramic industry today a broad capability and a body of empirical knowledge that can be applied to attain excellent surface finishes and dimensional tolerances. Many of these abrasive processes, based on existing knowledge, are operator-dependent, time-consuming, and costly. Their proper selection, controlled operation, and understanding will improve the quality of the final product and also offer a potential for considerable cost savings.

Chemical and energy-beam methods of material removal currently in the research or experimental stages represent possible revolutionary solutions to some ceramic-finishing problems and must therefore receive serious long-range consideration. Chemical methods, in particular, offer potential opportunities for economical processing and controlled results not readily envisioned for mechanical methods.

Ceramic surface and body treatments used for producing physical, chemical, or mechanical changes in ceramic parts must also be considered as finishing processes. Some, such as annealing, fire polishing, and the application of various coatings and glazes, are commonly used and well understood. New processes such as chemical strengthening of ceramics give promise for significant enhancement in strength, reliability, and other properties. The capabilities and limitations of these processes warrant careful study and evaluation.

The character of ceramic surfaces has such a marked influence on properties and, in turn, is so significantly altered by most finishing operations that surface characterization must logically be treated as part of the over-all ceramic-finishing problem area. It is a complex subject with limited experimental data and is faced with serious deficiencies in instrumentation and techniques.

Joining and assembly of ceramic parts to other ceramic or metal parts is also considered as a finishing process. Many ceramic surface-finish and tolerance requirements arise directly from joining and subassembly considerations. Furthermore, the frequently observed inverse relationships between size of manufactured ceramic parts and their strength, reproducibility, and quality emphasize the need for the component build-up approach by joining and assembly.

The Panel considered these various aspects of ceramic finishing, and the study results are presented under five headings: (a) Character of Finished Ceramic Surfaces, (b) Material-Removal Processes, (c) Surface-Treatment Processes, (d) Body-Treatment Processes, and (e) Joining and Assembly. An outline of the finishing processes studied by the Panel is shown in the Matrix Chart in Table 1.

CHARACTER OF FINISHED CERAMIC SURFACES

The character of finished ceramic surfaces is the sum of textural, structural, and compositional descriptions that identify a specimen uniquely and may be

Table 1. Matrix Chart of Material Removal and Other Finishing Processes

Type of Process	Function	Process Variables	State of Art (normal values)	Pertinent Characterization Parameters
MATERIAL REMOVAL				
<u>Mechanical</u>				_Process_
Grinding	Shaping	Machine tool:		Chips and breakage
Lapping	Dimensions	Speeds	4,000–6,500 sfm	Body cracks
Polishing	Surface finish	Feed rate	Variable (0.0005–0.05 in./rev)	Microcracks
Sawing	Cleaning	Depth of cut	Variable (0.0001–0.01 in./pass)	Pullout
Drilling		Pressure	Depends on other variables	Scratches
Crush-forming		Rigidity	Limited by part geometry	Residual surface material
Blasting		Loose abrasive	Al_2O_3, SiC, B_4C and diamond	Grain topography
Ultrasonic finishing		Grinding tool (wheel, belt):		Changes in surface chemistry
Tumbling		Type of bond	Metal, resin, and vitrified	_Body_
		Abrasive composition	Al_2O_3, SiC and diamond	Composition
		Grit size and shape	50–1,000 mesh	Voids (macro)
		Abrasive concentration	50–150 conc	Body porosity (micro)
		Tool dressing		Grain size
		Coolants	Water	Grain orientation
			Water-soluble oils	Grain boundaries
			Water-based solution	Nonuniformity
			Nonhydrous fluids	Residual stress (micro and macro)
		Part character:		Solute segregation
		Size and geometry	Machines available in wide range of sizes and compound shapes	Stoichiometry
				Glass–phase concentration
		Surface finish	2–5 μ in. on small pieces; 10–20 μ in. on large pieces	Component hardness
				Superficial hardness
		Tolerances	0.0001 in. for small pieces; 0.002 in. for large pieces	Resilience
		Material characterization	Rate of material removal increases with grain size and/or porosity	Toughness
<u>Chemical</u>				_Process_
Polishing	Shaping	Reagent	Mostly experimental	Loose grains
Machining	Dimensions	Reagent concentration		Residual compound
Etching	Surface finish	Time		Nonuniform removal
Electrochemical	Cleaning	Temperature		Residual crystal orientation
		Pressure		_Body_
		Effective potential		Same as for Mechanical Removal above

137

Table 1. (continued)

Type of Process	Function	Process Variables	State of Art (normal values)	Pertinent Characterization Parameters
Energy Beam Electron beam Plasma jet Laser	Holes Cutting	Energy Atmosphere	Mostly experimental	Process Grain size Composition Surface integrity Body cracks Microcracks Body Same as for Mechanical Removal above

SURFACE TREATMENT
 	
Coatings
 	
Ceramics:
  Glass
  Crystalline
  Metallizing
Films:
  Inorganic
  Organic
  Metallic
	Control surface properties
	Chemical
	Mechanical
	Thermal
	Optical
	Texture
		Geometry
		Density
		Thickness
		Composition
		Time, temperature
		Crystallization
		Atmosphere
		Pressure
		Electrical potential
		Vacuum
			Processes and materials available
			Specific to process and materials
			Characterization, evaluation, and control are needed
				Process
				
				Composition
				Chemical interaction
				Thickness
				Residual stresses
				Adherence
				Continuity
				
				Body and Surface
				
				Same as process and body parameters in sections above

Chemical
 	
Diffused:
  Surface layers
  Stuffing
  Low expansion phase
  New phases
  Solid solution
Healing of surface defects
Cleaning
	Compressive stresses
	Control surface properties
	Mechanical
	Electrical
	Chemical
	Thermal
	Optical
	Texture
		Composition
		Temperature
		Pressure
		Time
		Atmosphere
		Solvent reagent conc
		Agitation
			Mostly experimental
			Specific to materials
			Characterization, evaluation and control are needed
				Process
				
				Composition
				Crystalline phase
				Grain boundary
				Grain growth
				Solute segregation
				Residual surface stresses
				Microcracks
				Etching
				
				Body and Surface
				
				Same as process and body parameters in sections above

138

Table 1. (continued)

Type of Process	Function	Process Variables	State of Art (normal values)	Pertinent Characterization Parameters
Thermal				Process
Annealing	Compressive stresses	Time, temperature	Mostly experimental	Surface character
Tempering	Control surface properties	Medium	Specific to materials	Stresses
Degassing of surface	Chemical	Environment	Characterization, evaluation, and control are needed	Body and Surface
Redox surface	Electrical	Geometry		Body strength
Fire polishing	Texture			Same as process and body parameters in sections above
Thermal etching	Cleaning			
BODY TREATMENT				
Thermal				Process
Annealing	Stress relief	Time	Process well known	Composition
		Temperature	Proper control and evaluation needed	Grain size
				Grain growth
				Grain boundaries
				Phase changes
				Residual stresses
				Body and Surface
				Same as process and body parameters in sections above
Chemical				Process
HF Leaching	Purification	Time	New application not widely used	Composition
Fluorination	Machinability	Temperature		Grain size
Dehydroxylation	Reduce defect concentration	Concentration		Grain boundaries
		Agitation		Phase changes
				Density
				Body and Surface
				Same as process and body parameters in sections above

139

Table 1. (continued)

Type of Process	Function	Process Variables	State of Art (normal values)	Pertinent Characterization Parameters
ASSEMBLY				
Bonding				**Process**
Fusion	Attachment	Geometry	Specific for materials	Composition
Ceramic – metal seal	Sealing	Composition	and design	Interaction and diffusion
Cement adhesive	Component buildup	Size	Processor–dependent	Bond integrity
	Joining	Time	Characterization, evaluation	Bond structure
		Temperature	and control needed	Bond dimensions
		Surface condition (chem)		Size
		Mating geometry		Design
				Body and Surface
Mechanical				Same as process and body
	Attachment	Geometry (part and mating)		parameters in sections
	Sealing	Size		above
	Component buildup	Time, temperature		
	Joining			

140

correlated with its properties. Since the characterization of ceramic surfaces is a very complex subject, with limited experimental data, it is appropriate to discuss here some of the most obvious aspects of ceramic surfaces.

Surface microstructure of commerical oxide ceramics such as beryllia, alumina, and zirconia may exhibit different characteristics from those found internally. In general, an as-fired ceramic surface exhibits the greatest integrity of the entire sample, even though the surface may not be smooth. A ceramic surface will not show voids that are perhaps inherent in the system nor will it show the same glass phase that exists internally.

Methods of Surface Characterization

Finishing processes required to attain surface finish, dimensions, or properties will certainly affect the character of the surface. It is important to be able to determine the character of the surface of a finished ceramic product so that proper controls can be applied to the processes. Methods now available for evaluation of surface include: surface-roughness measurements, optical- and electron-microscope studies, electron-microprobe analyses, x-ray investigations, and residual-stress measurements.

SURFACE-ROUGHNESS MEASUREMENT

When smoothness of the surface is important, the specifications for ceramic products often include a maximum roughness number. This is expressed in microinches AA (arithmetical average), microinches CLA (center line average), or microinches rms (root-mean-square). Theoretically, rms numbers are about 11% larger than the equivalent AA and CLA.

Although a number of instruments for measuring surface roughness have been devised which employ optical, acoustical, mechanical, or pneumatic principles, nearly all manufacturers of ceramics use a stylus instrument with electrical amplification of the motion of the stylus perpendicular to the surface over which the stylus is traversed. The measurement of the roughness of the surface will depend primarily upon the diameter of the stylus point because this determines the width and depth of the surface crevice it will measure.

The stylus measurement of surface roughness is a helpful process guide, but its limitations should be kept in mind in using it as a sole characterization of the surface obtained from a grinding operation. It does not tell the presence or extent of those microchecks occuring in the surface that are smaller than the stylus diameter, nor does it measure the subsurface damage which may result from a harsh, rough grind.

Surface-roughness measurements should be related only to materials of the same composition produced by the same process if the values are for product evaluation or specification.

MICROSCOPY

The visual character of the grain structure after surface finishing is an important observation for the control of the process.

If surface-removal processes are required, the surface skin must be completely removed to obtain a uniform and reproducible surface, since the interior body is quite different from the unfinished surface. The measurement of the size of the exposed grain and the proportions or orientation of the different crystalline phases present could be a significant control method. The nature of the grain boundary, grain pullout, and any apparent grain or boundary damage are critical criteria.

In other surface-finishing processes, including coatings, chemical treatments, and thermal treatments, the visual character of the resulting finished surface is

142

equally important. A study of a section taken through the surface, showing coating interfaces and diffusion layers, may be essential to the control of the process. Similar observations of a joint made in an assembly operation may be needed for proper control of the finished product.

The optical microscope, both petrographic and metallographic, is the most common microscope used for the inspection of ceramic surfaces. Unfortunately, it is often necessary to remove a specimen from the product for observation, and in this case the test is destructive. Table 2 shows the range of magnification, resolution, and depth of focus for optical microscopes.

The electron microscope is almost essential today for characterization of the grain structure of our fine-grained ceramics. Although improved transmission techniques have recently been developed, usually a replica of the surface is prepared for actual observation. The surface is often treated with an etchant to obtain the relief necessary for proper contrast. The depth of focus is limited by the technique, but high magnification is possible. The range of capabilities of the electron microscope is also given in Table 2.

Recently, a scanning electron microscope has been developed that provides a greater ability for visual characterization of ceramic surfaces than those described above. This instrument fills in a nearly blind range between the optical and the electron microscopes. It observes the specimen directly and thereby avoids the limitations of the replica technique. As shown in Table 2, it has an unusual depth of focus. Here again it is necessary to obtain a specimen limited to about 1/4-in. in diameter.

ELECTRON-PROBE ANALYSIS

The electron-probe analysis of a finished surface, a glaze interface, a diffusion layer, or a ceramic-to-ceramic or ceramic-to-metal seal yields significant data on composition changes from grain to grain and grain boundary. Recently improved instruments have the capability of showing composition changes over an area of about 1μ in diameter as an electron beam traverses a specimen. Using x-ray emission techniques, these instruments are capable of analyzing for elements as light as boron.

X-RAY DIFFRACTION

The uses of x-ray diffraction for surface characterization include identification of the phases present and study of solid-solution composition, phase composition, degree of reaction and reaction rates, degree of preferred orientation, topography, particle size, and large-scale stresses. The use of x rays for residual-stress determination is covered in the section on that topic.

Identification of the phases present is extremely useful for surface characterization in cases in which the surfaces are treated to form new phases or to

Table 2. Comparison of Optical, Scanning, and Transmission Electron Microscopy

Comparison Factors	Optical Microscope	Scanning Electron Microscope	Transmission Electron Microscope
Magnification range	Up to 1,200x	50 to 50,000x	500 to 250,000x
Resolution possible	~2,000 Å	~200 Å	~5 Å transmission ~30 Å replica
Depth of focus	~1 μ at 100x	~100 μ at 1,000x ~1 μ at 10,000x	Limited by specimen

remove unwanted ones. The phase profile can be determined by grinding away the outermost surface layer and examining the material at each level.

Solid-solution composition is determined by measuring the lattice constants of the crystals and comparing these lattice constants with known standards. The concentrations of various phases that are present affect the intensity of the diffraction peaks so that by comparison of these intensities with the intensities for known standards the phase compositions can be determined. Using either of these techniques, the progress of chemical reactions can be followed and reaction rates can be determined.

Preferred orientation (that is, the departure from random orientation) of the crystals in the surface affects the intensities of the diffraction peaks. X-ray methods are widely used to determine the degree of preferred orientation.

Defects in the surface affect the degree of scattering, and low-angle x-ray examinations based upon this effect can be used to study surface structure and topography.

The width of the x-ray diffraction peaks depends upon the crystallite size, among other things, when the crystallite size is less than about 1 μ. Therefore, in the size range below 1 μ, x-ray diffraction is used as a method of grain-size determination.

Numerous methods of x-ray examination exist. The methods just described are expected to find increased use in examination of surfaces, and other methods will be adapted for this purpose.

LIQUID-PENETRATION METHODS

The characterization of the surface finish and integrity with dye tests and radioactive penetrants is being applied in some process-control procedures and has appeared in product specifications.

Colored and fluorescent dyes are applied to the surface and then removed by washing or rubbing; this cleaning will not remove that which has penetrated into cracks or checks. This system is used with visual inspection, sometimes with magnification. Large cracks are made very apparent. Numerous small checks in grains or grain boundaries will produce an area discoloration.

Radioactive penetrants can be measured with radiation counters.

It is important that the exact condition causing the nonremoval of dyes and radioactive penetrants be known in order to apply this method properly.

DIMENSIONAL AND GEOMETRIC MEASUREMENTS

Many mechanical, optical, and electronic supermicrometers are available for measuring exact dimensions. The most sensitive measurements require accurate temperature control and temperature corrections for the instruments. Flatness can be determined to a fraction of a wavelength of light with properly calibrated optical flats. For precision measurements it is important to know the conditions of calibration and to completely fulfill these requirements for the measurement. The proper selection of the method of measurement to fit the accuracy required is of prime importance.

RESIDUAL-STRESS MEASUREMENTS

The presence of residual stresses in ceramic bodies may enhance or limit the use of ceramics in structural applications. It is likely that inadequate characterization of these stresses is directly responsible for many of the unexplained variations in strength reported by many investigators.

Properly controlled stresses in a product can increase its strength and toughness. Systems of surface compression for increased strength and toughness are now being used. Compression glazes, tempered ware, and chemical strengthening are designed to enhance the strength of ceramic products. The proper control of these processes is necessary for reproducibility and reliability.

Conversely, the presence of stresses in a ceramic body often limits its use as a structural material. In massive pieces, the shrinkage, bond development, and grain growth may follow different timing schedules owing to temperature lag of a heavy section from outside to interior. Different parts of a piece may receive different heat treatments. This may cause a difference in body character toward the interior. Additionally, on cooling massive pieces or pieces with different cross-section thicknesses, various sections will cool at different rates, causing zonal stresses. Uncontrolled stresses of this kind will reduce strength and toughness and can result in spontaneous failure.

Grinding and polishing of the surfaces of ceramic pieces can change stress distribution and distort thin sections. This is sometimes quite troublesome where very accurate flatness or dimensions are required.

There are two principal types of residual stresses. Local stresses exist among the grains of all ceramic bodies. These stresses arise in several ways. They may result from unequal contractions of anisotropic crystals during cooling after sintering. They may result from unequal contractions of different phases in the same body. They may result from unequal transmission of large-scale stresses due to elastic anisotropy or variations in elastic properties from one phase to another. Large-scale stresses are characterized by the fact that tensile and compressive stresses may exist throughout large volumes of the body. These stresses may arise from differences in degree of preferred orientation, thermal expansion, plastic flow, and other ways because of different cooling rates.

There are many examples of the effect of residual stresses on the properties of ceramic bodies. In cases of extreme thermal-expansion anisotropy of the crystals in single-phase bodies with medium or large crystal size, the crystals contract unequally on cooling after sintering and form microcracks between the grains. Where the cracks have formed, the stresses are relieved. Where the cracks have not formed, the stresses may be very large, up to the strength of the bonds between the grains. Bodies of ths type may be very weak. These effects have been observed in alumina, titania, aluminum titanate, graphite, and lithium aluminum silicate bodies.

In polyphase bodies, the presence of phases with different expansion coefficients results in localized stresses among the grains when the bodies cool after sintering. In extreme cases, these stresses may be relieved by crack formation. In alumina bodies, the effectiveness of thermal conditioning in improving strength has been attributed to reduction of localized stresses among grains of the different phases. Local stresses may contribute significantly to pullout during mechanical material removal.

The most striking example of the importance of large-scale stresses is the use of compressive surface layers to strengthen glass, glass ceramics, and conventional polycrystalline ceramic bodies. After these successes, it is obligatory for each investigation of the effect of various factors on the strength to provide for characterization of the large-scale residual stresses, in order to assure that variations in residual stresses are not the reason for the observed variations in strength. There are encouraging signs of progress in this direction.

X-ray diffraction measurements of unit-cell dimensions show distortion in crystals. The strain thus measured may result from macrostress in zones of the piece.

There are no other good methods of determining stress in a ceramic piece. Certain shapes can be tested by sectioning the piece and determining the distortion that results when stress is released, but this is a destructive test and is limited to specific shapes.

Limitation of Techniques of Surface Characterization

None of the methods of surface evaluation discussed above, in themselves, gives adequate characterization of the surface. Correlation between these measurements and the product properties is often obscure. New tests and measurement techniques are needed. Better correlation of the effect of the character of the surface and properties of the product are essential to improved control of finishing processes.

Factors of surface character involved are: chemical composition, including absorbed layers; crystalline phase and morphology of the surface; grain boundaries; the nature of the interfaces between surface coatings and the body; micro- and macrostress of the surface layer; contour and dimensions; and surface defects.

Recommendations for Research on Characterization of Ceramic Surfaces

1. Develop improved methods of characterizing the surface of ceramic products. This should include an evaluation of present methods to determine their significance and limitations. This project may be divided into four sub-projects: topography, composition, morphology, and constitution.

2. Determine the character of localized stresses and develop methods of measurement.

     a. Develop a unique mathematical analysis of localized stresses, particularly those resulting from differential expansion properties of anisotropic crystals and multiphase systems.

     b. The x-ray method of strain (stress) measurement should be further developed and other methods should be studied.

MATERIAL-REMOVAL PROCESSES

The purpose of material removal is to obtain specific final shape, accurate dimensions, and surface finish, or to eliminate surface contaminants. The various processes are listed in Table 1 and are classified as mechanical, chemical, and energy beam; process variables, state of the art, and pertinent characterization parameters are also tabulated.

Mechanical Material-Removal Processes

The most common material-removal processes for structural ceramics are mechanical in nature and can be categorized as abrasive machining. Both loose and fixed abrasive methods are included, encompassing sawing, drilling, and contouring, and ranging from mass removal with coarse abrasives to surfacing with fine abrasives in lapping and polishing operations.

STATE OF THE ART OF ABRASIVE MACHINING

The state of the art of abrasive machining is defined as the sum of the technologies of the suppliers of machines, abrasives, and coolants coupled with the specific skills of the individual finishing processors and the knowledge and understanding of the investigators of the various abrasive processes.

Machine Tools

Machine tools are available for grinding large and complicated shapes and thus are not the limiting factors in the majority of grinding operations. Most of this equipment has been developed for metal and natural-stone finishing and has been or can be adapted to the finishing of ceramics. Surface speeds of the abrasive, pressure on the workpiece, and depth of cut are reasonably adjustable for ceramic grinding. This is not to say that there are no machine-tool problems. Hand finishing is often required for surface finishes below 32 μ/in., probably because the machining methods are generally developed from a metalworking technology and the machining characteristics of ceramics are frequently observed to be quite different from those of metals. Machining of ceramics is often done in the bisque state prior to hard firing, using single-point lathe tools or soft alumina abrasive wheels. This is analogous to machining of metals before hardening and might profitably be expanded.

Abrasive machining is usually done with one operator per machine, and generally only a few pieces are undergoing simultaneous treatment, so that labor costs are high. However, it is usually economics (volume of demand vs cost of automation) rather than technology that is limiting; great numbers of inexpensive and high-quality ceramic parts are produced daily for the electrical and electronic industries.

Grinding Wheels

The grinding wheel may be regarded as a multipoint cutting tool with irregularly shaped cutting points. The type of abrasive grain used, the size of the grains, the matrix of binder holding the grains together, the number of grains per unit area, and the interactions of these features are the wheel parameters that contribute to the efficiency of the grinding operation. The processes for the manufacture of grinding wheels are usually proprietary, and proper characterization of these tools is unknown or unavailable.

The most frequently used grains in a grinding wheel are silicon carbide, aluminum oxide, and diamond. Use of diamond abrasives is increasing because of hardness, stability of the grinding surface and, with the advent of the manufactured diamond, development of an ability to relate diamond properties to specific applications. For example, with proper selection of the type of manufactured diamond, it is claimed possible to change the volume of workpiece material removed per volume of wheel wear by a factor of two. Properties of selected abrasive materials are given in Table 3.

A friable or frangible grain is one that readily shatters or breaks apart, forming sharp new cutting edges and points. A tough grain is one that will round over the cutting edges and points. In reality, tiny chips are broken from the cutting edges, thereby rounding them, rather than gross pieces being removed to form new cutting edges.

The size of the abrasive grain in the wheel is one of the factors controlling

Table 3. Properties of Selected Abrasive Materials

Material	Density (g/cc)	Knoop Hardness (kg/mm^2)	Compressive Strength (psi x 10^{-6})	E (psi x 10^{-6})	Resistivity (ohm/cm)	Thermal Conductivity (btu/hr/ft^2/°F/in.)	Capacity (cal/g/°C)
Diamond (natural)	3.5	7,000	1.2	156	10^{10} - 10^{15}	1,040 (70°)	0.18
Diamond (manufactured, semiconducting)	3.5	7,000	1.2	168	10^{-2} - 10^{10}		
Boron-carbide		2,750-3,000	0.41		10^6		
Silicon-carbide	3.2	2,480	0.22	55	10^5	620 (400-1,600°F)	0.22
Aluminum-oxide	4.0	2,100	0.2-0.65	57	10^{11} - 10^{15}	160 (200-1,600°F)	0.21
Tungsten-carbide	15.6	1,550-1,800	0.54	<95		1,360 (70°F)	0.04

the depth of cut per pass, and vice versa. If the ratio of depth of cut to grain diameter is greater than 50%, the matrix or binder holding the grain together is brought into contact with the workpiece, injuring the bond, tearing out abrasive grains, generating excess heat, and wearing the wheel excessively. Effects on the workpiece are equally drastic. The surface finish is injured by chatter, glazing, burning, and deep scoring. Excessive pressure can build up rapidly and fracture the workpiece, the wheel, and the machine setup. On the other hand, a grain size which greatly exceeds the depth of cut can also be destructive. The desired surface finish on this and subsequent operations will be difficult to achieve, edge chipping will be prevalent, the surface-grain boundaries will be in a fractured state, and it will be hard to obtain accurate dimensions.

The types of materials used to bond the grains in grinding wheels contribute materially to the performance of the abrasive. They range in consistency from resilient to brittle. A resilient bond is tough, energy-absorbing, and resistant to grain pullout but must be cooled to prevent grain shifting. It is especially good for finishing, with light cuts at high speeds. A brittle bond supports the grains very well and is self-cleaning but is subject to fracture. It is good for heavy cuts (stock removal) and accurate dimensions.

Binder materials include resins, rubbers, metals, vitrified materials, shellac, and silicates. Vitrified bonds are most common, but diamond wheels are frequently metal-bonded, and resin bonds are not uncommon. The resin bond has the characteristics of a resilient bond. The vitrified bond has the characteristics of a brittle bond. The metal bond has a high modulus of elasticity and provides an abrasion-resistant bond with good mechanical support. It has high thermal conductivity but may also create more heat during grinding, thereby requiring slow grinding and more wheel dressing. A metal-bonded wheel is ideally applied on nonmetallic intermediate or moderately "high-modulus-of-resilience" materials.

The number of grains per unit area in a diamond cutting wheel will obviously influence the rate at which a wheel will cut and the rate at which it will wear. There are optimum levels, controlled by the type and size of grain, the type of binder, the nature of the workpiece, and the goal of the operation, viz., stock removal or surface finishing.

Of equal importance is the structure of the wheel. An open-structure wheel consists of grains, binder, and air pores, like a heavy foam; it cuts faster, cools and self-cleans better, but wears faster and loses shape and dimension more quickly. A tight structure contains, to the extent possible, only grains and binder; it provides better dimensional control, a better surface finish and longer wheel life. The structure or spacing between the grains (from "0" for dense to "15" for open) is often indicated separately when specifying a wheel.

Grinding wheels are often known as "hard" or "soft," with the hardness grade indicated by a letter system—from A for soft to Z for hard. Wheel hardness does not reflect the real hardness or strength but rather the performance of the over-all aggregate; it is a complex factor. At the extremes, a hard wheel will consist of a tough grain in a resilient bond with a tight structure, while a soft wheel will consist of a friable grain in a friable bond with an open structure. A soft wheel will cut rapidly, wear rapidly, and require little cooling or cleaning; it will allow an increase in work speed or depth of cut or a reduction in grains per unit area. A hard wheel will provide tighter dimensional control and a better finish and will hold its shape better, but it will require better cooling and more frequent dressing to avoid glazing and will provide a lower rate of stock removal.

Dressing is a means of putting a grinding wheel in optimum condition to grind efficiently: Sometimes it is removing the swarf or grinding debris from between the abrasive grains so the cutting edges of the grains can be exposed; sometimes it is removing the glazed or worn areas, causing and exposing new cutting edges; and sometimes it is changing or truing the shape of the wheel. Generally, two or more of the above operations are combined and the term "dressing" is used to describe the whole operation. Because of the expense involved in diamond wheels and their ability to withstand wear for long periods of production, dressing is generally limited to maintenance of wheel form, with abrasive wear being minimized by optimizing operating conditions. Therefore, it is frequently desirable to clean the cutting surface by removing workpiece swarf or matrix material that has "mushroomed out" under grinding pressure. This is generally accomplished by using a soft abrasive stick or by grinding with a soft (aluminum oxide) wheel which will remove surface detritus without affecting the diamond grain.

Loose Abrasives

Loose abrasives are commonly used in wire saw cutting, in some flat grinding, in lapping, and in polishing. Diamond dust, aluminum oxide, silicon carbide, and boron carbide are the usual abrasive materials. Quartz sand and garnet are also used in grinding; and cerium oxide, zirconia, and rouge (iron oxide) are common polishing materials.

Lapping is done to control geometry and size as well as surface finish—that is, it is used to achieve flatness, perpendicularity, and accurate dimensions. Polishing is primarily a surface-finishing operation.

Coolants and Lubricants

The four major classes of coolants and lubricants are water, oil-water emulsions, water-based solutions, and nonhydrous compound mixtures. Usually these fluids are complex mixtures of proprietary composition that cannot easily be characterized by the users.

There has been extensive work on finding suitable fluids for grinding metals, but relatively little work has been done on fluids for grinding oxide-ceramic materials; however, there is some evidence that glass can be cut or polished better by using particular types of coolants or lubricants.

The primary uses of coolants are to remove the products of grinding and to control the temperature at the tool-workpiece interface. The use of coolants is particularly important where high thermal-stress failures are encountered in grinding, such as in the low thermal-conductivity systems. The coolant usually acts also as a lubricant, reducing friction and thereby further augmenting the coolant function, but probably also reducing or promoting chemical interaction between the tool and the workpiece, usually through the control of absorbed surface films. The grinding fluid, acting as a boundary lubricant, may prevent oxidation of boron carbide or the dissolution of silicon carbide in steel, for example, or may promote the formation of antiwelding films on chips; in metal cutting, additions of sulfides, chlorides, and chlorates are often used for this purpose.

It is generally recognized that there are basically two surfaces to be protected by a lubricant: the workpiece and the abrasive. This may apply to aluminas, especially if a glass phase is present. Major diamond suppliers believe that although one can reduce friction and wear by using lubricants tailored to the workpiece, the greatest benefits will come from grinding fluids that effect direct protection of the diamond surface.

Before an effective lubricant can be developed, there must be an understanding of the various categories of lubrication and a realization of which type is present during grinding. It has been shown that friction conditions can be classified by the coefficient of friction. Below a coefficent of friction of 0.02, hydrodynamic lubrication is present. In this case, there is complete separation of the solid surfaces, which means there is no transfer (metal) between solid surfaces, and therefore no possibility of chemical reaction between the two solids. Above a coefficient of 0.02, boundary lubrication is present, which signifies that unless special precautions are taken, there will be solid-to-solid contact, and chemical reaction may take place. There is another defined area of lubrication called mixed lubrication that exists between coefficients of 0.005 to 0.1. In this case, both hydrodynamic and boundary lubrication can be present. In the grinding of metals, investigators have shown that the coefficient of friction is always above 0.02 and generally greater than 0.1, which denotes that one is always dealing with boundary lubrication. This indicates that distinct measures must be taken to limit the rate of solid transfer and chemical reactions.

It has been shown that such protection can be provided if the lubricant is capable of forming a protective layer on one or both of the solid surfaces. The family of fatty acids falls into this category for many applications. These illustrate three main points indicative of all good boundary lubricants. First, the film must be a solid to afford maximum protection of the surface, and since the friction process generates heat, the melting point of the lubricant will be of importance; the higher the melting point, the lower the coefficient of friction and the lower the rate of solid transfer. Second, if the friction is to be low, the solid film must be an easily sheared solid, which is the case for long-chain fatty acids. Third, the lubricant should adhere to the surface.

Although some of the requisites of the boundary lubricants for diamond abrasive have been identified above, it is a difficult problem to develop an end product specifically synthesized to meet these requirements.

Current Abrasive Machining Capabilities
(Industrial State of the Art)

Grinding   Although machines and technology are available for precision grinding and finishing of large parts for various special applications such as radomes, the present industry capability for general products is limited to about 14 in. in diameter, and this size is downgraded if the part geometry is too complex. Flat surfaces of considerable size (multiple square feet) can be ground on bed-type machines. Surface finish and tolerances attainable are usually better on smaller pieces. On the smaller parts, surface finishes of the order of 2-4 microinches and tolerances of the order of 0.000010 in. are not uncommon.

Knowledge of precise mechanisms and quantitative relationships relating to the grinding process is virtually nonexistent, but current technology extends somewhat beyond the information in the preceding sections. It is known, for example, that high body strength does not result from abrasive-machining operations, but that the strength of a body can be reduced by abrasive machining. Fast hogging (gross-stock removal) followed by polishing will leave a weak body. Fast hogging must be followed by successively more shallow cuts, where each cut can remove the scratches or gouges left by the preceding cut, and where the total material removed by the last stages is sufficient to remove the intergranular cracks, pullouts, and other damage generated by all the preceding operations. These are, however, empirical observations. They are usually true, but there is no public knowledge of techniques whereby any exceptions can be predicted or even isolated after the fact without destructive testing (assuming no gross and obvious flaws are present).

There is little information on the tool-workpiece interaction. Research has shown that the interface temperatures are quite high but it is not known how high they may be in most commercial grinding operations. This local heating may generate stresses that could have a major effect on microchecks, pullout, and chip formation. The combination of temperature and pressure alters permanent stresses in the surface to an extent that thin plates often distort when released from the grinding bed. This area of the correlation of the mechanical material-removal processes with the character of the final surface, to enhance reliability and reproducibility, remains virtually unexplored.

There are several gross reasons for rejection of a part, such as chips,

150

breakage, and body cracks. These defects may result from the harshness of the grinding operation, as indicated in the previous paragraph, but may also be due to excessive feed rate or excessive pressure on the workpiece, for example. They may also be due to the character of the workpiece. For example, grain pullout may be due to underfiring or local stresses, and inability to achieve a particular surface finish may be due to oversize grains or pores in the workpiece.

Many decisions in setting up a grinding operation are affected by multiple and sometimes interrelated parameters. The choice of the wheel type will depend on the workpiece, the volume of material to be removed per pass (i.e., stock removal vs surface finishing), and the dimensional accuracy or surface finish desired. A major criterion for the choice of a wheel for initial stock removal is the grinding ratio, G, or wheel efficiency, which is defined as:

$$G = \frac{\text{volume of material removed}}{\text{volume of wheel wear}} .$$

A plot of material removed vs the volume of wheel wear for metals is shown in Figure 1. The middle region, where the grinding ratio is high, is preferred. Similar information for ceramic grinding is desirable.

The feed rate, d, and the grinding ratio, G, are related by:

$$dG^n = C ,$$

where n and C are constants. Thus, the grinding ratio is related to the feed rate.

Typical wheel speed is 4,000 to 7,000 surface feet per minute. Doubling this rate and reducing the pressure on the workpiece will often increase efficiency, but the wheel may fly apart due to centrifugal forces.

Ultrasonic Material Removal   An interesting and valuable industrial application of ultrasonics is the process known as ultrasonic cutting or ultrasonic machining of brittle materials. The ultrasonic method is a form of abrasive machining. The brittle material (e.g., carbides and aluminas) is removed by blows from grains of a harder abrasive, which is under the control of a tool that vibrates with a comparatively small amplitude. Of course, the abrasive also causes wear in the tool, but this is minimized by making the tool of a viscous material (one that has no tendency to cleave). The particles of abrasives are themselves cleaved in the process and so must be gradually replaced by running an abrasive slurry into the working area, which also serves to flush away the abrasion products. The material is cut away as very small particles, but these are produced by many abrasion grains, and the tool vibrates at a high frequency (18,000 to 24,000 cps), so that the total rate of removal can be sufficient for practical purposes.

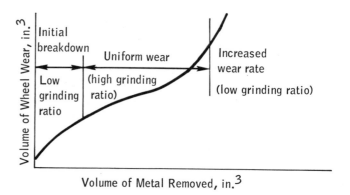

FIGURE 1. Schematic representation of grinding ratios found in grinding metals.

The tool may be advanced in the direction of vibration, in which case a cavity is produced whose profile corresponds precisely to that of the tool. Combinations of movements allow one to perform a variety of operations on brittle materials analogous to those of ordinary drilling, shaping, and profile milling, for example.

Ultrasonic cutting, however, is a technique as yet far from perfected, and existing machines have many deficiencies; i.e., they are costly and operate at very low efficiency. Ultrasonic cutting techniques are only beginning to be exploited. No reliable methods are available for calculating the dimensions of components, especially cutting tools.

At present, the process is in use in this country in dental drilling and dental prophylaxis, machining die cavities in hard metals, machining ceramics and other nonconductive materials, machining cemented carbides for special nozzles, and cutting and drilling holes in glass and ceramics.

Other Mechanical Material-Removal Processes   Nearly all ceramic companies use either tumbling or vibrating to remove setter sand from ceramic parts. Some use tumbling to produce a mirror finish on certain parts where surface roughness is not critical. This is usually done on ceramics softer than alumina.

Grit blasting is also used frequently to remove setter sand from fired ware. Some experimental work has been done with grit blasting in an attempt to obtain very intricate patterns on cylinders and plates, mainly for the inertial guidance and for electronic industries. The grit used on alumina parts is either silicon carbide or boron carbide; the finish and straightness of the walls in the indentations leave much to be desired.

Current Understanding of Abrasive Machining
(Scientific State of the Art)

Grinding of ceramics is presently an art based on experience. No scientific knowledge exists, and such technical information as is available has to do with empirically established procedures for obtaining particular results. The meager published information about the effects of grinding on the workpiece is limited to materials like metal-bonded carbides, glass, and semiconductors, which bear an uncertain relationship to alumina and other ceramics.

This lack of scientific information is not due to experimental difficulties, because the nature of the breakdown of hard and brittle materials has been studied extensively in somewhat related operations. Sheldon and Finnie (1965a) have observed both brittle and ductile behavior in the erosive cutting of brittle materials. Tsuwa has made electron-microscope studies of fracture and plastic flow in abrasive grains while grinding steel. Eiss and Fabiniak have made similar studies in which sapphire spheres were rubbed at high speeds against a steel plate. King has also studied the wear of ceramic tools when cutting steel, and the Air Force has supported recent efforts to improve ceramic cutting tools. Recent Japanese studies have shown how abrasive grains are affected by diamond dressing.

The techniques used in these and other studies might be applied to the study of what happens when ceramics are machined. A better understanding could lead to more rapid improvement in the art than is realized by present empirical methods. In the meantime, hypotheses concerning the mechanisms involved in abrasive machining of ceramics are confirmed by the scope and applicability of information generated in studies on glass, metal-bonded carbides, and, in some cases, metals.

The mechanism of chip formation, which affects the rate of removal and finish, has been studied in glass. Smekal found that in sawing glass with a diamond cutoff wheel, glass was all splintered by being crushed into particles ranging from 10 μ to below 1 μ. The glass cracked ahead of the abrasive grain, to a depth equal to the grain depth of cut. There was no evidence of any deeper cracks or of any plastic flaw. On the other hand, Ishida and Ogawa obtained spiral chips when they cut glass with a diamond point, and they did not observe any glass splinters. Ryshkewitch observed very similar spiral chips in sapphire cut slowly with a diamond tool. Kobayashi ground an unspecified ceramic material with a diamond wheel and found that all material came off in the form of brittle particles, some of which were partly fused.

An immediate generalization seems possible, based on the foregoing paragraph: Fast machining, done at random (no predetermined path—using an abrasive wheel rather than a single-point tool), will cause splinters; slow machining with a controlled path (single-point lathe tool) allows crystalline fusion and the production of strands or spiral chips (length of sheared particle many times the diameter).

A few attempts have been made to find relationships of physical properties and grindability of brittle materials (Gielisse). One of these proposes a ductility index, which is defined as a ratio of surface energy to the hardness of the workpiece or abrasive grain. Another study relates the "modulus of resilience," expressed as a function of strength and modulus of elasticity, to the grinding performance of metal-bonded tungsten carbide. This modulus of resilience expresses the material's ability to resist impact before failure. These studies have not been applied to ceramic materials.

Interesting as these concepts are, they remain qualitative since they are based on parameters pertaining to the abrasive, the matrix, or the workpiece alone. Furthermore, they presuppose that wear on both the abrasive and the workpiece is essentially a mechanical process rather than a thermal or chemical one.

Interface friction, which causes thermal damage and enhances the various chemical effects that accompany the mechanical-wear process, was found to be expressed by the relationship $K = cf^n$, where K = wear factor, c = constant, f = coefficient of friction, and $n = 3$. This indicates that small changes in friction can cause large changes in the wear factor. Thus, lubricants, not just coolants, have a large effect on grinding performance.

In grinding any material, at least one other factor must be taken into account—namely, that of the temperatures developed at the wheel and workpiece interface. The temperature developed in the diamond on the periphery of the grinding wheel is reported to be proportional to the reciprocal of the square root of the thermal conductivity of the workpiece, when that workpiece is a metal-bonded tungsten carbide.

To assist in the selection of an abrasive system that will generate the least amount of heat, Gielisse developed an intermittent-transient heat-transfer model as shown in Figure 2.

Here,

$$q_t = q_w + q_m + q_c ,$$

where q_t = total heat flow, q_w = heat flow in the wheel, q_m = heat flow in material, and q_c = heat flow into the chips produced during grinding.

Now, assuming

$$q_t \propto F_t \propto \sigma_{(T)} ,$$

where F_t = tangential load, and $\sigma_{(T)}$ = total ultimate strength at temperature, and setting

$$O_w = \frac{1}{V_w} \text{ and } O_m = \frac{1}{V_m} ,$$

where O_w = contact time of the wheel, O_m = contact time of the workpiece, 1 = length of the contact zone, V_w = speed of the wheel, and V_m = speed of

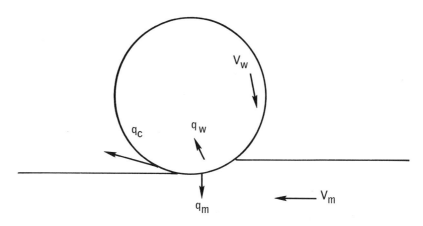

FIGURE 2. Transient heat-flow distribution at a wheel-workpiece interface.

the material to be ground, the interface temperature, T, as related to the physical parameters of the system may be expressed as follows:

$$T \propto \left[1 / \left(\frac{K_m}{O_m} + \frac{K_d}{O_w} \right) \right]^{1/2} ,$$

where K_m = thermal conductivity of the workpiece, and K_d = conductivity of abrasive grain.

Using, as an example, the grinding of glass with Al_2O_3 and diamond, we can illustrate what happens. In the case of Al_2O_3 on glass:

$$T_{Al_2O_3 - glass} = \left[1 / \frac{K_G}{O_m} + \frac{K_A}{O_w} \right]^{1/2} = 0.4 ,$$

where $O_w = 0.01 \, O_m$, $K_G = 0.0017$ cal/cm sec °C, and $K_A = 0.0016$ cal/cm sec °C.

For the diamond - glass system: $T_{diamond - glass} = 0.17$, or the temperature developed at the diamond - glass interface would be estimated at only 40% of that developed at the Al_2O_3 - glass interface. This implies that for the particular application, the diamond grinding wheel provides for a lower interface temperature.

An interesting experiment that measured the interface temperature was reported by Gielisse. By using a semiconducting manufactured diamond, connected as a thermistor, as the abrasive tool, he was able to measure the temperature of the diamond grain while it was cutting.

RECOMMENDATIONS FOR FUTURE RESEARCH AND DEVELOPMENT

General

It is known that improper grinding and finishing techniques can seriously degrade the inherent properties of ceramic parts by causing surface cracks, residual stresses, particle pullout, and roughness. The problem seems to be more serious as one develops higher-strength materials. Apparently, the high-strength materials have fewer natural defects, such as porosity or inclusions, and hence the surface flaws become the prime loci of failure initiation.

There is evidence that the various types of commercially available alumina bodies respond quite differently to cutting, grinding, and polishing. It is recommended that for any study of ceramic finishing the aluminas studied should cover reasonable ranges of composition, grain size, and processing. The ranges are identified as follows:

Composition
1. 85 to 94% alumina
2. 95 to 99% alumina
3. 99 to 99.9% alumina

Grain Size
1. Fine   up to 5 μ
2. Small   5 to 15 μ
3. Medium   15 to 30 μ
4. Large   30 to 50 μ

Porosity
1. Up to 1%
2. 1 to 5%
3. Over 5%

To minimize body variables it is recommended that all alumina test pieces in any specific test program be made by the same process (e.g., isostatic pressing and sintering) and by the same manufacturer. When comparing data from different test programs, particular attention should be paid to differences in character and resultant differences in abrasive machining behavior due to the forming process.

It is also recommended that simple shapes be employed; that the surfaces studied include cylindrical OD's, cylindrical ID's, and flats; and that at least one complex shape from each category be employed, especially when residual or induced stresses are to be studied. The purpose is to isolate the different surface character that may ensue from different types of abrasive machining that are used to achieve the various shapes.

It is further recommended that, when applicable, investigations be conducted on as-fired surfaces, ground surfaces, lapped surfaces, and polished surfaces.

Recommendation for Specific Investigations

Abrasive Machining   The recommendations that follow are discussed under four headings: Engineering Study, Basic Study of Mechanisms of Material Removal, Coolants and Lubricants, and Ultrasonic Material Removal.

Engineering Study. The purpose of this program should be to explore the function and reproducibility of each step of the abrasive machining process and the relationship of each step to the preceding and following steps.

The objectives should be to assess the nature, extent, and predictability of the influence of abrasive machining on the character and properties of the workpiece; to explore, if necessary, the prospects for preventing, minimizing, or removing any deleterious results; and to examine the long-range prospects of abrasive machining vs chemical, energy-beam, or other material-removal processes.

The scope of the program should including the following factors:

1. Temperature gradients and temperature levels developed in ceramics and the interface during grinding; thermal stresses

2. Grinding forces; forces necessary for grit movement, penetration, and cutting; tangential and radial forces on the workpiece; signature analysis of the vibrational spectrum

3. Workpiece alterations; residual-stress distribution, deformation, surface stoichiometry, microcracking, incipient melting, hardness changes, recrystallization, physical and mechanical properties

4. Workpiece properties such as type of finish, dimensional accuracy, and form

The variables included in this program should include but not necessarily be limited to:

1. Machine condition such as wheel speed, workpiece speed, depth of cut
2. Properly characterized abrasive type

3. Type of bond system
4. Coolants and lubricants
5. Grinding mode

From Table 1 (Material-Removal Processes) the Type of Process would be sawing, grinding, lapping, and polishing; the Function would be surface finish; the Process Variables would be machine tool (all those listed) and grinding tool (all those listed, and the abrasive is to be diamond); nearly all factors listed under State of Art; and nearly all features listed under Pertinent Characterization Parameters.

The surface character after each material-removal or polishing operation could be studied by the following methods: electronic contact analysis (profilometer, Talysurf), interferometric methods, microscopy (optical, electron, scanning electron), radiography, fluorescent dye penetration techniques (Zyglo, Spot-Chek), or other methods found suitable.

Basic Study of Mechanisms of Material Removal. At least four mechanisms have been suggested as being involved in material removal: (a) atomic, i.e., diffusion, submicroscopic bonding; (b) adhesional wear; (c) shear deformation into chips; and (d) chipping and fracture. Their presence or absence, the conditions for any mechanism, and the conditions for transition from one to another must be established. However, while these suggestions provide an initial reference point, any intense investigation of the basic mechanisms of material removal should not be limited to such current conjectures.

A modest initial effort is suggested, concurrent with the Engineering Study recommended above. As specific objectives are defined and the work leaves the exploratory category, an increase in effort is recommended for as long as necessary to achieve a fundamental understanding of abrasive machining. The outcome of such knowledge may be the means of optimizing abrasive machining or it may provide unequivocal evidence favoring other means of material removal.

Coolants and Lubricants. There is a need for a systematic study of the functions that may be served by a grinding fluid in the abrasive machining process and the subsequent development of an optimum fluid. The progress already realized from studies of the contributions of fluids to the grinding of metals may provide substantial background, but it must be recognized that physical and chemical differences in the abrading medium and the workpiece from one system to another can materially alter the utility of the fluid. For example, a metal workpiece can be an effective heat sink, while a low-conductivity ceramic may trap the heat at the working surface; similarly, one grinding medium or workpiece may be far more susceptible to oxidation or other chemical reaction than another.

To bound the problem to workable proportions, it is suggested that efforts be confined to the alumina bodies described in the preceding section. Once knowledge and understanding of one family of the wheel-workpiece system is realized, techniques and probable routes should facilitate progress in other systems.

Ultrasonic Material Removal. As an auxiliary effort to the Engineering Study recommended above, a study of the mechanisms, techniques, and competitive or unique advantages of ultrasonic abrasive cutting is recommended.

Chemical Material-Removal Processes

STATE OF THE ART

Chemical material-removal processes are currently used mainly for experimental purposes. A comprehensive body of knowledge exists concerning the use of reagents to bring out various microstructural features in samples used for microscopic examination. Techniques for chemical polishing have been investigated, and a modest technical capability exists for polishing a small number of different materials. The chemical methods used to put ceramic materials into solution for chemical analysis or chemical processing provide another source of information that can be used for development of practical methods of chemical material removal.

Opportunities for economical processing of polycrystalline ceramics exist because the parts can be processed in groups rather than singly, as is the case for mechanical material-removal operations on ceramics for structural applications. Good results may be achieved because of the absence of the types of surface damage that are characteristic of mechanical material-removal processes as they are now performed. In addition, processing in groups by chemical methods may lead to reliable results through the use of chemical process control procedures.

Chemical methods can be used to remove material from all types of polycrystalline ceramic bodies. For example, 96% alumina bodies packed in mixtures of Cr_2O_3 powder, plus more than 20 wt% $CrF_3 \cdot 3\text{-}1/2H_2O$, and refired at 1,400°C for approximately one hour, lost weight and the dimensions became smaller. In an extreme case when 100% $CrF_3 \cdot 3\text{-}1/2H_2O$ packing material was used, and the escape of the decomposition products was prevented by a refractory tube, the diameter of an alumina rod was reduced from 0.150 in. originally to about 0.100 in. after treatment at 1,450°C for 4 hours. The large proportion of material removed indicates that more than just intergranular siliceous material was removed by the reaction.

Either acids or bases can be used to remove material from alumina bodies. For example, boiling phosphoric acid can be used to reduce the dimension of alumina bodies. In processes using boiling reagents, refluxing of the evaporated material is useful in reducing the deposition of reaction products on the surface of the body. Some materials are less soluble than the alumina bodies in boiling phosphoric acid, so that formation of these materials on the portions of the body that are not to be removed may constitute an approach to localizing the chemical material removal.

Possibilities also exist for combining chemical processes with other processes to achieve efficient material removal. For example, the intergranular material in conventional alumina bodies can be removed by leaching with aqueous hydrofluoric acid or other reagents. In a current program, this leached material is machined to form complex shapes and then refired to form dense, strong bodies. Several hundred parts have been processed by these methods. Much remains to be learned before this process can be applied with optimum results, but the practicality of this method for machining alumina has been established. This new process has the following advantages over conventional processes that may involve shaping the part in the green or semifired condition followed by diamond grinding of the fired part.

1. It represents a substantial step toward establishment of an industry that can create a large variety of complex shapes from a small number of stock shapes, much as machine shops usually do with metals.

2. Complex shapes can be formed. Some of these shapes can be formed in no other way.

3. Higher-alumina bodies can be produced from lower-alumina bodies.

4. A higher-alumina surface layer can be produced on a low-alumina body.

5. More rapid production of design prototypes may speed up the design process and allow designers to try out more of their ideas.

6. Tooling (dies for pressing) can be eliminated in many cases, so that production of small numbers of special shapes may be practical.

RECOMMENDATIONS FOR FUTURE RESEARCH AND DEVELOPMENT

1. Research on chemical methods of material removal is recommended. One or two reagents should be chosen for reaction with a particular polycrystalline ceramic body. Techniques for localizing the chemical material removal should

be investigated. The effect of the reactions on the character of the surface should be investigated and compared with the character of surfaces resulting from mechanical material removal. Methods of process control and the uniformity of the resulting materials should be studied. Some properties of the treated parts, including flexural strength, should be determined and, if possible, correlated with the observed changes in character.

2. Continued development of leaching and machining as a method of material removal is recommended. This investigation should have the following objectives:

1. Development of an alumina body in which the intergranular phase has a composition selected specifically for controlled reaction with the reagent selected for leaching.

2. Development of improved methods of reconstitution or refiring.

3. Development of processes that combine the leaching and machining process with chemical strengthening processes.

Energy-Beam Material-Removal Processes

STATE OF THE ART

To date, the energy-beam methods of material removal have been essentially experimental in nature. The machining techniques employed include electron beam, ion beam, plasma arc, and laser.

Electron-Beam Machining

Electron-beam machining is a fusion process utilizing heat provided by the degradation of the kinetic energy of a beam of rapidly moving electrons. The energy conversion occurs at the point of impact of the beam with the workpiece. It is reported that this process allows for drilling holes as small as 0.0005 in. in ceramics, cutting thin slots about 0.005 in. wide, and scribing thin films. This technique is most frequently used for precision drilling of small holes in thin wafers or crystals. Precision drilling has been demonstrated by the cutting of 0.001-in.-diam holes in quartz crystals on 0.005-in. and 0.010-in. centers. Where the holes were cut on 0.005-in. centers, a density of 40×10^3 holes per sq in. was achieved. For example, a high-density "screen mesh" obtainable by an electron-beam cut can provide fluid regulation for nuclear or space applications and filtering for cryogenic fluids used in high thermal environments.

Ion-Beam Machining

The ion-beam machining technique employs a stream of high-velocity ions that impinge on the surface of a sample and thereby effect material removal. This technique is presently experimental in nature and has been employed for thinning nonmetallic samples in preparation for examination under a transmission electron microscope. The rates of material removal by this process are extremely slow.

Plasma-Arc Machining

Plasma arcs have been used primarily with metals—for cutting, repairing blow holes in casting, and correcting machining errors. (Plasma arcs have also been used to apply composite coating and to coat ferrite parts, for example.) They could probably be used for profiling or line-cutting operations on low-expansion materials. However, the nature of plasma arcs and the generation of intense heat at the cutting faces make it doubtful that plasma-arc cutting will find wide use in ceramic machining.

Laser Machining

Laser machining, the newest of the energy-beam techniques, is finding limited uses on a small scale. Holes as small as 0.0002 in. (5 μ) have been drilled in all types of materials by vaporizing small increments of material. The laser does not require any physical contact with the workpiece, and only a negligible temperature rise occurs in the surrounding region.

RECOMMENDATIONS FOR FUTURE RESEARCH AND DEVELOPMENT

As the energy-beam methods of material removal are still in the developmental and limited-application stages, it is recommended that the processes, limitations, and applications be investigated to determine the potential of these processes for ceramic machining and material removal.

SURFACE-TREATMENT PROCESSES

State of the Art

Surface treatments are presently used to enhance the strength, reliability, resistance to environmental degradation, smoothness, and other properties that are important in structural applications. Progress in the area of surface-treatment processes must be accelerated in order to take advantage of the inherent advantages of ceramics in structural application. The treated materials may find applications in ceramic armor, impact-resistant goggles, radomes, leading edges, bearings, electrical insulation, and so forth.

Surface treatments include penetrating solid-solution coatings; superficial coatings consisting of inorganic crystalline phases, glass (glazes), organic compounds and metals; thermal treatments including annealing, tempering, degassing, fire polishing, and etching; chemical treatments including etching, polishing, oxidation, and reduction; and others. These treatments serve many purposes, including those listed in the previous paragraph.

Chemical strengthening by surface treatments has been found effective for improving the strength of glasses, glass ceramics, and oxide single crystals. Abraded flexural strengths in excess of 200,000 psi, a 10-fold increase, have been observed for chemically strengthened glass ceramics, as well as a 4-fold increase for an abraded aluminum-oxide single-crystal rod. The standard deviations of the flexural strengths are very low. Recently, the feasibility of this approach for strengthening conventional polycrystalline ceramics was established. Chemical strengthening may be accomplished by formation of compressive surface layers. Compressive stresses in the surface prevent surface flaws from acting to cause failure.

The processes and their effects on the character of finished parts are summarized in Table 1 of this report. Specific areas of interest in surface treatment are discussed below.

COATINGS

Glazes are common on ceramic products, and the general processes are well known and amenable to control. Good methods of characterizing the surface of the substrate, the proper character of the glaze - body interface, and nondestructive measurement of thickness of the coating are not readily available or commonly used. This is also true of crystalline coatings from engobes to flame-sprayed materials. It is questioned whether full use is being made of these types of coatings to enhance the properties of ceramic products; e.g., increased strength, cleanability, weather resistance and surface hardness, and friction characteristics. Porosity of flame-sprayed and plasma arc-sprayed coatings is a problem and may detract from the usefulness of these materials.

Metallizing is commonly used for decoration, ceramic-metal seals, and electrical contacts or shielding.

Special films can be used for optical, thermal, mechanical, or electrical purposes. The proper characterization of the substrate and the film is not generally available. The processes are often specific to the processor. Although the application of films to ceramic products is not now in broad use, future demands may increase their importance.

CHEMICAL TREATMENT

It is believed that chemical treatments of the surfaces of polycrystalline ceramic bodies will become more important in the future, particularly in the area of enhancing the mechanical properties of ceramic products. Diffusion of ions into the surface may create composition or phase changes or structural stuffing that will affect surface stress, thermal expansion, grain size, grain boundaries, and local stresses between grains.

Among the approaches that can be used for formation of compressive layers are the following:

1. Chemical reactions at high temperatures to form low-expansion solid-solution surface layers. During cooling, the main body tends to contract more than the surface layers, resulting in compressive stresses in the surface layers. An example of such a process is the formation of Al_2O_3-Cr_2O_3 solid solutions on the surface of alumina by packing the alumina in Cr_2O_3 powder and refiring. Compressive surface layers are formed, and the strength of the resulting bodies is improved, demonstrating the feasibility of this approach to chemical strengthening.

2. Chemical reactions at high temperatures to form new low-expansion compounds on the surfaces. The compressive stresses result in the same way as described above. The strengthening of magnesia by means of a forsterite surface layer as described by Rhodes et al., is an example of this approach.

3. Phase transformations in the surface layer that result in an increase in volume. If the phase transformation occurs at a temperature that is low enough, the underlying body restrains the expansion of the surface layers, resulting in compressive stresses. At higher temperatures, the stresses may be relieved by plastic flow. An example of this approach is the "Marstressing" process described by Koistinen and used to improve the durability of steel bearings.

4. Chemical reactions that result in an increase in volume of the reacted surface. If the reaction occurs at a temperature that is low enough, the underlying body may restrain the tendency of the reaction layer to expand, resulting in compressive stresses. An example of such a reaction may be formation of spinel ($MgO \cdot Al_2O_3$) from corundum (Al_2O_3) and periclase (MgO) on the surface of an alumina ceramic. In this case the volume of the products is about 7% greater than the volume of the reactants. At higher temperatures the stresses may be relieved by plastic flow.

5. "Stuffing"—that is, substitution of a larger ion for a smaller ion at low temperatures in the surface layer. An example of this process is substitution of sodium or potassium ions for lithium ions in a crystalline lithium aluminum silicate phase. In some instances two ions (such as lithium) may be substituted for one (such as magnesium). The lattice tends to expand because of the greater volume of the substituted ions but is restrained by the underlying material, leading to compressive stresses in the surface.

6. Chemical reactions that deposit a layer of crystals with preferred orientation with the low-expansion direction parallel to the sample surface. For example, corundum (Al_2O_3) is anisotropic and has its low-expansion direction parallel to the "a" crystallographic axis. If the crystals of an alumina body are

oriented with the "a" axis parallel to the surface in the surface layers and randomly in the interior, the surface will be in compression after cooling.

Other methods of chemical strengthening may include removal of secondary phases from the surfaces of polyphase bodies to avoid the localized stresses associated with these secondary phases and thereby obtain improved strength. Another approach is to reduce the thermal-expansion anisotropy or elastic anistropy of the crystals in the surface layers by composition variations. This reduction in crystal anisotropy may have similar consequences.

The use of chemical surface treatments to reduce the severity of other types of surface defects has the possibility of enhancing the strength of polycrystalline ceramics. The extent to which this is used or can be used has not been determined.

THERMAL TREATMENT

Thermal treatment to affect the surface properties of ceramic products includes the quenching (thermal conditioning) of ceramic bodies to obtain a surface compression. This process is commonly used for glass products and, in this case, is commonly called tempering. Quenching of glazed bodies results in much higher stresses in the surface layers compared with the same glazed bodies cooled slowly. These higher compressive stresses result in much higher flexural strengths. The use of these treatments on ceramic products has not been determined, but experiments have been reported that indicate possible application.

Recommendations for Future Research and Development

Of the processes discussed above, the chemical strengthening of Al_2O_3 and other conventional ceramics by compressive surface layers has been demonstrated to be an effective process. This research is in progress and should be continued. It may be noted that most of the research recommended here relates to strengthening, but it is also obvious that surface finish and surface character will play an important role in affecting the properties of the finished parts.

STRENGTHENING PROCESSES BY SURFACE TREATMENT

Chemical strengthening of brittle materials by compressive surface layers has amply demonstrated its potential for improving the flexural strength of brittle materials. Several methods, as outlined earlier, are available for forming compressive surface layers. It is recommended that new programs be initiated to concentrate on each of these methods of forming compressive surface layers and such other new methods as may be conceived. In order to arrange these approaches into a manageable number of programs, somewhat similar approaches have been combined to give programs of broader scope. The suggested programs are described below together with recommended priorities and levels of effort.

1. Use of chemical reactions at high temperature to form low-expansion solid solutions or compounds in the surface layers. During cooling after treatment, the main body tends to contract more than the surface layers, resulting in compressive stresses in the surface layers. Recent research indicates that these approaches are feasible and very fruitful.

2. Use phase transformations that occur with an increase in volume to obtain compressive stresses in the surface layers. The tendency to increase in volume, restrained by the underlying material, results in compressive stresses in the surface layers. This approach is commercially important in improving the wear resistance of metal-bearing materials. The feasibility of this approach has not been established for ceramics but it is considered promising. It is especially important because the stresses will not be relieved when the temperature is

raised, as is the case with the methods using the thermal-expansion differences.

3. Use chemical reactions to form less dense phases or to exchange larger ions for smaller ones to increase the volume of the surface-layer material (stuffing). This tendency to increase in volume, restrained by the underlying material, results in compressive stresses in the surface layers. "Stuffing" is used successfully for glass ceramics. The feasibility has not been established for conventionally sintered and hot-pressed ceramics, but these approaches are considered promising.

4. Use reactions that form a layer of crystals with preferred orientation so that the low-expansion direction is parallel to the sample surface to form compressive surface layers. During cooling after the surface-layer formation, the main body tends to contract more than the surface layer, resulting in compressive stresses in the surface layers.

5. The effect of compressive surface layers in improving the resistance of ceramics to environmental factors should be investigated. The following factors are among those to be considered: (a) thermal shock—in downshock, the compressive stresses must be relieved before the surface can go into tension and failure can occur; (b) static fatigue and stress corrosion; (c) abrasion and rain erosion; and (d) weathering and chemical attack.

Strengthening of brittle materials by compressive surface layers formed by physical methods. For example, quenching of glazed bodies leads to higher compressive-surface forces than are observed in slowly cooled bodies. Superficial crystallization and the resulting compressive layer may be induced on the body or glaze with proper heat treatment. Investigation of other physical methods for forming compressive surface layers is to be included.

Chemical strengthening by methods other than by compressive surface layers. For example, the following approaches might be used:

1. Remove phases, such as sintering aids and grain-growth inhibitors, by chemical methods. Reduction of local stresses between phases is expected to lead to increased strength.

2. Chemical strengthening by reduction of thermal-expansion and elastic anisotropy of surface-layer materials. The thermal-expansion anisotropies of several oxides can be modified by addition of solid-solution atoms as follows: (a) TiO_2 (rutile) by VO_2 or GeO_2, (b) SnO_2 (cassiterite) by VO_2, and Al_2O_3 (corundum) by Cr_2O_3.

If the thermal-expansion and elastic anisotropies of the surface-layer crystals can be reduced, the local stresses between the grains will be lower and presumably the strength will be increased.

3. If dislocations can be pinned at the surface by chemical methods, they may be prevented from moving. Therefore, formation of new flaws may be prevented and the strength and reliability improved.

BODY-TREATMENT PROCESSES

State of the Art

The finishing processes that affect the entire body include both thermal and chemical treatments. The state of the art is described in the following sections.

THERMAL TREATMENT

Thermal treatments applied after the body is fired include annealing (reheating, holding at high temperatures, followed by controlled cooling), quenching (reheating, followed by rapid cooling), and other processes. These processes may be used to relieve stresses, induce beneficial stress patterns, cause grain growth, precipitate new phases, and so forth. Some of these processes are discussed below.

In the normal firing and cooling of ceramic parts, particularly massive pieces or those with major differences in cross section, large residual stresses can result if the cooling is too rapid. This will cause the product to have reduced mechanical strength and toughness. When subsequent grinding is required, high losses due to breakage and chipping may result, and close tolerance finishing may be impossible.

Although it is here recommended that the original cooling after firing be scheduled to minimize large residual stresses, these stresses can be removed by an additional heating to near the original sintering temperature and slow controlled cooling. This process is usually called annealing.

The quenching processes described under surface treatments may also affect the entire body. As a specific case, if Insley and Barzak's explanation of the strengthening effect on thermal conditioning is correct, then these should be considered as body treatments.

Thermal treatments can be used to precipitate secondary phases in ceramic bodies. These precipitates may have substantial effects on the mechanical properties of these materials. In some cases, the results are similar to precipitation hardening of metals.

CHEMICAL TREATMENT

Chemical body-treatment processes depend upon diffusion of chemical species into the body. In spite of this limitation, a wide variety of reactions can be carried out that will affect the entire body rather than just the surface. These reactions include oxidation, reduction, dehydroxylation, and chemical leaching, among others. It does not appear that chemical treatments are broadly used.

Recommendations for Future Research and Development

Although surface treatments are considered to have the greatest potential for achieving strength and reliability in polycrystalline ceramics in the near future, it is evident that progress in treating the surface will soon result in evidence of the deficiencies in the main body. Therefore, rather fundamental long-range research on problems related to the enhancement of strength of the main body after firing is recommended.

An experimental investigation of precipitation of secondary phases and their effects on local stresses, dislocation processes, and strength is recommended. Heat treatments would be used to obtain various degrees of precipitation. This research would be related to earlier work on thermal conditioning and to more recent investigations of the effect of dispersed metal phases on alumina. Chemical treatment prior to heat treatment may develop phases that are not possible with normal processing.

JOINING AND ASSEMBLY

State of the Art

In most applications of structural ceramics, parts must be joined or assembled into a final structure. Thus, assembly and joining normally constitute the final steps of the total processing and finishing cycle to which a ceramic piece is subjected during its incorporation into a useful structure or component. A primary requirement in the assembly of ceramics, whether with similar or dissimilar ceramic components or with metals and other materials, is that the desirable characteristics and properties of the material not be lost or compromised by the assembly operation. In general, an improved capability for assembly and joining is essential if full advantage is to be realized from the unique properties of ceramic materials.

A further need for improved ceramic-joining techniques and processes arises from the fact that the strength, density, and uniformity of structure of ceramic parts usually vary inversely with size. In other words, substantial difficulties are frequently encountered in the scale-up of manufactured ceramic-part size. Reliable and efficient ceramic-joining processes, such as are available for metals, would permit the buildup of small parts into larger components or assemblies having higher and more-uniform properties. Practical realization of the concept of ceramic "mill products" may also be an eventual outgrowth of major advancements in ceramic-joining technology.

Ceramic attachment and joining techniques can be categorized into two broad types: "mechanical" and "bonded." The various mechanical joints and attachments are so numerous and so closely oriented with specific designs and uses that a further subdivision would be unnecessary for the purpose of this report. They would include such types as bolted, riveted, or pinned joints, clamps, shrink fits, snap rings, and threads, for example—many of which may be used with or without intermediate gasketing materials. Bonded joints, however, have been further broken down into brazed, adhesive, and sintered or fused types for consideration in this report.

As reflected in the following discussion, the philosophy employed in analyzing research and development requirements in the area of ceramic assembly and joining was to determine the state of the art as related to general requirements and needs that could be visualized. The desirability of such an analysis or study has been pointed out by the MAB Ad Hoc Committee on Design for Brittle Materials (Report No. MAB-198-M). Recognition of this problem area was also acknowledged by the previous Ad Hoc Committee on Processing of Ceramic Materials (Report No. MAB-195-M). One of the most comprehensive recent research efforts on the study of attachments for brittle components was accomplished by Hofer (1965) under Air Force Flight Dynamics Laboratory sponsorship.

State-of-the-art capabilities in the area of mechanical joining of ceramics are closely related to specific applications and designs. This fact, plus the availability of considerable technical literature dealing with brittle-material designs and attachments, obviates the need for additional discussion here. The lack of such a discussion does not imply a lack of potential for further research and development in this area.

There appear to be several bonding techniques that offer a distinct potential for certain types of ceramic applications. These are: organic adhesive bonding, ceramic adhesive bonding, sinter joining, ceramic welding, and high-temperature brazing.

ORGANIC ADHESIVE BONDING

Various organic adhesives, such as the epoxies, bond very well to ceramic bodies and are used in specialized applications for joining and attaching ceramics. Examples include the bonding of alumina pump plungers to metal actuating shafts and the bonding of ceramic composite armor facing tiles to glass-reinforced plastic backup. The joints demonstrate shear strengths of 5,000 psi or more at room temperature in metal-to-ceramic bonds. The maximum service temperature of epoxy-type adhesives is low—approximately 300°F. This, plus relatively poor over-all environmental resistance as compared with ceramics, limits their utility for many ceramic applications.

Reliable design and performance data on the utility of the newer, more heat-resistant resins for ceramic joining, attachment, and bonding are almost completely lacking. The availability of such data should broaden the use spectrum of organic adhesive bonding for ceramics and permit greater exploitation of its utility, versatility, and economy.

CERAMIC ADHESIVE BONDING

The various commercially available and useful ceramic cements or adhesives (many of which are based on phosphoric acid, potassium silicate, and calcium aluminate) are relatively poor performers when considered in the light of their ability to produce efficient tensile and shear joints in high-strength ceramics such as dense alumina. Joint efficiencies under these conditions have been found to be generally in the order of a few percent. If ceramic adhesive bonding is to "come of age" as a method of joining high-strength ceramic parts or segments, it must be developed to the extent that joint strength approaches that of the basic material being joined. Based on the current state of the art, this would appear to be a difficult but not impossible or unrealistic goal.

A significant step toward indicating the potential of high-temperature and high-strength ceramic adhesive bonding is described by Jones and Barr. This report covers an Air Force-sponsored program for fabricating a large prototype ceramic radome by adhesively bonding together thin trapezoidal-shaped high-strength alumina tile segments. The glassy adhesive used had a bonding temperature of about 2,150°F, wetted the alumina well, and closely matched it in thermal coefficient of expansion. It developed a room-temperature joint shear strength of up to 11,000 psi with the dense alumina material.

Fusion bonding, or soldering, is commonly used in the glass industry to join and seal glass and glass-metal components. Likewise, ceramic glazes are sometimes employed as an adhesive for joining ceramic components—as for attaching the handles on certain dinnerware cups, and for the assembly of large porcelain insulators. General requirements for such adhesives are similar in many respects to those of ceramic glazes. They must melt or mature at temperatures below those at which the base body is softened or otherwise affected. They must also wet and adhere to the body without appreciable interaction and should match or "fit" the body with respect to thermal expansion. They should, in addition, produce a high-strength void-free joint when applied to the faying (bonding) surfaces of the ceramics to be joined and heated to the softening or maturing temperature under slight contact pressure.

Of particular interest in connection with the development of ceramic adhesives and joining techniques is the experience of the glass industry with devitrifying solder glasses. These glasses are used in much the same manner as the common vitreous solder glasses, but once the joint or seal has been made, further heat treatment produces crystallization. This not only results in a stronger joint but also permits use or reheating at somewhat higher temperatures without affecting the vacuum holding ability. In addition, devitrifying glass compositions are obtainable with a wide range of thermal-expansion coefficients, which spans the expansion range of most common ceramic bodies.

On the basis of this background experience and state of the art, it is concluded that there is considerable potential for improving the utility of high-strength ceramics through the development of better ceramic adhesive-bonding materials and techniques. Glass, devitrifying glass, and crystalline-type adhesives should be investigated and developed for use with the common high-performance ceramics such as dense alumina. The objectives should include both high- and low-melting adhesive compositions to meet a range of requirements and ceramic applications with bonded-joint efficiencies severalfold higher than are currently considered practical.

HIGH-TEMPERATURE BRAZING

Brazing is widely used commercially for gastight joints or seals between ceramics or glass and metal. The procedures are generally available in the open literature; however, the joints have limited mechanical and thermal capabilities that do not meet present requirements. The primary problem areas in direct metal-to-ceramic bonding or brazing are fairly well understood from a practical standpoint at least. These areas are the wetting of ceramics by metals and the matching of the ceramic and metal expansion coefficients.

"Active" metals such as titanium or zirconium are often added to the filler metal to enhance wetting on oxide ceramics. The required thermal-expansion match is obtained by proper metal or alloy selection. Kovar alloy, for example, provides a fairly good match with the expansion of alumina. Thus, Kovar, with small additions of an "active" metal, has shown considerable promise as a braze metal for joining alumina to high-temperature alloys and refractory metals.

The existing state of the art in ceramic-to-metal and ceramic-to-ceramic brazing falls short of needs and requirements in at least three respects. First, available braze alloys that are otherwise suitable are limited to moderate-temperature applications. Second, joint-design data are very limited in both quantity and reliability, and joint efficiencies are low. Third, test methods and lack of understanding of the residual stress fields represent serious side problems that should be investigated further.

The current state of the art of ceramic-to-metal and ceramic-to-ceramic brazing is well summarized by Lintner et al.

SINTER JOINING

Although it is well known that grains of ceramic oxides can be sintered into a strong body at temperatures well below the melting point, little practical use has been made of this for joining purposes. In the case of alumina, for example, solid-phase sintering takes place appreciably at about 3/4 of the melting point, and the rate is increased significantly under pressure. This, of course, is the basis of hot-pressing techniques for pure oxides. Taking alumina as an example again, pure Al_2O_3 powder can be sintered to theoretical density in a few minutes under 150-200 atmospheres of pressure and a temperature of $1,800°C$.

The primary problem in achieving a good sintered bond between two oxide body surfaces held in contact under heat and pressure is that of obtaining intimate and uniform contact between the surfaces. The surface tolerance and finish requirements can be decreased to practical limits by use of a small amount of the finely powdered oxide as a "filler" between the surfaces. Vacuum-tight sintered joints in alumina bodies have been reported at temperatures of about $1,500°C$; however, little strength data or experience on this bonding technique are available.

Research to develop and assess the potential of sinter bonding of oxide and perhaps other ceramics further should include investigations of surface preparation by leaching. This should reduce localized stresses and permit more-uniform contact when the surfaces are pressed together. Vibration might also aid in achieving a better fit between such surfaces.

Another possibility that could be considered is the use of a radiation field to promote sintering and joint strength. Sinter bonding offers the potential of joints in pure oxide bodies that approach the strengths and characteristics of the basic sintered body. For certain specialized applications, this may be the only acceptable type of bond; hence the process warrants further development.

CERAMIC WELDING

During the past several years considerable interest has developed in the use of high-energy beams and plasmas for localized fusion and welding of refractory ceramic materials. The more commonly considered approaches include electron beams, laser beams, and various high-energy plasma beams. The potential attractiveness of such joining techniques stems from the facts that they introduce no foreign bond material into the joint which will compromise the essential characteristics of the ceramic; no pressure contact is required; fusion can be localized; a wide range of dissimilar materials may be welded; and the operation may be made in air or in a controlled atmosphere. These are especially important relative to various electronic applications where ceramics are finding increased use in power electron tubes, microwave windows, and similar components. The advantages of ceramics, such as alumina, for these applications are not being fully realized because of difficulties in joining the ceramic parts and sections into vacuum-tight, structurally strong components. Organic or ceramic adhesive bonds lack the necessary strength or thermal resistance, while metallized and brazed joints present problems of thermal-expansion matching, reduced service temperatures, and lowered dielectric properties.

Direct fusion welding of small ceramic sections has been accomplished experimentally by the use of controlled high-energy beams and plasma torches; however, several problems remain to be solved. Chief among these appear to be equipment and techniques developed to control heating and cooling rates within the weld area and in the surrounding body. It has been reported that welds can be made in alumina, beryllia, fused silica, magnesia, and other ceramic bodies, but that factors affecting welding quality and crack prevention must be better understood and controlled. In the case of electron-beam welding, these factors include accelerating voltage, beam current, and welding speed, plus preheating and cooling rates.

On the basis of experiments to date, it appears that weld-joint efficiencies of 40 to 50% are attainable, at least in small sections, and further improvements in joint strengths and size capabilities should be possible with additional development.

Recommendations for Future Research and Development

BONDED CERAMIC JOINTS

The term "bonded" is employed here to designate all the various types of non-mechanical joints and joining techniques for ceramic materials. The ultimate design and development objective for any joint is 100% efficiency; i.e., the joint properties should equal those of the limiting material being formed. Secondary objectives may also include such factors as thermal and electrical conductivity and transition for thermal-expansion differences between materials being joined. Since maximum efficiency and other required properties are difficult to achieve in a simple butt joint, there is a requirement for geometric joint design developments for the various bonding techniques. Suitable joint-testing procedures may also need developing in connection with the research and development programs suggested.

Organic Adhesive Bonding

Considerable progress has been made in raising the operational temperature limits of organic adhesives, the heterocyclic resins being an example. The utility of such high-temperature resins as adhesives for ceramic-to-ceramic and ceramic-to-metal joining should be investigated, and design guidance data should be developed.

High-Temperature Joining Techniques

Ceramic joining techniques that utilize high-temperature processing may affect the characteristics of the bodies being joined. The recommended research and development in all these areas should include: technique development for making joints; effects of these techniques on both body and joint characteristics; and joint strengths and the effects of joint design on strength.

Ceramic Adhesive Bonding   Research and development is needed to develop ceramic adhesive compositions and procedural techniques for making bonded joints in high-strength ceramics. Both low- and high-temperature ceramic bonding compositions should be investigated, with emphasis on devitrifying glasses and crystalline ceramic compositions, in order to develop much higher tensile and shear strengths than are currently attainable. The objective should be a ceramic bonding or joining technology analogous to brazing and soldering for metals.

Sinter Joining   The potential of the buildup of ceramic components by pressure-sintering of prefired segments should be investigated. Investigations should include such approaches as leaching of the contact surfaces to minimize surface-fit and tolerance problems, and the use of a high-radiation field to reduce sintering temperatures.

Ceramic Welding   The fusion welding of ceramics by the use of high-energy beams offers a unique potential for ceramics-joining applications and should receive further research and development support.

High-Temperature Brazing   Braze alloy and technique developments should be accomplished to obtain high-temperature performance more compatible with the service-temperature capabilities of various high-strength ceramics and the refractory metals. Such brazes are needed for ceramic-to-ceramic and ceramic-to-metal joining.

Mechanical Joints and Attachments

Generation of design-guidance information, or refined design philosophies for typical (model) mechanical joints and attachments for a few characterized high-strength ceramic bodies should be undertaken. Emphasis should be on a determination of the statistical distribution and value of joint and attachment efficiencies in relation to the statistical distribution of the strength of the ceramic materials used.

ACKNOWLEDGMENTS

Special recognition and thanks are offered by the Panel for the helpful assistance and technical contributions of: Louis R. McCreight, General Electric Company; George S. Reichenbach, Norton Company; Leo P. Tarasov, Norton Company; Peter J. Gielisse, General Electric Company; Wilfred Mathewson, General Electric Company; and R. L. Williams, Air Force Machinability Data Center.
The Panel is particularly indebted to the gentle guidance and wise counsel of Donald G. Groves, Materials Advisory Board Staff Engineer.

BIBLIOGRAPHY

Character of Finished Ceramic Surfaces

"ACMA - Standards of the American Ceramic Manufacturers Assn. for High Alumina Ceramics," 2nd Edition, 1964. Can be obtained through George P. Byrne, Jr., Secretary, Alumina Ceramic Manufacturers Assn., 53 Park Place, New York, New York. Three grades of surface finish as listed by using ASA B.46.1-62 methods but with stylus of 0.0005 in. radius and 0.030 in. cutoff. Use AA (arithmetic average) expressed in MU. As-fired alumina is listed as 30-60 AA, ground surfaces from 15-30 AA, and polished or glazed surfaces from 1-15 AA.

"Alumina Specifications for Ceramic to Metal Seal Applications," ASTM Tentative Specifications, Comm. F-1, Sub-Comm. V, Task Force B-5, under direction of Dr. Wing Lo, Bell Tel. Lab., Allentown, Pa. To be voted on in 1967. Tentative specifications on surfaces include the following values: as-fired, from 5-65 AA; ground surfaces from 10-50 AA; and polished or glazed surfaces from 0-30 AA.

W. Buessem, "Internal Ruptures and Recombinations in Anisotropic Ceramic Materials," Proceedings of a Conference on Mechanical Properties of Ceramic Materials, Interscience Publishers, Inc., New York, 1961.

W. R. Buessem and F. F. Lange, "Residential Stresses in Anisotropic Ceramics," Interceram., 15(3), 229-231, 1966.

F. R. Charvat and W. D. Kingery, "Thermal Conductivity, XIII, Effect of Microstructure on the Conductivity of Single-Phase Ceramics," J. Am. Ceram. Soc., 40, 306-315, 1957. (Cracks in rutile [TiO_2] bodies caused by expansion anisotropy.)

D. H. Chung and W. R. Buessem, "The Elastic Anisotropy of Crystals," International Symposium: Anisotropy in Single-Crystal Refractory Compounds, June 1967, to be published.

R. L. Coble and W. D. Kingery, "Effect of Porosity on Physical Properties of Sintered Alumina," J. Am. Ceram. Soc., 39(11), 377-385, 1956. (Cracks in alumina caused by expansion anisotropy.)

Jaroslov Feifer, "Roentgenographic Measurement of the Elastic Stresses in Ceramic Insulators of Sintered Corundum," Czech. J. Phys., 8, 322-331, 1958.

L. N. Grossman and R. M. Fulrath, "X-Ray Strain Measurement Techniques for Ceramic Bodies," J. Am. Ceram. Soc., 44, 567-571, 1961.

D. P. Koistinen and R. E. Marburger, "A Simplified Procedure for Calculating Peak Position in X-ray Residual Stress Measurements on Hardened Steel," Trans AIME, 51, 537-555, 1959.

Kenneth B. Lewis, "The Grinding Wheel," Grinding Wheel Institute. Chicago, Ill. Revised Edition, 1959.

V. A. Likhachev, "Microstructural Strains Due to Thermal Anisotropy," Soviet Phys. Solid State, 3, 1330-1335, 1961.

R. C. Mielenz, V. E. Wolkodoff, J. Backstrom, and R. Borroughs, "Origin, Evolution, and Effects of the Air Void System in Concrete; Part 4—The Air Void System in Job Concrete," J. Am. Concrete Inst., 30(4), 1958. (Appendix gives details on methods of measuring voids and methods of calculation and calculation of distribution.)

R. E. Reason, "Significance and Measurement of Surface Finish," reprinted from Grinding and Finishing, Engis Equipment Co., Chicago, Illinois, 1965.

D. H. Rice and R. W. Stowe, "Research on Anisotropy in Polycrystalline Dielectric Materials," Melpar, Inc. Final Report, Contract NOw 66-0440-d, June 1966.

H. Schwartsbart, "Development of Nondestructive Testing System for Analysis and Control of Residual Machining Stresses," IIT Research Institute Engrg. Prog. Report IR-7-718 (VI), Contract AF33(615)-1400, August 31, 1966.

"Surface Roughness, Waviness and Lay," MIL-STD-10A, U.S. Government Publications, 1965.

"Surface Texture—Surface Roughness, Waviness and Lay," ASA B46.1-1962, UDC 621.9.015, published by the Amer. Soc. of Mech. Eng. (cosponsored with Soc. of Automotive Eng.), United Engineering Center, 345 East 37th St., New York, 17, New York, 1962.

L. P. Tarasov and N. W. Thibault, "Determination of Knoop Hardness Numbers Independent of Load," Trans. Am. Soc. Metals, 38, 331-353, 1947.

V. E. Wolkodoff and L. E. Ferreira, "Ceramic Surfaces and Relationship to Internal Microstructure," Third International Materials Symposium, Univ. of Calif., June 1966. To be published by John Wiley & Sons.

V. E. Wolkodoff and R. E. Weaver, "Microscopical Examination of Ceramic Surfaces for Substrates and Related Applications," presented at the Pacific Coast Regional Meeting of the American Ceramic Society, Los Angeles, California, Oct. 27, 1965.

Mechanical Material-Removal Processes

F. P. Bowden and D. Tabor, "The Friction and Lubrication of Solids—Part II," Oxford at the Clarendon Press, 182-183 and 336-370, 1964.

Bulletin of Japan Society of Grinding Engineers, by the Japan Society of Grinding Engineers. A good publication on grinding in general. Typical references are made to Vol. 1, 1961;

Vol. 2, 1962; and Vol. 3, 1963, which contain several excellent articles on abrasive grains and diamond wheels.

"Carbide Cutter Grinding—Laboratory Evaluation of Diamond Wheel Size and Surface Speed," ASTME Manufacturing Seminar, Paper No. SP 64-65, 1963-1964.

N. S. Eiss, Jr., and R. C. Fabiniak, "Chemical and Mechanical Mechanisms in Wear of Sapphire on Steel," J. Am. Ceram. Soc., 49(4), 221-226, 1966.

P. Gielisse (private communication, January 1967).

K. Gillis, "Plating with General Electric Man-Made Diamond," American Machinist, May 9, 1966.

K. W. Hards, "Ultrasonic Speed Diamond Machining," Ceramic Age, 34-36, December 1966.

E. H. Hull and G. T. Malloy, "The Strength of Diamond," presented at the Winter Annual Meeting, Chicago, Illinois, November 7-11, 1965. ASME Paper No. 65 - WA/Prod-2.

"Industrial Diamond Review" (Incorporating Industrial Diamond Abstracts), which can be obtained through the Subscription Department, 131 Fleet St., London, E.C.4, England. The publication is international in scope and includes a wide variety of categories, including Properties of Diamond, Properties of Hard Materials, Grinding, Lapping, Honing and Polishing, and many other topics of interest in finishing materials. Under Properties of Diamond, a typical abstract is "A Means of Increasing the Oxidation Resistance of Diamond," by E. L. Simons and P. Cannon, General Electric Research Lab., Schenectady, New York; Nature, 210 (5031), 90-91, London, 1966.

Ishida and Ogawa, "Bulletin of the Japan Society of Precision Engineering," published semiannually by the Japan Society of Precision Engineering, Bunkyo Mansion 401, Maruyama-cho 35, Bunkyo-ku, Tokyo, Japan. Many of the articles and abstracts deal directly with grinding, grinding mechanisms, surface finishes, and abrasives. A typical abstract is "Theory and Measuring Method of the Temperature Distribution in Ground Surface Layer—Theoretical Analysis on the Grinding Temperature (1st Report)," Koya Takazawa, 30(11), 1964.

E. L. Kapenavos, "Effect of Diamond Content on Grinding Wheel Performance," 19th Annual Convention of the Industrial Diamond Assn. of America, March 9, 1964. Reprints available from Met. Prod. Dept., General Electric Co., Detroit, Michigan 48232.

E. L. Kapenavos and E. Ratterman, "High Efficiency Approach to Diamond Carbide Grinding," Grinding and Finishing, August-October 1963.

A. G. King, "Ceramics for Cutting Materials," Am. Ceram. Soc. Bull., 43(5), 1964. (Part of the article deals with chemical polishing.)

S. Kobayashi, J. Ind. Eng., 82, 324-332, 1960.

H. R. Letner, "Stress Effects of Abrasive Tumbling," Trans. Am. Soc. Metals, 51, 402-420, 1959.

Kenneth B. Lewis, "The Grinding Wheel," (Revised Edition), Grinding Wheel Institute, 1959.

R. E. Lintner, V. E. Wolkodoff, L. E. Ferreira, and L. C. Hageman, "New Horizons for Industrial Ceramics," Metal Progr., 84(5), 1963.

R. E. Lintner, V. E. Wolkodoff, L. E. Ferreira, and L. C. Hageman, "Fabricating and Joining High Strength Ceramics," Metal Progr., 84(6), 1963.

W. F. Mathewson, Jr., "The Role of Lubricants in Diamond Grinding," presented before a seminar conducted by Industrial Diamond Assn. of America, April 7, 1965. Reprints available from Met. Prod. Dept., General Electric Co., Detroit, Michigan 48232.

E. Ratterman, "How Tungsten Carbide Properties Affect Diamond Wheel Life," Cutting Tool Engineering, 17-20, June 1966.

L. D. Rozenberg, V. F. Kazantsev, L. O. Makarov, and D. F. Yakhimovich, "Ultrasonic Cutting," Consultants Bureau, New York, 1964.

E. Ryshkewitch, Brichrite Glastech. Niche Guelschaste, 20, 166-174, 1942.

D. Sato, Bulletin of Japan Society of Grinding Engineers, 3, 87-102, 1963 (Lubricants).

R. Sedlacek and E. P. Farley, "Processing of Ceramics—Surface Finishing Studies." Final Report under Contract NOw66-0383-d, May 1967.

G. L. Sheldon and I. Finnie (1965a), "On the Ductile Behavior of Nominally Brittle Materials During Erosive Cutting." Presented at the Winter Annual Meeting, Chicago, Illinois, November 7-11, 1965. ASME Paper No. 65-WA/Prod-7.

G. L. Sheldon and I. Finnie (1965b), "The Mechanisms of Material Removal in the Erosive Cutting of Brittle Material." Presented at the Winter Annual Meeting, Chicago, Illinois, November 7-11, 1965. ASME Paper No. 65-WA/Prod-8.

A. Smekal, Naturwiss. 30, 204-205, 1942.

L. P. Tarasov, "Grinding Fluids," Tool and Manufacturing Engineer, June-August 1961.

L. P. Tarasov, "An Introduction to Abrasive Machining," American Machinist Metalworking Manufacturing, Special Report No. 520, 125-136, April 16, 1962.

170

L. P. Tarasov, W. S. Hyler, and H. R. Letner, "Effect of Grinding Conditions and Resultant Residual Stresses on the Fatigue Strength of Hardened Steel," Proc. ASTM, 57, 601-622, 1957.

L. P. Tarasov, W. S. Hyler, and H. R. Letner, "Effects of Grinding Direction and of Abrasive Tumbling on the Fatigue Limit of Hardened Steel," Proc. ASTM, 58, 528-539, 1958.

Hideo Tsuwa, "An Investigation of Grinding Wheel Cutting Edges," Trans. ASME, J. Eng. Ind., 86, 371-382, 1964.

E. D. Whitney et al., "Development of Improved Cutting Tool Materials," AFML-TR-65-306, October 1965. [AF33(657)-9789].

Chemical Material-Removal Processes

W. J. Alford and D. L. Stephens, "Chemical Polishing and Etching Techniques for Al_2O_3 Single Crystals," J. Am. Ceram. Soc., 46(4), 193-194, 1963.

W. B. Harrison, "Influence of Surface Condition on the Strength of Polycrystalline Magnesia," J. Am. Ceram. Soc., 47(11), 574-579, 1964.

A. G. King, "Ceramics for Cutting Metals," Bull. Am. Ceram. Soc., 43(5), 395-401, May 1964.

H. P. Kirchner, R. M. Gruver, D. R. Platts, and R. E. Walker, "Chemical Strengthening of Ceramic Materials," Linden Laboratories, Inc. Summary Report, Contract No. NOw 66-0441-c, April 1967.

H. P. Kirchner, J. M. Infield, H. L. Brungard, and S. J. Beyer, "Machining High Purity Alumina," Linden Laboratories, Inc. Final Engineering Report, Contract No. DA-36-039 AMC-03634(E) (to be published).

R. D. McBrayer, H. Palmour III, and Povindar Kumar Mehta, "Chemical Etching of Defect Structures in Alumina-Rich Spinel Single Crystals," J. Am. Ceram. Soc., 46(10), 504-505, 1963.

R. C. McVickers, S. D. Ford, and R. A. Dugdale, "Polishing and Etching Techniques for Dense Alumina," J. Am. Ceram. Soc., 45(4), 199, 1962.

N. M. Parikh, "Fracture Mechanisms in Polycrystalline Nonmetallic Materials," IIT Research Institute, Final Report AMRA CR 66-09(F), Contract No. DA-19-066-AMC-288(X), October 1966.

D. R. Stiefbold, J. R. Boston, and R. A. Huggins, "New Dislocation Etchant for Magnesium Oxide," J. Am. Ceram. Soc., 46, 507, 1963.

Energy-Beam Material-Removal Processes

"Energy Beam Processes," DMIC Report, Inquiry 174, September 15, 1962.

C. F. Luck, Jr., and W. Prifti, "Machining with Laser," ASME Publication presented at Design Engineering Conference, Chicago, Illinois, May 9-12, 1966.

"Plasma Arc Machining," U.S. Army Material Research Agency, Report AMRA CR-66-03-F, May 1966.

Roy L. Williams, "Energy Beam Technique," AFMDC Inquiry #10368, Air Force Machinability Data Center, July 14, 1966.

Surface-Treatment Processes

G. H. Beall, B. R. Karstetter, and H. L. Rittler, "Crystallization and Chemical Strengthening of Stuffed β-Quartz Glass-Ceramics," J. Am. Ceram. Soc., 50(4), 181-190, 1967.

F. J. P. Clarke, "Residual Strain and the Fracture Stress - Grain Size Relationship in Brittle Solids," Acta. Met., 12, 139-143, 1964.

D. A. Duke, J. F. MacDowell, and B. R. Karstetter, "The Crystallization and Chemical Strengthening of Nepheline Glass-Ceramics," J. Am. Ceram. Soc., 50(1), 67-74, 1967.

R. H. Insley and V. J. Barczak, "Thermal Conditioning of Polycrystalline Alumina," J. Am. Ceram. Soc., 47(1), 1-4, 1964.

L. A. Jacobson and L. L. Fehrenbacher, "Surface and Microstructural Influence on Flexural Strength of Dense, Polycrystalline MgO," AFML-TR-66-91, May 1966.

B. R. Karstetter and R. O. Voss, "Chemical Strengthening of Glass-Ceramics in the Li_2O-Al_2O_3-SiO_2 System," J. Am. Ceram. Soc., 50(3), 133-137, 1967.

H. P. Kirchner and R. M. Gruver, "Chemical Strengthening of Ceramic Materials," Linden Laboratories, Inc. Summary Report, Contract No. NOw-64-0381-c, May 1965.

H. P. Kirchner and R. M. Gruver, "Chemical Strengthening of Polycrystalline Ceramics," J. Am. Ceram. Soc., 49, 330-333, 1966.

H. P. Kirchner, R. M. Gruver, D. R. Platts, and R. E. Walker, "Chemical Strengthening of Ceramic Materials," Linden Laboratories, Inc. Summary Report, Contract No. NOw 66-0441-c, April 1967.

H. P. Kirchner, R. M. Gruver, and R. E. Walker, "Chemical Strengthening of Ceramic Materials," Linden Laboratories, Inc. Summary Report, Contract No. NOw 65-0407-c, May 1966.

H. P. Kirchner, R. M. Gruver, and R. E. Walker, "Chemically Strengthened Leached Alumina and Spinel," J. Am. Ceram. Soc., 50(4), 169-173, 1967.

H. P. Kirchner, R. M. Gruver, and R. E. Walker, "Chemical Strengthening of Polycrystalline Alumina," Paper No. 9-J2-67. Joint Session on Compaction and Sintering, 69th Annual Meeting, American Ceramic Society, May 3, 1967. Submitted for publication.

D. P. Koistinen, "The Generation of Residual Compressive Stresses in the Surface Layers of Through-Hardening Steel Components by Heat Treatment," ASM Transactions Quarterly, 57(3), 581-588, 1964.

M. Macha, "A Critical Survey of Ceramic Thin Film Technology," General Precision, Inc., Librascope Group, AFML-TR-67-226, July 1967.

K. M. Merz, W. R. Brown, and H. P. Kirchner, "Thermal Expansion Anisotropy of Oxide Solid Solutions," J. Am. Ceram. Soc., 45(11), 531-536, 1962.

N. M. Parikh, "Studies of the Brittle Behavior of Ceramic Materials," IIT Research Institute, ASD-TR-61-528, Part III, Contract AF33(657)-10697, June 1964.

N. M. Parikh, "Fracture Mechanisms in Polycrystalline Nonmetallic Materials," IIT Research Institute, Final Report AMRA CR 66-09(F), Contract No. DA-19-066-AMC-288(X), October 1966.

W. H. Rhodes et al., "Microstructure Studies of Polycrystalline Refractory Oxides," Avco Corp., Summary Report, Contract No. NOw-65-0316-f, March 1966.

D. H. Rice and R. W. Stowe, "Research on Anisotropy in Polycrystalline Dielectric Materials," Melpar, Inc. Final Report, Contract NOw-65-0440-d, June 1966.

Body-Treatment Processes

J. O. Brittain, "Plasticity and Fracture of Ceramics," Northwestern University, Final Report, Contract Nonr 1228(17), December 31, 1966.

J. J. Burke, N. L. Reed, and V. Weiss, Editors, "Strengthening Mechanisms," Syracuse University Press, 1966.

G. W. Groves and M. E. Fine, "Solid Solution and Precipitation Hardening in Mg-Fe-O Alloys," J. Appl. Phys., 35(12), 3587-3593, 1964.

G. W. Groves and D. A. Shockey, "The Fracture Toughness of Impure MgO Crystals," Carnegie Institute of Technology, Technical Report No. 2, Contract Nonr-760(29), November 1966.

C. W. Hewson and W. D. Kingery, "Effect of MgO and $MgTiO_3$ Doping on Diffusion Controlled Creep in Polycrystalline Aluminum Oxide," J. Am. Ceram. Soc., 50, 218-219, 1967.

S. E. Hsu, W. Kobes, and M. E. Fine, "Strengthening of Sapphire by Precipitates Containing Titanium," J. Am. Ceram. Soc., 50(3), 149-151, 1967.

R. H. Insley and V. J. Barzak, "Thermal Conditioning of Polycrystalline Ceramics," J. Am. Ceram. Soc., 47(1), 1-4, 1964.

C. O. McHugh, T. J. Whalen, and M. Humenik, Jr., "Dispersion-Strengthened Aluminum Oxide," J. Am. Ceram. Soc., 49(9), 486-491, 1966.

C. J. Phillips and S. Divita, "Thermal Conditioning of Ceramic Materials," Bull. Am. Ceram. Soc., 43(1), 6-8, 1964.

Joining and Assembly

F. Anthony, A. H. Blessing, W. H. Buckley, and W. H. Dukes, "Analytical Methods and Design Studies," Vol. 2, AF33(616)-6034, March 1961.

F. Anthony, F. Merrihew, A. Mistretta, and W. Dukes, "Investigation of Feasibility of Utilizing Available Heat-Resistant Materials for Hypersonic Leading Edge Applications," Vol. 1, Summary, AF33(616)-6034, June 1961.

J. L. Arnquist, "Design Considerations and Structural Usage of Brittle Materials," in Symposium on Design with Materials that Exhibit Brittle Behavior, MAB-175-M,

National Academy of Sciences - National Research Council, Washington, D.C., pp. 232-260, October 20, 1961.

R. L. Barnett, "Review of Structural Design Techniques for Brittle Components under Static Loads," May 1963.

"Calcium Aluminate Cement CA-25," anonymous, Alcoa Product Data, Form 13-11753, Alumina Company of America, 1963.

J. F. Clarke et al., "State-of-the-Art Review of Ceramic to Metal Joining," Texas Instruments, Inc., AFML TR-65-143 (AD-465809), May 1965.

K. W. Cornely, "New Cements Prove Suitable for Applications Above 4000°F," Ceramic Age, January 1962.

F. W. Diederich, W. C. Broding, A. J. Hanawalt, and R. Sirull, "Reliability as a Thermo-Structural Design Criterion," Report prepared by Avco Corp., Research and Advanced Development Div., for Air Force under Contract No. AF04(647)-16 and -36, NASA Doc. No. N63-10388.

W. H. Duckworth, A. D. Schwope, O. K. Salmassy, R. L. Carlson, and H. Z. Schofield, "Mechanical Property Tests on Ceramic Bodies," WADC TR 52-67, March 1952.

M. M. Frocht and H. N. Hill, "Stress Concentration Factors Around a Central Circular Hole in a Plate Loaded Through a Pin in the Hole," Trans. ASME, J. Appl. Mech., 62, March 1940.

W. H. Gitzen, L. D. Hart, and G. MacZura, "Phosphate-Bonded Alumina Castables: Some Properties and Applications," Bull. Am. Ceram. Soc., 35(6), 1956.

W. H. Gitzen, L. D. Hart, and G. MacZura, "Properties of Some Calcium Aluminate Cement Compositions," J. Am. Ceram. Soc., 40(5), 1957.

H. H. Gregor, "Aluminum Phosphates—New Bonds for Refractories," Brick and Clay Record, 117 (2), 1950.

R. A. Heindle and W. L. Pendergast, "Bonding Strength of Cold-Setting Refractory Cements," Bull. Am. Ceram. Soc., 15 (5), 1936.

K. E. Hofer, Jr., "Utilization of Refractory Nonmetallic Materials in Future Aerospace Vehicles: Part II, Study of Attachments for Brittle Components," FDL-TDR-64-123, August 1965.

K. E. Hofer and A. J. Durelli, "Stress Distribution at the Fillet of an Internal Flange," J. Appl. Mech., 618-623, December 1961.

H. A. Hokanson, S. L. Rogers, and W. I. Kern, "Electron Beam Welding of Alumina," Ceramic Industry, August 1963.

R. E. Horton, "Joining Methods for Brittle Materials," Allowables Research Memorandum No. 8, Boeing Aircraft, 1959.

R. A. Jones and F. A. Barr, "Composite Ceramic Radome Manufacture by Mosaic Techniques," Technical Report AFML TR-65-418, 1965.

P. F. Jordan and W. F. Barrett, "Foamed Ceramics in Heat Shield Design," in Symposium on Design with Materials that Exhibit Brittle Behavior, 1, MAB-175-M, National Academy of Sciences - National Research Council, Washington, D.C., pp. 288-303, October 20, 1961.

W. D. Kingery, "Fundamental Study of Phosphate Bonding in Refractories; I-III," J. Am. Ceram Soc., 33 (8), 1950.

R. Lintner, V. Wolkodoff, L. Ferreira, and L. C. Hageman, "Fabricating and Joining High-Strength Ceramics," Metal Progress, December 1963.

J. W. Lobbett and E. A. Robb, "Thermomechanical Analysis of Structural Joint Study," WADD TR 61-151, January 1962.

J. Lynch, C. Ruderer, and W. Duckworth, "Engineering Properties of Ceramics," AFML-TR-66-52, June 1966.

A. L. Mistretta, W. H. Dukes, and F. M. Anthony, "Attachment Design Studies, Chapter VIII of Vol. II: Analytical Methods and Design Studies—Investigation of Feasibility of Utilizing Available Heat Resistant Materials for Hypersonic Leading Edge Applications," Report No. WADC TR 59-744, March 1961.

R. E. Peterson, "Stress Concentration Design Factors," John Wiley & Sons, Inc., New York, 1953.

"Report of the Ad Hoc Committee on Design for Brittle Materials," MAB-198-M, National Academy of Sciences - National Research Council, Washington, D.C., May 1964.

"Report of the Ad Hoc Committee on Processing of Ceramic Materials," MAB-195-M, National Academy of Sciences - National Research Council, Washington, D.C., October 1965.

"Report of the Ad Hoc Committee on Refractory Inorganic Nonmetallic Structural Materials," MAB-169-M, National Academy of Sciences - National Research Council, Washington, D.C., January 15, 1961.

E. A. Robb and J. W. Lobbett, "Thermo-Mechanical Analysis of Structural Joint Study," WADD TR 61-151, January 1962.

O. K. Salmassy, E. G. Bodine, W. H. Duckworth, and G. K. Manning, "Behavior of Brittle-State Materials," Parts I and II, WADC TR 53-50, June 1955.

W. L. Schleyer, "Refractory Specialties and the Properties of Potassium," Bull. Am. Ceram. Soc., 38 (7), 1959.

H. D. Sheets, J. J. Bulloff, and W. H. Duckworth, "Phosphate Bonding of Refractory Compositions," Brick and Clay Record, July 1958.

F. C. Smith, "Design and Fabrication of Refractory Composite Structures," November 10, 1961. Paper presented at SAMPE Mtg. on November 14-15, 1961.

R. Steimitz, "Borides - Part B: Fabrication, Properties and Applications," Modern Materials, Vol. II, 191-224, 1960.

"Studies of the Brittle Behavior of Ceramic Materials," edited by N. A. Weil, ASF TDC No. ASD-TR-61-628, April 1962.

H. Switzky, M. J. Foray, and M. Newman, "Thermo-Structural Analysis Manual," 1, Sec. 5, "Thermoelastic Analysis of Joints," WADD TR 60-517, pp. 5.1-5.40.

J. P. Taylor, R. D. Guyton, J. N. Krusos, and J. L. Pentercost, "Ceramic-Metallic Structural Design for Hyperthermantic," in Symposium on Design with Materials that Exhibit Brittle Behavior, Vol. 1, MAB-175-M, National Academy of Sciences - National Research Council, Washington, D.C., pp. 199-231, October 20, 1961.

P. S. Theocaris, "The Stress Distribution in a Strip Loaded in Tension by Means of a Central Pin," J. Appl. Mech., Paper No. 55-A-34.

PANEL ON FINISHING

GEORGE J. BAIR, <u>Chairman</u>
Director, Technical Staff Services
Corning Glass Works

N. M. PARIKH, <u>Cochairman</u>
Director, Metals Research
Illinois Institute of Technology Research
Institute

Members

DONALD A. HALLOCK
Manager, Accuramics
Greenfield Tap and Die, Division of
United Greenfield Corporation

RODNEY A. JONES
San Diego, California

HENRY PAUL KIRCHNER
Linden Laboratories, Inc.

VLADIMIR E. WOLKODOFF
Senior Research Scientist
Research Department
Coors Porcelain Company

LIAISON REPRESENTATIVES

CHARLES F. BERSCH
Materials Engineer
Naval Air Systems Command
U.S. Department of the Navy

SAMUEL W. BRADSTREET
(Air Force Representative from
March 8, 1965 to September 6, 1966)

SAM DIVITA
U.S. Army Electronics Command
Electronic Components Laboratory
Electronic Parts and Materials Division

BARRY R. EMRICH
Air Force Materials Laboratory
Applications Division
U.S. Department of the Air Force
Wright-Patterson Air Force Base

ALFRED GUY EUBANKS
National Aeronautics and Space
Administration
Goddard Space Flight Center

PROFESSIONAL STAFF

DONALD G. GROVES
Staff Engineer
Materials Advisory Board

CHAPTER 5

Report of the Panel on Evaluation

ABSTRACT

A principal difficulty in the use of ceramics for critical applications is associated with their apparent lack of uniformity, reproducibility, and reliability. The Panel on Evaluation examined methods and techniques used for evaluating ceramics in an effort to determine their ability to identify the sources of variability in these materials. It also examined the methods and techniques used for relating properties to character. In order to be sure that the needs of the user of ceramics were being considered, the Panel reviewed the property data required by the designer.

It was found that the state of art of evaluation (characterization and testing) was such that current techniques have not provided the information necessary to determine the degree to which the variability of ceramics may be assigned to processing parameters or testing techniques, or may be an intrinsic property of brittle materials. Also, these techniques, as presently employed, have not been successful in relating the character features of ceramics to their properties. These deficiencies appeared to be due as much to the lack of adequate application and control of the techniques as to the techniques themselves. In order to improve our understanding of the behavior of ceramic materials and to assist in the development of a science of ceramic processing, it was recommended that research be supported in the areas of developing improved characterization techniques, improving property measurement methods, and in studying property-character relationships. It was also recommended that, as a minimum requirement, the DOD make maximum use of current evaluation techniques in future materials-development programs. As an aid to the more effective use of ceramics for future DOD applications, it was also recommended that a program be initiated to advance the state of the art of design with brittle materials.

SUMMARY OF RECOMMENDATIONS

The primary objective of the Panel on Evaluation has been to examine that part of the Committee's activities that deals with the coupling of processor with user through evaluation. Although the state of the art of ceramic processing may be improved substantially by developing better evaluation techniques, it has become apparent that significant improvement in control of ceramic processing is possible through the proper application of currently available techniques. This situation suggested that the recommendations of the Panel should be presented in two parts. Part 1 recommends areas for research and development to improve evaluation techniques. Section A recommends research which offers the greatest probability for immediate payoff. Section B recommends research that is of a long-range nature. Part 2 is directed toward encouraging the wider use of present evaluation procedures.

Part I. Improvement of Evaluation Techniques

A. HIGH PROBABILITY FOR IMMEDIATE PAYOFF

1. Improve techniques for the characterization of surfaces.

2. Develop standard materials both to improve communication concerning character features and for calibration.

3. Mechanical tests should be improved to permit attainment of uniform stress distribution in the specimen over a wider range of environmental test conditions and specimen size.

4. Conduct experiments and analytical studies of different test techniques to establish the criticality of the test conditions.

5. Stress analyses of mechanical tests should be evaluated, developed, and organized (extended if necessary) to provide comparison of different tests and to determine how undesired variation in test equipment and operation affect stress distribution.

6. Develop test methods for studying stress and strain in the microstrain region, fracture-surface energy, fatigue behavior, creep behavior, and multi-axial stress - strain behavior.

7. Develop standard materials for elastic moduli and for tests of behavior in tension, compression, and flexure.

8. Initiate studies to relate properties by nondestructive test techniques (NDT) with properties by destructive techniques. Surplus materials should be provided as a part of future material-development programs involving controlled processing, careful characterizing, and accurate property measurement. These samples would be stored for future characterization and testing as significant improvements in characterization and property measurement techniques are realized.

9. Initiate a study of the mechanisms of crack initiation and propagation.

10. Initiate a study of processing variables that are responsible for character features which in turn control properties.

B. LONG-RANGE PROGRAMS

1. Improve methods for measuring residual microstrain.

2. Improve the resolution of the electron microprobe or develop some other fine-scale analytical tool.

3. Develop statistical measures of grain shape, relative orientations (other than crystallographic orientation), and description of the morphology of a second phase.

4. Improve techniques for the characterization of grain boundaries.

5. Improve techniques for using high-resolution instruments to examine areas substantially larger than the field of view.

6. Develop NDT techniques for characterizing ceramics.

7. A program of mechanical testing should be carried out to support flaw-characterization techniques (as they are developed) to help identify and determine the significance of those flaws controlling strength.

8. Initiate studies to determine the dependence of mechanical and thermal properties on character features.

9. Initiate a study of the mechanism of mass transport of ceramics including bulk and boundary transport.

10. Initiate a study of solid solutions including their range of occurrence and the kinetics of precipitation.

11. Initiate studies of the mechanism of inelastic deformation and the quantitative development of constitutive equations for mechanical behavior.

12. Undertake a program to advance the state of the art of design with brittle materials. Particular attention should be given to the use of realistic models to describe the behavior of ceramic materials.

Part 2. Use of Current Evaluation Techniques

1. Character features influencing properties of interest should be determined and recorded as part of any meaningful physical test program.

2. Property test procedures should be carefully evaluated to determine the scatter in the results caused by the procedure itself.

3. Character features as well as physical properties should be determined and recorded as part of any meaningful material program.

INTRODUCTION

The properties and behavior of a ceramic are related to its character (sum of compositional and structural descriptions that identify a specimen uniquely and may be correlated with its properties). The Committee has recognized the central role of characterization in linking processing with use; this linkage by characterization is shown graphically in Figure 1 on page 5 of this report.

A principal difficulty in the use of these materials is associated with their apparent lack of uniformity, reproducibility, and reliability. The viewpoint of the designers with respect to these factors is indispensable to the processor in understanding the degree to which use of ceramics is dependent on their supposed limitations. Much emphasis has been placed on the apparent relationship between the variability of ceramics and the lack of understanding and control of ceramic processing. However, inadequate test techniques may introduce apparent variability, and some degree of variability may be an inherent characteristic of brittle materials.

Empirical correlation of properties of ceramics with processing parameters has been a useful tool in past development of ceramics. Future development using this approach is fundamentally limited because it does not take into account how processing affects character and how character affects properties. Development of a science of ceramic processing depends strongly upon our ability to characterize ceramics.

The complete or total characterization (including bulk and surface) of a ceramic (C_T) would include all features of composition and structure that affect properties. For convenience, total character is separated into atomic character (C_A), microcharacter (C_μ), and macrocharacter (C_M). Their separation is represented by writing

$$C_T = C_A + C_\mu + C_M. \tag{1}$$

Ideally, total characterization would serve as the link between processing and properties and accordingly between processing and use. Unfortunately, total characterization of a ceramic is not presently possible because of experimental limitations and because all the features of character may not yet be known. As a practical compromise the available features of character combined with sufficient property data (P) and historical data (H) to uniquely describe the ceramic may be employed as the linkage between processing and use. This combination is called description (D) and may be expressed as:

$$D = XC_T + (1 - X)(P + H), \tag{2}$$

where X would be 1 if complete characterization were possible.

Evaluation is concerned with methods and techniques for determining the character, properties, and behavior of ceramics, and the relationship between character and properties. The Panel on Evaluation examined that part of the Committee's activities that dealt with the coupling of processor with user as exemplified by the character-property relationship and its relevance to processing and to design. The objectives of the Panel may be summarized as follows:

1. To assess the capability of current characterization techniques to determine adequately the character of ceramic products, and to recommend areas for research.

2. To review and evaluate the capability of property test methods and associated analysis of data to determine quantitatively the properties of ceramic materials and to recommend areas for the improvement of test methods and procedures.

3. To examine means of relating the property data available from these test methods to the character of ceramic products, with special reference to the sources of variability, and to recommend areas for study and improvement.

4. To review special procedures required for quality control, and procedures to evaluate the environmental behavior of ceramics for specific applications.

5. To review properties that will provide the data that are required in the design of ceramic hardware.

The relation of these objectives to the Committee's over-all view of the coupling between processing and use is illustrated in Figure 1.

To carry out the objectives outlined above, the Panel on Evaluation addressed itself to the following three areas: Description of Ceramic Materials, which covers objectives 1 and 3, as shown in Figure 1; Properties of Ceramic Materials and Test Methods to Detect Them, covering objective 2; and Interactions Among Properties, Structural Design and Analysis, Environmental Behavior, and Quality Assurance, which covers objectives 4 and 5. In addition, objectives 4 and 5 are supported by detailed coverage in Appendix 1, Structural Analysis and Design in Ceramics Using Statistical Fracture Theory; Appendix 2, Environmental Behavior; and Appendix 3, Quality Control and Proof Tests. These appendixes represent material outside the Committee's primary responsibility but are given detailed treatment because they are important to better under-

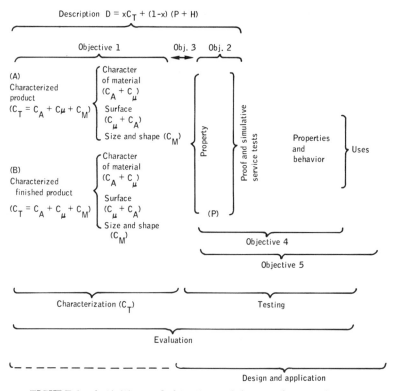

FIGURE 1. Activities and objectives of the Panel on Evaluation.

standing of the user's needs and because processors have not generally had access to this material.

It was pointed out at the beginning of the Committee report that the use of ceramics for DOD applications has been restricted because of their apparent lack of reproducibility and reliability as exemplified by a scatter of property and test data obtained under a set of fixed conditions. Later it was stated that it was the scatter of data that was normally the basis on which charges of poor ceramic-processing capability are made, rightly or wrongly. It thus becomes extremely important to determine unequivocally the reason for the scatter in data. Therefore, throughout its deliberations, the Panel on Evaluation has kept before it the primary objectives of determining the extent to which current evaluation procedures are capable of identifying the sources of the scatter in data of ceramics, and the amount of scatter in property data that can be attributed to the testing methods and techniques themselves.

STATE OF THE ART

Description of Ceramic Materials

INTRODUCTION

As has been stated previously in this report, the central motivation of the parent Ad Hoc Committee is ultimately to enhance the suitability of ceramic materials for structural and high-temperature applications and to direct research, development, and manufacturing attention to those areas that are currently limiting. It is generally recognized that if a ceramic material is reproducible, within well-defined limits, it will be appropriate for certain structural uses. As the property reliability is increased and as selected properties are improved, the material will find an increasing number of critical applications, particularly in the DOD. In attempting to attain the desired material characteristics, the ceramic processor is therefore concerned with how to describe and thereby reproduce his product adequately. This description must include all factors that in some way influence specific application-oriented properties.

TOTAL CHARACTERIZATION

The precise and detailed description of an object as complex as a ceramic body is indeed a difficult problem. Unfortunately, words such as "description" and "characterization" carry different connotations for each individual. Therefore, to ensure that the scope and intent of the Committee's deliberations are clear, the following definitions and interrelationships have been developed.

The total character of a body (C_T), as defined by this committee, is composed of several constituents: an atomic character (C_A), microcharacter (C_μ), and macrocharacter (C_M).

Atomic characterization is concerned with the determination of the chemical identity and location of all the atoms in a solid. Such characterization leads directly or indirectly to the knowledge of the point- and line-defect nature and the chemical bonding in the material. (In practice, however, microcharacterization techniques are used to determine defect nature and concentration.) Microcharacterization, however, deals with the scale of things that in principle can be seen directly by microscope techniques: the existence of particulate inclusions; the size, shape, and relative orientation of grains; the distribution of dislocations; the nature of interfaces and grain boundaries; and intergranular stresses. Macrocharacterization is concerned with the size and shape, density, bulk chemical composition, homogeneity, surface topography, and gross stress distribution. The sum of these types of character, then, comprises the total character,

$$C_T = C_A + C_\mu + C_M. \tag{1}$$

This is referred to as linkage 1 in the functional chart (Figure 1) developed by the Evaluation Panel.

Information contained under total characterization, when combined with and related to certain properties of the body (P), provides a useful and meaningful description (D) of the material (linkage 3). In addition, because the present state of the art in characterizing and measuring the properties of ceramics is still limited, it is necessary to introduce into a useful working definition of description the concept of sample history (H)—an accurate record of the conditions of fabrication.

$$D = C_T + P + H. \tag{2}$$

The properties utilized in this relationship may vary widely. Most common are those of direct application interest such as elastic moduli, strength, and dielectric constant. However, to permit meaningful correlations, basic intermediate properties, not themselves of direct structural interest but underlying the structural properties, are often required.

The relative importance of properties, history, and the body character in describing a ceramic body is not fixed. At the present state of the art, primary evaluation is based on property measurements. In accordance with the objectives of the Ad Hoc Committee, however, this situation should be reversed. Equation (2) can thus be rewritten as:

$$D = XC_T + (1 - X)(P + H), \tag{3}$$

where as X approaches 1 the dependence of description on properties and history will disappear.

The question then arises as to the extent to which we can actually describe a ceramic body. At the present state of the art, the character parameters most commonly determined fall under the micro- and macro- categories. This is primarily because of the gross effects imposed by the polycrystallinity and the multiphase nature of ceramic materials. Atomic character, on the other hand, derives from the character of the raw materials and the details of processing and is fundamental to the behavior of all materials. This part of the characterization process is covered quite extensively by the report of the MAB Ad Hoc Committee on Characterization of Materials (MAB-229-M).

In attempting to maintain some degree of realism in the amount of character and property information that can be obtained for a specific piece of material, it is first necessary to determine what properties are most significant for the specific use, how one can best measure them, and which character features influence the properties of interest. For example, different sets of properties will be of interest if we are trying to describe the inherent properties of the material, as determined by processing conditions, from those desired if we wish to design a structure using the material or those needed to evaluate a material's response in a particular application. Similarly, we may wish a precise description of the surface condition if we are measuring ultimate strength, but the elastic modulus would be little affected by surface alterations.

This section of the report deals only with the character-property relationship; that is, the relationship of a selected group of inherent properties to well-defined character features so that we can evaluate material uniformity and reproducibility and deviations therefrom. How these properties are to be measured, the relationship of properties to design, and the relationship of properties to applications evaluation are considered in subsequent sections of this report.

In Table 1 (p. 184) are listed many characterization factors known or suspected to be influenced by processing operations and known to be related to the properties of the body. Categories 1 and 2 in the first column of this table are included to provide a general processing reference. At the present time these factors provide the best means for obtaining reproducibility. With improved body description, however, it is hoped that these factors will become less essential.

The remaining categories, 3 and 4, include those factors that are presently considered to be important for complete body characterization. Certainly, if each of these items could be specified exactly, we would know a great deal about body variability. Unfortunately, it is not generally possible to examine a practical material to the extent suggested by this table. Some of the factors, such as strain in individual grains, cannot be measured with a meaningful degree of precision. It is therefore essential that at least those factors that can be measured and that are recognized to have a significant effect on the property being measured, be specified to the greatest extent possible.

The major characterization features in the first column are arranged in a logical order for examining a polycrystalline structure. First, one would wish to know the general body composition. Subsequently, one would examine the grains that predominate the body and then any additional phases dispersed in the body. Grain boundaries would then hold one's attention, followed by the presence of pores or cracks in the structure. Finally, one might consider the surface condition over the entire piece and its possible influence on properties.

Each of these features may receive an initial minimum examination and then, depending on the interest of the investigator, may be considered in much greater detail, as is shown by the subject breakdown in the first column. Phase identification of the predominant grains would tell whether they were alumina or mullite, for example. Quantity of these grains may be listed as a percentage to show if the body is essentially single phase or if a large amount of another phase is also present. Grain size has been reported to influence strength significantly, but size distribution may be an equally significant variable. Grain shape and relative orientation are other descriptive factors that may be altered by processing conditions and may, in turn, influence properties. Internal strain in grains is a more difficult factor to observe or to place on a quantitative basis but it is suspected to exert a strong influence on properties dependent upon ultimate strength.

The internal composition and dislocation structure of grains are strongly influenced by the processing conditions and in turn may affect a variety of properties. Stoichiometry of tantalum carbide (TaC), for example, may vary from $Ta_{0.7}C$ to $Ta_{0.98}C$ before either Ta_2C or C may appear in the body as a second phase. Impurities may tend to concentrate at boundaries or surfaces or may move into ordered networks throughout the grain structure under suitable processing conditions. Similarly, the density, type, and arrangement of dislocations depend to a considerable extent on certain processing conditions, frequently indicating the onset of plastic flow or showing other signs of response to severe external or internal stresses.

Similar considerations are essential for other observed phases in a ceramic body. These phases may also occur as individual grains or as boundary phases—continuous or discontinuous—or as solid-state precipitates. Heading 4.2 in the first column of Table 1 permits a complete description of any such phases.

Grain boundaries are considered to be the interfaces between grains or between phases. They do not include the bulk of identifiable phases segregated between grains. Thickness of a grain boundary is difficult to define but for this characterization table is considered to be that region that differs structurally and identifiably from either bordering bulk phase. Thus, for low-angle grain boundaries, it may be only a few atomic spacings across the region of lattice distortion. In other cases, where both compositional and structural discontinuities occur, it may be quite thick and continuously varying across the thickness. Means are provided in Table 1 for describing the composition and composition distribution across the region as well as any observable lattice structure. The relative orientation of grains on either side of the boundary may influence considerably the state of strain in the boundary, particularly in anisotropic materials. However, this factor generally cannot be specified as a general feature in a ceramic body.

Pores, microcracks, and cracks generally occur throughout a polycrystalline body. Normally, we are concerned with delineating the total number of pores. However, this is undoubtedly less critical than the distribution of these pores throughout the body (concentration or depletion at grain boundaries) or the size and size distribution in the structure. Similarly, Table 1 has a heading to include the shape and shape distribution to indicate the sphericity and connectivity of pores. Relative orientation is included to indicate whether cracks and pores follow grain boundaries or are oriented along crystallographic planes in grains. The effect of the composition of the gas held within a pore or crack is largely unknown at the present time.

Subheadings for detailing surface characterization appear to be few but are extremely inclusive. Topography is not limited to an rms finish but includes microfissures, notches, and blebs, as well as gross corners and curvatures. The state of stress refers to the entire region at the surface, which deviates significantly from the condition of the bulk material. By this definition, a surface as defined in terms of the stress state may penetrate a considerable distance into the bulk. Stress distribution as a function of depth should be reported but such data are clearly years away. Adsorbed gases at the surface may or may not be a significant factor. Chemistry of the surface again includes any deviations from bulk compositions that may occur as a result of volatilization, contamination, or leaching during firing, finishing, or use. Such chemical changes may cause other variations such as an altered grain size or the development of a residual-stress state at the surface.

Extrinsic defects include such factors as blebs, inclusions, and isolated massive grains. These are generally isolated features which may be extremely difficult to locate or to describe in any programmed manner. In some cases, if they are sufficiently large and well separated, nondestructive tests such as radiography or ultrasonic procedures may be effective. Otherwise, examination of fracture surfaces may be the only way to assure that such features are not responsible for failure.

On occasion such defects reportedly have been found in fractured surfaces. If they are the primary cause of failure, additional care will be required in control of raw material, prevention of agglomeration, and mixing, for example. It may, in fact, be necessary to make major alterations in processing methods in order to eliminate such defects. At the present time, however, the extent of influence of such defects is unclear, and improved characterization methods for locating flaws are urgently needed.

The second column in Table 1 lists analytical techniques currently available for evaluating the character features listed. Table 2 lists the referenced techniques and shows the generally accepted analytical limits of these methods. These limits are also graphically illustrated in Figure 2. From these two tables, several limitations in our present capabilities are apparent:

1. Measurement of strain and stoichiometry both depend on diffraction techniques. Neither technique (electron diffraction or x-ray diffraction) for measuring strain is accurate within several thousand psi and both are confounded by slight shifts in stoichiometry. Neither can examine submicron areas, which are of interest in examining localized stresses in grains or boundaries.

2. The electron microprobe and the scanning electron microscope are

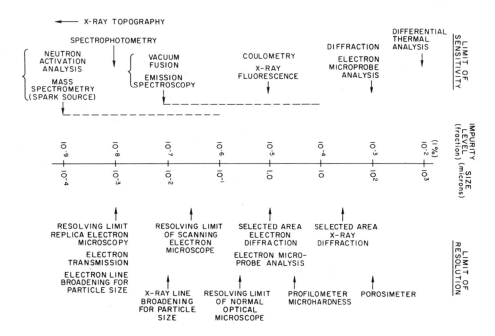

FIGURE 2.

essentially the only tools available for observing localized impurities, and their resolution limits are quite high.

3. There are no suitable techniques at the present time for characterizing grain boundaries or surfaces.

4. All high-resolution analytical techniques are incapable of surveying sufficiently large areas to permit useful conclusions to be drawn.

RELATING CHARACTER TO PROPERTIES

In attempting to specify which elements of character may influence specific properties, it should be recognized that a considerable amount of interplay exists between the various character factors. For example, tensile-strength measurements on ceramic bodies having rough and heavily damaged surfaces would not be expected to show a large dependence of strength on grain size or porosity. However, as the quality of the surface is improved, the strength may be increased until it is influenced by the grain size utilized and a grain size effect is observed. As the grain size is altered to affect higher strength, the surface condition or some other factor may become limiting. It would then appear that beyond a certain grain size no size effect would exist. Contrarily, as the grain size of a body is changed by altering the thermal treatment, the extent of segregation of impurities to the grain boundaries may cause significant property variations quite unrelated to the grain size itself. Thus, before judging that a certain factor does or does not significantly influence some property, it must be established that another factor is not obscuring the test results. This also emphasizes that when one factor is judged, the state of several other potentially limiting factors must be specified.

In the third column of Table 1 are shown some of the specific descriptive properties of a ceramic body reported in the literature to be affected by individual character features. An attempt has been made to limit the properties listed to those most sensitive to the character category. All properties will, of course, depend upon the grain composition of the body, but gross composition will be established by other means, and many properties will not be affected by minor changes that may result from variations in processing. The referenced properties are explained in Table 3. Unfortunately, in almost every case

184

Table 1. Total Characterization of Ceramics

Characterization	Analytical Techniques[a]	Descriptive Properties Known or Suspected to be Affected by Small Character Variations[b]
1. Description of material		
1.1 Nominal composition		
1.2 Trade name, code No., etc.		
2. Sample history		
2.1 Method of preparation		
2.2 Potential sources of contamination		
2.3 Special treatment—thermal, chemical, etc.		
2.4 Shaping technique		
2.5 Specimen size and shape		
3. Average composition (C)	ES, CA, MS, XF, NA, S, VF, C	UTS, SASI, SLSI, F, DC, FSE, DVSE, ϵ, δ, ρ, E, SCor, Cor, TS, IR, TC, TD
4. Geometrical factors		
4.1 Grains (G)		
4.1.1 Phase identification (GI)	TS, XD, ED, PE, CA, DTA	SAS, SASI, SLS, SLSI, DC, FSE, ϵ, δ, ρ, T, Cor, TS, TE, HC, TC, TD
4.1.2 Quantity (GQ)	PS, TS, XD, ED	UTS, SAS, SASI, SLS, SLSI, F, W, TS, IR, TC, TD
4.1.3 Size and size distribution (GS)	PS, TS, XD, ED	UTS, SASI, F, FSE, TS, IR
4.1.4 Shape and shape distribution (including connectivity) (GSh)	PS, TS	UTS, SASI, ρ, W, SCor, TC, TD
4.1.5 Preferred orientation (GRO)	TS, XD, ED	UTS, SAS, SLS, F, TC
4.1.6 Internal strain (GIS)	XD, ED	UTS, F, W, TS, IR
4.1.7 Composition (GC)		
4.1.7.1 Stoichiometry (GCS)	XD	DC, DVSF, ϵ, δ, ρ, E, R, T, H, W, TS, TC, TD
4.1.7.2 Impurity clustering and ordering (GICO)	PS, XD, ED, EMP, SEM	SASI, F, FSE, DVSF, ϵ, δ, T, Cor, TS
4.1.7.3 Impurity concentration distribution (GICD)	EMP, XF	SASI, DC, FSE, ϵ, SCor, Cor, TC
4.1.7.4 Impurity defect sites (GIDS)	EMP	DC, DVSF, δ, TC
4.1.8 Dislocations (GD)		
4.1.8.1 Density (GDD)	PS (EP), ET	UTS, SASI, F, DC, DVSF
4.1.8.2 Type (GDT)	PS	
4.1.8.3 Substructure (GDS)	ET, XT	UTS
4.2 Additional phases (2P)		
4.2.1 Phase identification (2PI)	CA, XD, ED, EMP, TS, PE, DTA	UTS, SASI, SLSI, ϵ, δ, ρ, DC, FSE, T, H, Cor, TS, TC, TD
4.2.2 Quantity (2PQ)	PS, CA, DTA	UTS, SAS, SASI, SLS, SLSI, F, W, SCor, TS, IR, HC
4.2.3 Size and size distribution (2PS)	PS, FS, SEM	UTS, SASI, SLSI, F, FSE, TS
4.2.4 Shape and shape distribution (including connectivity) (2PSh)	PS, TS	UTS, SAS, SASI, SLS, SLSI, FSE, δ, ρ, TC
4.2.5 Preferred orientation (2PRO)	TS, XD, ED	
4.2.6 Internal strain (2 PIS)	XD, ED	UTS, F, W, SCor, TS, IR
4.2.7 Composition (2PC)		
4.2.7.1 Stoichiometry (2PCS)	XD	F, ϵ, δ, ρ, T, SCor, TS, TC, TD
4.2.7.2 Impurity clustering and ordering (2PICO)	PS, XD, ED, EMP, SEM	SASI, F, FSE, DVSF, ϵ, δ, T, Cor, TS
4.2.7.3 Impurity concentration distribution (2PICD)	EMP, XF	SASI, DC, FSE, ϵ, SCor, Cor, TC

Table 1 (continued)

Characterization	Analytical Techniques[a]	Descriptive Properties Known or Suspected to be Affected by Small Character Variations[b]
4.2.7.4 Impurity defect sites (2PIDS)	EMP	DC, DVSF, δ, TC
4.2.8 Dislocations (2PD)		
4.2.8.1 Density (2PDD)	PS (EP), ET	UTS, SASI, F, DC, DVSF
4.2.8.2 Type (2PDT)	PS	
4.2.8.3 Substructure (2PDS)	ET, XT	UTS
4.3 Grain boundaries (GB)		
4.3.1 Composition and composition distribution (GBC)	TS, FS, EMP, XT	UTS, SASI, SLSI, F, FSE, ε, δ, ρ, T, SCor, Cor, TS, TC, TD
4.3.2 Structure (GBS)	TS	UTS, SASI, F, FSE, TS, IR
4.3.3 Relative orientation of grains (GBRO)	TS, XD(micro), ED	UTS, SASI, F, FSE, Scor, TS
4.3.4 Grain boundary strain (GBSt)		UTS, SASI, F, FSE, W, SCor, Cor, TS, IR, HC, TC, TD
4.4 Pores, microcracks, cracks (PMC)		
4.4.1 Quantity (PMCQ)	PS, DM, P	UTS, SASI, SLSI, F, DC, FSE, ε, T, H, W, Cor, TS, IR, HC, TC, TD
4.4.2 Distribution in structure (PMCD)	PS	UTS, SASI, F, FSE, T, H, W, Cor, TS, IR, TC
4.4.3 Size and size distribution (PMCS)	PS, P	UTS, SAS, F, FSE, T, Cor, TS
4.4.4 Shape and shape distribution (including connectivity) (PMCSh)	PS	UTS, SASI, F, FSE, W, Cor, TS, IR, TC, TD
4.4.5 Relative orientation (PMCRO)	PS	UTS, F, FSE
4.4.6 Gas composition (PMCGC)	MS	
4.5 Surfaces (S)		
4.5.1 Topography (ST)	Pr, SEM	UTS, SASI, F, E, R, W
4.5.2 State of stress (strain) (SS)	XD	UTS, SASI, F, W, Cor, TS, IR
4.5.3 Adsorbed gases (SAG)	MS	UTS, F, Cor
4.5.4 Chemistry (SC)	EMP	UTS, SASI, E, R, T, W, Cor
4.6 Extrinsic defects (ED)		
4.6.1 Type (EDT)	NDT, FS, PS, TS	UTS, F, FSE, W, Cor, TS, IR
4.6.2 Position (EDP)	NDT, FS, PS, TS	UTS, F, FSE, W, Cor, TS, IR

[a]See Table 2 and Figure 1.
[b]See Table 3.

Table 2. Analytical Techniques[a]

Abbreviation	Method	Limits of Resolution
XT	X-ray topography	$0 - 10^5/cm^2$
NA	Neutron activation analysis	$0.1 - 100$ ppm $\pm 5\%$
MS	Mass spectrometry	ppm – ppb range
S	Spectrophotometry	ppm $\pm 1 - 5\%$
ED	Electron diffraction	10 Å ultimate, 1μ selected area, 0.1%
ET	Electron transmission	10 Å
VF	Vacuum fusion	$0.1 - 100$ ppm
ES	Emission spectroscopy	$0.1 - 100$ ppm
XD	X-ray diffraction	100 Å ultimate, 50μ selected area, 0.1%
SEM	Scanning electron microscope	0.05μ
PS(EP)	Polished section (etch pit)	$0 - 10^7/cm^2$

Table 2 (continued)

Abbreviation	Method	Limits of Resolution
PS	Polished section	0.5μ optical, 10 Å electron replica
TS	Thin section	0.5μ optical
FS	Fracture surfaces	0.5μ optical, 10 Å electron replica
C	Coulometry	0.002%
XF	X-ray fluorescence spectrometry	20 - 200 ppm
EMP	Electron microprobe analysis	2μ, 0.1%
Pr	Profilometer	5μ diameter, 0.1μ vertical displacement
MH	Microhardness	5μ
DM	Density measurement	± 0.001%
P	Porosimeter	10^{-3} - $10^{-2}\mu$ ± 2%
CA	Wet chemical analysis	
DTA	Differential thermal analysis	1%
NDT	Nondestructive testing[b]	

[a]For additional information and references, see Characterization of Materials, MAB-229-M, pp. II3-II38.
[b]See Appendix 3.

Table 3. Properties Desired for Description of Ceramic Body (to permit identification and confirmation of reproducibility)

Property	Known (or Suspected) Critical Test Conditions	Critical Body-Character Parameters	Minimum Test Data Required	Remarks and Recommendations
A. Mechanical evaluation				
1. Ultimate tensile strength (UTS)	Temperature, stress rate, gage volume, stress distribution	C, GQ, GS, GSh, GRO, GIS, GD, GDS, 2PI, 2PQ, 2PS, 2PSh, 2PIS, 2PD, 2PDS, GBC, GBS, GBRO, GBSt, PMCQ, PMCD, PMCS, PMCSh, PMCRO, TS, SS, SAG, SC, EDT, EDP	Average + variability	Variations with temperature and stress rate may assist characterization
2. Stress-axial-strain—elastic (SAS) a. static (SASS) b. dynamic (SASD)	Temperature, stress rate (at high rates)	GI, GQ, GRO, 2PQ, 2PSh, PMCS	Average + variability	
3. Stress-axial-strain—inelastic (SASI)	Temperature, stress rate (at high rates)	C, GI, GQ, GS, GSh, GICO, GICD, GDD, 2PI, 2PQ, 2PS, 2PSh, 2PICO, 2PICD, 2PDD, GBC, GBS, GBRO, GBSt, PMCQ, PMCD, PMCSh, St, SS, SC	Average + variability	Includes creep at high temperatures and grain-boundary sliding
4. Stress-lateral-strain—elastic (SLS)	Temperature, stress rate (at high rates)	GI, GQ, GRO, 2PQ, 2PSh, PMCS	Average + variability	
5. Stress-lateral-strain—inelastic (SLSI)	Temperature, stress rate (at high rates)	C, GI, GQ, 2PI, 2PS, 2PSh, GBC, PMCQ	Average + variability	Includes creep at high temperatures and grain-boundary sliding

Table 3 (continued)

Property	Known (or Suspected) Critical Test Conditions	Critical Body-Character Parameters	Minimum Test Data Required	Remarks and Recommendations

6. Fatigue (F)
  a. Static (FS)
  b. Cyclic (FC)
	Temperature, amplitude, mode of loading	C, GQ, GS, GRO, GIS, GICO, GDD, 2PQ, 2PS, 2PIS, 2PCS, 2PICO, 2PDD, GBC, GBS, GBRO, GBSt, PMCQ, PMCD, PMCS, PMCSh, PMCRO, ST, SS, SAG, EDT, EDP	Average + variability	

7. Intermediate properties				
a. Diffusion constants (DC)		C, GI, GC, GICD, GIDS, GDD, 2PI, 2PICD, 2PDD, PMCQ		
b. Fracture surface energy (FSE)		C, GI, GICO, GICD, 2PI, 2PS, 2PSh, 2PICO, 2PICD, GBC, GBS, GBRO, PMCQ, PMCD, PMCS, PMCSH, PMCRO, EDT, EDP		
c. Dislocation velocity—stress function (DVSF)		C, GC, GICO, GIDS, GDD, 2PICO, 2PIDS, 2PDD		
B. Thermal evaluation				
1. Conductivity (TC)	Temperature, environment	C, GI, GQ, GSH, GRO, GC, GICD, GIDS, 2PI, 2PSh, 2PCS, 2PICD, 2PIDS, GBC, PMCQ, PMCD, PMCSh	Average + variability	Influenced by radiation at high temperatures
2. Diffusivity (TD)	Temperature, environment	C, GI, GQ, GSh, GC, 2PI, 2PCS, GBC, PMCQ, PMCSh	Average + variability	Influenced by radiation at high temperatures
3. Expansion (TE)	Temperature, environment	GI, 2PI	Average + variability	
4. Heat capacity (HC)	Temperature, environment	GI, 2PQ, PMCQ	Average + variability	
C. Electrical evaluation				
1. Dielectric constant (ϵ)	Temperature, environment	C, GI, GC, GICO, GICD, 2PI, 2PCS, 2PCIO, 2PCID, GBC, PMCQ		
2. Loss tangent (δ)	Temperature environment	C, GI, GC, GICO, GIDS, 2PI, 2PSh, 2PCS, 2PICO, 2PIDS, GBC		
3. Resistivity (ρ)	Temperature, environment	C, GI, GSh, GC, 2PI, 2PSh, 2PCS, GBC		
D. Optical evaluation				
1. Emittance (E)	Wavelength	C, GCS, ST, SC		
2. Reflectance (R)	Wavelength	GCS, ST, SC		
3. Transmission (T)	Wavelength	GI, GCS, GICO, 2PI, 2PICO, GBC, PMCQ, PMCD, PMCS, SC		

Table 3 (continued)

Property	Known (or Suspected) Critical Test Conditions	Critical Body-Character Parameters	Minimum Test Data Required	Remarks and Recommendations
E. Behavioral evaluation				
1. Hardness (H)		GCS, 2PI, PMCQ, PMCD		
2. Wear (W)		GQ, GSh, GIS, GCS, 2PQ, 2PIS, GBSt, PMCQ, PMCD, PMCSh, ST, SS, SC, EDT, EDP		
3. Stress corrosion (SCor)		C, GSh, GICD, 2PQ, 2PIS, 2PCS, 2PICD, GBC, GBRO, GBSt		
4. Corrosion (Cor)		C, GI, GICO, GICD, 2PI, 2PICO, 2PICD, GBC, GBSt, PMCQ, PMCD, PMCS, PMCSh, SS, SAG, SC, EDT, EDP		
5. Thermal shock (TS)		C, GI, GQ, GS, GIS, GCS, GICO, 2PI, 2PQ, 2PS, 2PIS, 2PCS, 2PICO, GBC, GBS, GBRO, GBSt, PMCQ, PMCD, PMCS, PMCSh, SS, EDT, EDP		
6. Impact resistance (IR)		C, GQ, GS, GIS, 2PQ, 2PIS, GBS, GBSt, PMCQ, PMCD, PMCSh, SS, EDT, EDP		

the relationships between body character and properties are at best qualitative. No clear-cut mechanistic relationships permitting a rigorous theoretical analysis are available. Further, the few experimental relationships that have been explored are open to much speculation, principally because the bodies being studied were not characterized in any meaningful way. In other cases, the property measurement procedures employed were not suitable for the generation of such property data. (This latter factor is discussed more extensively in the following section.)

In Table 3, the information contained in Table 1 is presented in reverse order. Here, properties considered to be of maximum importance for body description (P in Equation 3) are listed, and the body character features considered most critical to each property are noted.

Empirical correlations between descriptive properties and the character features controlled by ceramic-processing parameters are very useful in reproducing and improving desired properties of a product. However, to profit most rapidly from such correlations they must also be supported by an improved understanding of the factors controlling the property. This view leads to consideration of a number of intermediate properties not themselves of direct structural interest but underlying the structural properties. Thus, fracture mechanics indicate that the fracture surface energy is a property controlling brittle fracture. If the body character of a ceramic is completely specified, all properties are, by definition, fixed. However, one cannot yet calculate fracture surface energy accurately from a knowledge of character. Therefore, in addition to complete character determination, the measurement of fracture surface energy is needed to assess the mechanism by which a variation in ceramic processing affects the strength. Self-diffusion constants and the velocity-stress function for dislocations are additional examples of intermediate properties whose measurements are needed in order to determine the mechanism by which certain properties are affected by processing variables. Some of these intermediate properties have been listed as item A-7 in Table 3.

In order to illustrate the use of these tables, let us consider that we are interested in the effect of grain size and size distribution on the properties of a ceramic body. Looking under the heading 4.1.3 in Table 1, we see that this feature can best be characterized by microscopy using polished sections (PS) or thin sections (TS) or by x-ray or electron diffraction (XD or ED), depending on the size range. While these techniques give a very limited picture of grain size, particularly with respect to the size distribution, they are essentially the only analytical tools available. In the third column of the table, we see that the descriptive properties that appear to be seriously affected by variations in this character feature are the ultimate tensile strength (UTS), inelastic stress-axial strain (SASI) (this includes permanent deformation caused by the introduction of microcracks, plastic deformation, and grain boundary sliding, for example), fatigue strength (F), fracture-surface energy (FSE), thermal shock resistance (TS), and impact resistance (IR). All these properties involve failure of the specimen. It is noteworthy that purely elastic properties such as the elastic moduli are not seriously affected by grain size itself. Thus, in establishing property tests to evaluate process control over consistency of grain size and size distribution, one would utilize strength tests rather than sonic modulus measurements.

On the other hand, if an ultimate strength test is to be used to evaluate grain-size control, the other character features known to influence tensile strength must be maintained constant, and it must be ascertained that none of these factors is actually the limiting-strength feature so that the grain size effect is masked, as was discussed previously for the case of the surface finish. Table 3 was designed to assist in this type of an evaluation. Here, in column 3, the character parameters known to influence each descriptive property are listed. Thus, in the case of ultimate tensile strength, used as a descriptive property, there are 29 other character features which must be controlled and/or described in order to assure that grain-size and size-distribution effects are actually being examined. In addition, some of the critical testing conditions which must be controlled to provide meaningful data are shown in column 2. The types of test data that should be reported are indicated in column 4. Thus, an average value of tensile strength is of limited value, particularly in making comparisons between bodies, unless some indication of the variability of results is provided. The latter may consist of distribution curves or may be as simple as standard-deviation values if normal distributions are obtained. Frequently one is concerned with stress values causing a low probability of failure. In this case complete distribution curves are essential.

Table 3 points up several areas requiring additional work if property measurements are to be suitable for use in the total description of ceramic bodies:

1. Additional attention must be directed to providing improved control over the testing conditions in order to ensure that data generated are actually indicating true material properties. For example, if the specimen gage volume under maximum stress is nearly zero, effects that may result from changes in grain-size distribution will not be observed. Similarly, if the stress rate is not closely controlled and it influences strength data, variabilities reported will not represent material properties. Such features of specific tests will be

reported in the next section of this report, but the importance of these factors must be recognized in characterization studies.

2. Increased attention must be given to the interplay of various character features as they influence specific properties. In any study to ascertain the effect of a character change, other features that may change with a shift in processing conditions or techniques must also be evaluated.

3. Research effort should be directed to establishing which character features are currently limiting the properties of ceramic bodies processed by conventional techniques. In this way, for example, the list of 30 character features shown to influence tensile strength can at least be arranged in an order of importance; some may even be eliminated.

4. Further statistical work should be directed to the presentation of experimental data so that much of the information will not be lost or misinterpreted as a result of abbreviated reporting in the technical literature.

The tables presented in this section of the report are undoubtedly incomplete. Many of the entries may, in fact, be proven incorrect. As additional factors are recognized by individuals attempting to utilize this information, they should be added. Factors considered not applicable in a specific circumstance may be omitted. The tables are intended only as a guide for the producer and user, to permit them to organize some descriptive rapport in attempting to obtain a desired reproducibility in ceramic products and, ultimately, materials having radically improved properties which may be tailored to meet specific requirements.

Properties of Ceramic Materials and Methods to Detect Them

INTRODUCTION

When considering the properties of ceramics and test methods to detect them, the first problem involves relating properties to the total spectrum as it must be viewed by the tester. This interrelationship is discussed in detail in recent literature by several investigators.[1] If we restrict the review to mechanical properties, the total spectrum for strength of materials includes: mechanical behaviors, such as stress - strain, from which one can obtain properties; testing of specimens; stress analysis of members or analysis for theory studies; quality assurance; proof testing; and production control or feedback to material processors. A detailed discussion of the selection of these terms is also included in recent literature. The selection was based on an agreement with classic terms blended with interdisciplinary compatibility.

The mechanical behaviors include stress - strain diagrams, stress concentration, impact, fatigue, creep, hardness, modulus of rupture, thermal shock, and others. Certainly, there are some arguments here in listing all these items as behaviors. For example, stress concentration may be a behavior but could be a product of analysis. For metals it has been included under behaviors in much literature, probably because intensification factors were developed by experiment and simply "plugged into" subsequent analyses. For ceramics it seems doubtful that we know enough about it to delete it from this category of behaviors, even though we may wish to include it also under analysis.

But let us proceed to the general outline of strength of materials and find properties listed under the various behaviors. Specifically, under the behavior of stress - strain, the classic literature lists such properties as strength, elastic moduli, Poisson's ratio, and strain energy rate, among others. Certainly, these are properties obtained from the stress - strain curves. Now observe that there are "controlled conditions" and "observed conditions" that one encounters and that influence the value of the property. That is, the value for the strength (property) is influenced by such controlled conditions (controlled by the tester) as quality of influence, temperature, strain rate, specimen geometry, surface finish, anisotropy, and volume. The observed conditions (observed rather than controlled by the tester) are fractology, structure, variability, density, failure mode, and so on.

Perhaps all these controlled and observed conditions can be called simply "conditions" that alter the simpler concept of single intrinsic properties and that often operate differently than is commonly recognized from past studies on metals. Information concerning these conditions is necessary to isolate them, establish their unmasked influence, and permit the design of testing experiments. One logical approach to a study of the conditions is to explore different theoretical and empirical relations used in analyses, such as the ones for Weibull volume and Neuber notches, while controlling or isolating the conditions. Consistencies among theories will lead to confidence in their isolation.

This outline implies that one obtains behaviors and thus properties by specimen testing, makes a design and/or analysis, comes up with a stress member or a check of a theory, tests the member or structure in the case of a design, modifies the design and/or analysis as indicated by proof testing and/or model testing, and finally delivers a product or concludes that he has indeed checked a theory. This certainly sounds routine and easy! With metals that provide load distribution, and with structures that permit large factors of safety, the problems related to design requirements have been overcome with nominal difficulty. Also, with metals there is a sense of consistency developing between different properties, suggesting that the theories and empiricisms are becoming quite adequate.

With ceramics a few new actors enter the scene and the problems are magnified. There is little load relief and little boundary deformation; there is uncertain reproducibility; specimens may be unlike larger bodies; and analytical relations established for metals may not persist. The nature of brittle materials as related to their constitution and their use is discussed further in the literature.[3,4]

Once the properties and conditions of interest are defined, the problem of selecting a suitable test method remains.[2,5] Because of the stringent requirements introduced by the nature of ceramics, this selection demands extreme care and demands further that the tester be oriented to the total problem. There is no single simple test that can be recommended for all properties under all conditions. The chances are that there is no single value for any property but that each is a function of "conditions," among other things. Hence, a detailed discussion of the influence of conditions on properties is necessary as a prelude to discussing test methods. See Table 4 for one arrangement of the properties, test methods, and conditions that are of interest in this discussion.

INFLUENCE OF CONDITIONS ON PROPERTY VALUES OBTAINED

When considering the relations between properties and conditions, one major problem area is immediately obvious in that there are properties of "materials" and properties of "specimens" evaluated or tested in a particular way. Webster defines property as "a quality belonging specially to something." For this discussion, the property is intended to relate to the inherent or constitutuve response of the material and not the specimen. Now let us observe how the problem operates.

If the temperature is varied in a perfect test on a perfect material, one might obtain the material property as a function of temperature unconfounded by any other condition. However, it would be perfectly possible to have an unwanted condition in surface finish or residual stress that created as big an influence as temperature on the value obtained so that the change in property observed was not really a function of temperature as far as the constitution of

Table 4. Test Methods and Conditions Influencing Properties

		Controlled Conditions	Observed Conditions
Property or Behavior	Test Method	Quality of Influence / Temperature / Strain/Stress Rate / Specimen Geometry / Surface Finish / Anisotropy / Volume / Environment / Number of Specimens / Time to/at Temperature / Residual Stress in Specimen / Triaxial Conditions / Failure Mode / Method of Loading / History of Specimen / Amenability of Analysis	Fractology / Macro- and Microstructure / Reproducibility / Variability / Density / Residual Stress / History / Failure Mode
Tensile ultimate strength (homogeneous)	Gas-bearing system / Monitoring system / Pressurized ring / Indirect		
Tensile stress – axial strain (homogeneous)	Gas-bearing system / Monitoring system / Pressurized ring		
Tensile stress – lateral strain (homogeneous)	Gas-bearing system / Monitoring system		
Tensile fatigue (homogeneous)	Gas-bearing system / Monitoring system / Pressurized ring		
Tensile creep (homogeneous)	Gas-bearing system (short time) / Pressurized ring (short time)		
Flexural MOR (behavior)	4 point		
Flexural midpoint deformation (behavior)	4 point		
Flexural stress – lateral strain (behavior)	4 point		
Flexural fatigue (behavior)	4 point		
Flexural creep (behavior)	4 point		
Compressive ultimate strength	Gas-bearing system / Precision guides and universals		
Compressive stress – axial strain	Gas-bearing system / Precision guides and universals		
Compressive stress – lateral strain	Gas-bearing system / Precision guides and universals		
Compressive fatigue	Gas-bearing system / Precision guides and universals		
Compressive creep	Gas-bearing system / Precision guides and universals		
Shear properties[a]	Gas-bearing system with slotted tensile		

Table 4 (continued)

Property or Behavior	Test Method	Controlled Conditions																Observed Conditions							
		Quality of Influence	Temperature	Strain/Stress Rate	Specimen Geometry	Surface Finish	Anisotropy	Volume	Environment	Number of Specimens	Time to/at Temperature	Residual Stress in Specimen	Triaxial Conditions	Failure Mode	Method of Loading	History of Specimen	Amenability of Analysis	Fractology	Macro- and Microstructure	Reproducibility	Variability	Density	Residual Stress	History	Failure Mode
	Slotted tensile with universals Pin Torsion																								
Fatigue	Pressurized ring Gas-bearing																								
Dynamic modulus (behavior)	Flexing reed Sonic																								
Combined stress[b] (behavior)	Pressurized cylinders axially loaded Gas-bearing system and torsion Cubes face loaded																								
Thermal conductivity	Have methods to 2,000°F ± 3% Have methods from 2,000°F to 4,000°F ± 15%—need better																								
Thermal expansion	Have methods to 5,000°F ± 5%—need better																								
Heat capacity	Have methods to 5,000°F ± 5%—need better																								
Thermal diffusivity[b] (behavior)	Have methods to 5,000°F—need better																								
Emittance	Have methods to 2,000°F ± 5% Have methods from 2,000°F to 5,000°F ± 20%—need better																								

[a]MAB should recommend work to develop the problems and solutions, but not recommend methods now—use torsion for modulus and slotted tensile for ultimate.

[b]MAB should recommend work to develop the problems and solutions, but not recommend methods now.

the material was concerned. This very result has been observed many times where the strength at the lower temperatures was lower than at the higher one, probably from surface-finish effects and residual stresses being more influential at lower temperatures. Thus the molecular or ionic bond could not be studied as a function of temperature since the overriding influences of surface finish and residual stress were masking the results. It would be desirable to inspect any given behavior while holding all conditions either negligible, well defined, or on a plateau. There is a word of warning here. The plateau must exist where the effect of the condition under inspection is not negated by other effects. That is, an extremely rough surface finish might provide a strength plateau where small variations in surface finish did not change the strength, but volume effect could not be explored because the rough surface condition reduced the strength of all specimens to a common value.

There is a second major problem area related to the conditions. In some test methods it is possible to control or know most conditions but in others it is not. For example, in tensile testing, parasitic (unknown and unwanted) stresses must be minimized and the initial fracture must be preserved and identified to permit studies of fractology. Some test methods that permit good definition of these conditions may not be amenable to other controls such as quite high stress rates, and, conversely, high-stress-rate systems may not be capable of providing uniform stress fields in the gage length. Careful selection of the test method for a given property and set of conditions is mandatory.

Another problem area involves the uncertainty of theoretical behavior and the many unknowns that still surround the behaviors of brittle materials, leading to the lack of control in test conditions that unwittingly results. For example, since smaller volumes have larger strengths, it is obvious that studies of, say, notches, must consider not only the theoretical stress intensification involved in a notch geometry but also the volume upon which this peak stress is imposed. Another even more subtle effect may involve variability as it is used to deter- mine material constants or statistical response; that is, surface finish may induce failures and influence the variability in a manner that precludes the accurate study of strength of an internal increment of material. As another example of uncertainty in theoretical understanding, the influence of conditions is not always the same for different types of tests; that is, surface finish has a definite and orderly influence on the tensile strength of uniaxially loaded rods, while there is not a demonstrated quantitative agreement with results from the flexural test.

A final problem involving studies of properties and conditions is the vari- ability of the material within a piece and reproducibility from piece to piece and between lots. This has been a major problem in the past in that failure to recognize the degree of variability and reproducibility has resulted in insuffi- cient control, and there has been more difference in specimens than in the property or condition under study. Work has been started in characterizing the basic powders[6] as well as the final bodies.

Thus, the major problems related to property values, condition, and testing have been interaction of "conditions" confounding results; unsatisfactory test methods; uncertain theoretical relationships; and specimen reproducibility, variability, and control.

There is another general area involved in property studies, which involves the use of the property values and the motivating reasons behind the particular investigator. This consideration has an influence in the selection of some of the controlled conditions.

Properties are obtained for the following reasons: as a guide to the material developer, particularly in quality control and processing; to assist in the development of theories for mechanics (Griffith crack theory, Weibull volume theory, Neuber notch theory, and others); to assist in the development of theories for the stress analysis of complicated pieces and structures; and for the design of components and structures. To further confound the problem, there may be screening tests, engineering tests, and statistical tests, all re- quiring different precision and accuracy, different stress states, and different numbers of specimens. Unfortunately, each of these areas is quite extensive in itself, and the generalizations are difficult.

Influence of Conditions for Tension

Now let us consider the influence that the following conditions have on proper- ties as related to uniaxial tension in a rod or uniform stress in a pressurized ring.

Quality of Influence   When studying the tensile response of a brittle material, it is mandatory that the stress field be well defined (no parasitic stresses). In a rod or pressurized ring, this proper definition demands a stress field that is constant or homogeneous within a few percentage points. Attempts to accept minimum parasitic stresses have been unsuccessful, resulting in low corrected average values, standard deviations unrelated to theory, and the inability to relate the property to a consistent analysis of any type. As examples, volume effects have been missed, surface-finish effects have been random, stress-rate effects have gone undetected, and attempts to explain failures in terms of probability of fracture have been rather futile. The single most important condition is to provide a uniform stress field.

One literature source[5] has put it very well: "Intrinsic and intensive properties should be established first, whenever possible. Test methods should be designed so that only one of those properties is being evaluated at a time. One way of achieving this will be the use of a simple and homogeneous state of stress or strain."

Macro- and Microstructure   First, consider a hot-pressed alumina, well characterized and reported in the literature.[7] Out of 24 tiles of this material (about 1-1/8 in. thick by 12 in. sq.) most had a rather uniform structure with a grain size of 2 to 5 μ. A few of the tiles had large 25-μ grains scattered through the matrix. An electron micrograph of the adjacent fine and large grains revealed a third structure that contained the original flour essentially in an unsintered condition. The weaker specimens of this total lot (24 tiles) had the mixed structure of small and large grains and, had this structure not been detected, these weaker values may well have confounded other parts of the study of things such as volume, surface finish, and strain rate.

The inclusion of macroflaws or voids in an otherwise dense structure can confound the study of properties. Observe in Figure 3 that macroflaws in the range of 1/64 in. to 1/32 in. in the same hot-pressed alumina reduced the strength of small specimens, 1/8 in. in diameter, quite significantly (25 to 30%) and had only a minimum effect of about 5% on larger specimens about 3/4 in. in diameter. This effect is more than "area accountability" and is not consistent with the theoretical prediction of a critical stress for a given flaw.

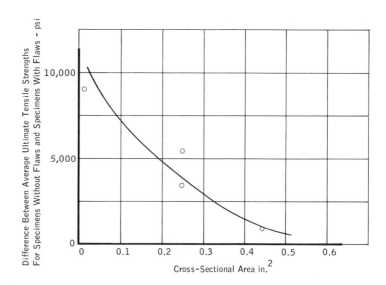

FIGURE 3. Influence of visual macrocracks on strength of different volume specimens of a hot-pressed alumina (Source: Pears and Starrett, "An Experimental Study of the Weibull Volume Theory," AFML-TR-66-228).

The influence of grain boundaries could come here under Microstructure but is discussed later under Temperature, where the influence is more dramatic.

Reproducibility   When several ceramic pieces are made in a kiln or by hot-pressing, there is not total consistency between pieces, even though processing schedules have supposedly remained constant.[4,8] Observe in Figure 4 that the average strengths of the different hot-pressed alumina tiles of the prior reference varied from about 22,000 psi to about 48,000 psi. Both small and large specimens were investigated and the results for both are shown.

In another instance the strengths of a pressed and fired alumina varied as much as 10% from lot to lot. Three different investigators eventually recognized this difference after trying to conduct comparable variability studies. These were competent investigators. This particular material also is well characterized in the references[9,10,11,12] and is referred to later in this report.

Thus, different lots of materials introduce a reproducibility question, not necessarily intrinsic to the material, that can confound studies of mechanical responses unless one looks for and detects them.

Density   The literature contains considerable evidence that strength is a function of density[4] and/or porosity. In general, large differences in density can be related to strength differences by modifications of the law of mixtures and other empiricisms. For small differences in density, the correlations become more questionable and certainly must be limited to a given material. One mistake often made is to try to "normalize" results to a common density, irrespective of other considerations. As often as not, density probably is only an indication of some other operating mechanism such as incomplete sintering. Density normalizing requires care.

Fractology   The type of fracture can indicate uniform loading, structural deformities, surface nonuniformity, and other points of vital interest in the

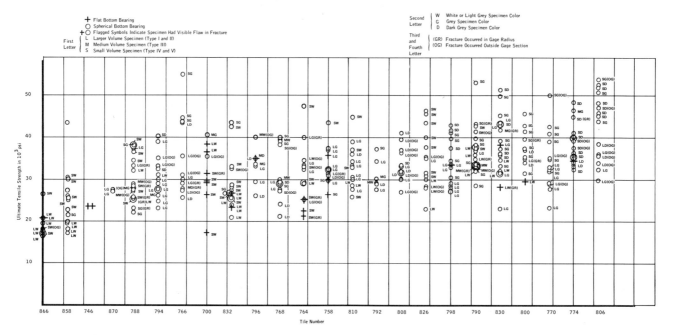

FIGURE 4. Influence of furnace lots on strength of a hot-pressed alumina (Source: Pears and Starrett, "An Experimental Study of the Weibull Volume Theory," AFML-TR-66-228).

evaluation of results; for example, the large grains discussed for the hot-pressed alumina, and their influence on strength. Other experiments have been reported in the literature[12] where extensive macrocrack systems were visual in the unbroken ends of the specimen; that is, several macrocracks were generated before one proceeded to failure. More sophisticated explanations have been offered in terms of dislocation tangles and grain-boundary arrest.[14] This geometric event probably explains the range in elastic moduli that can be obtained for a given material, since the deformation is not truly elastic but includes macrocrack generation and its geometric contribution to strain. Other work on precision elastic limit and dimensional stability[15] suggests that these irreversible strains and visual macrocracks are generated in beryllia at about 50% of the ultimate tensile strength at room temperature, and hence have a geometric and hidden influence on supposed "elastic responses," particularly as related to crack blunting.

Temperature   As shown in Figure 5, the strength and elastic modulus of the pressed and fired alumina decreased quite drastically at about 2,500°F, or well below the melting point of the parent material.[9,10] The total unit strain showed a sharp increase. (Incidentally, one can observe in the same figure that the room temperature tensile and flexural strengths are about equal on some brittle materials when the tensile values are obtained properly. Concern remains about flexural responses, particularly where early macrocracking occurs and/or at temperatures where the tensile and compressive elastic moduli may be varied and the force centroid of the flexural specimen may shift.[16,17] More study is required here.)

A major conclusion here is that studies at temperature can be made in tension, but that material characterization by the tester is mandatory and that one must be cautious in assigning temperature effects to the parent grain material. Grain boundaries or other anomalies may be controlling and their analysis is extremely difficult.[9,10,14]

Figure 6 provides additional information on the influence of temperature on the strengths of a brittle material, this time beryllia.[18] Observe that the 98% dense hot-pressed beryllia was stronger at 70°F than the 95% dense one, but that their strengths were about equal at 2,000 and 3,500°F. Also observe

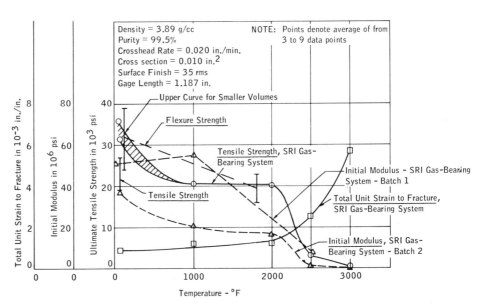

FIGURE 5. Ultimate tensile strength and initial modulus of a pressed and fired alumina from 70°F to 5,000°F (Source: Pears and Digesu, "The True Stress-Strain Properties of Brittle Materials to 5000°F," AEC ORO 461, 1961).

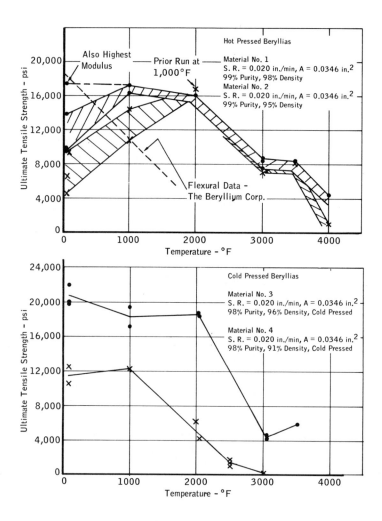

FIGURE 6. Ultimate tensile strength of some beryllias as a function of temperature (Source: Pears et al., "The Tensile and Compressive Ultimate Strengths and Moduli of Beryllium Oxide," presented at Ceramics Society Meeting in Seattle, Washington, October 1962).

that one of the cold-pressed beryllias had strength through 3,500° F about equal to the hot-pressed ones, but that the strength of another cold-pressed one decreased to practically zero at 2,500 to 3,000° F. It seems apparent that grain boundaries or other structural anomalies were confounding the study of the parent beryllia. The weaker material was only 91% dense; however, it seems obvious that density cannot explain the difference since a theoretical accounting of this variable is not nearly sufficient. Silica in the grain boundaries seems a more probable explanation. Thus, again, temperature studies require extreme care in the drawing of conclusions concerning the parent material. It is interesting that the approach of mechanics uncovered these effects in 1962, as reported by Pears et al.,[18] but that general understanding is still subject to arbitration.

Volume   The strength of alumina does decrease with larger volumes, and the Weibull analysis permits a reasonable estimate of the order of this decrease. Figure 7 shows that the strength of the pressed and fired alumina with 35 rms surface finish decreased from 39,000 to 26,000 psi as the volume was increased by a factor of about thirteen.[9,10] With a surface finish of 120 rms, the strengths

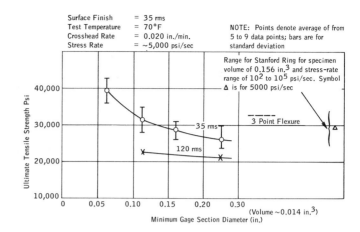

FIGURE 7. The effect of volume on the ultimate tensile strength of a pressed and fired alumina at two different surface finishes (Source: Pears et al., "Evaluation of Tensile Data for Brittle Materials Obtained with Gas-Bearing Concentricity," ASD-TDR-63-245; Pears and Digesu, "The True Stress-Strain Properties of Brittle Materials to 5000°F," AEC ORO 461, 1961).

of the different volumes tested were about equal. Additional values on the same material (but a different lot) were reported on the pressurized ring[11] for a much larger volume, indicating a lower strength than for the smaller uniaxial rod specimens. The range for the rings is shown in the figure to cover different stress rates, but a comparable stress rate would give 29,000 psi compared with the 39,000 psi for the small rod specimens. The reported conclusion for the ring was that there was no volume effect; but results on the uniaxial rods would refute this.

Additional data on the hot-pressed alumina[7] are shown in Figure 8, where the strength of the smaller-volume specimens (0.031 in.^{3}) was 43,000 psi and that of the larger volume (1.33 in.^{3}) was 29,800 psi. Some curves are shown in the figure indicating the predicted strength for different volumes when using a given volume as a base point and applying the Weibull analysis. For those who are interested in this particular analysis, Figure 9 shows the frequency plots for different-sized specimens. A total analysis of this aspect

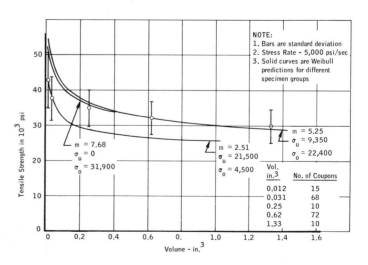

FIGURE 8. Influence of volume on strength of hot-pressed alumina (Source: Pears and Starrett, "An Experimental Study of the Weibull Volume Theory," AFML-TR-66-228).

200

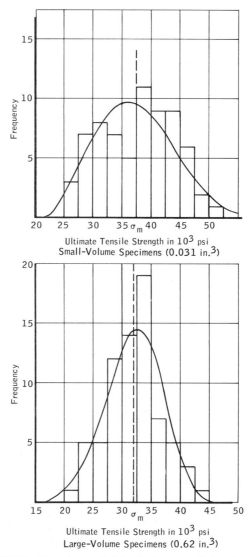

FIGURE 9. Frequency plot for hot-pressed alumina specimens (Source: Pears and Starrett, "An Experimental Study
of the Weibull Volume Theory," AFML-TR-66-228).

also is given in the literature.[7] Observe the dual node in Figure 9 suggesting
that the smaller-volume specimens failed by two mechanisms of fracture.
Perhaps undetected macroflaws would explain this; recall that the evidence is
that these macroflaws do not respond in a theoretically predictable fashion and
have a disproportionately large effect on the strength of the smaller volume
specimens. It is also possible that a different mode of fracture becomes controlling for the smaller-diameter specimen.

Figure 10 contains a plot of the probability of fracture for these hot-pressed
alumina specimens vs applied stress. A total discussion of this curve is in the
reference and further discussion is in the literature,[19] but observe that one
could test the smaller specimens and predict a safe working stress for the
larger ones. Also observe that the lower portion of the curve for the smaller-
volume specimens does not tail off toward a zero stress allowable. Rather, a
working stress of over, say, 20,000 psi is indicated and, indeed, no specimens
of any sizes (including the specimens with macroflaws) failed at less than
16,000 psi.

The conclusion is that there is a volume effect that must be considered

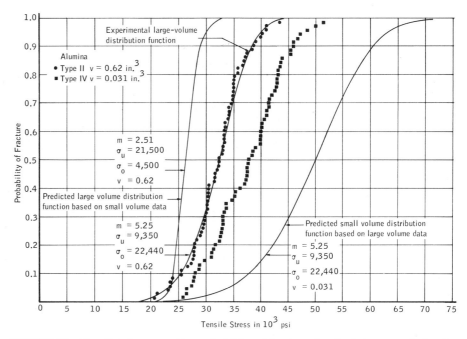

FIGURE 10. Tensile stress vs the probability of fracture for the hot-pressed alumina (Source: Pears and Starrett, "An Experimental Study of the Weibull Volume Theory," AFML-TR-66-228).

when studying conditions and properties and that the test method must accommodate it. Extreme caution is necessary to isolate conditions without directing the results; for example, surface finish can negate the volume effect, and gross macroflaws can have a different influence on different volumes. Yet one cannot indiscriminately discard all specimens with obvious flaws or the calculated volume effect can be shifted drastically.

If one is studying intrinsic material behavior of a given microstructure, it is reasonable to discard all specimens that have an abnormal structure; however, if one is interested in obtaining statistical strength for designs of a material as it is produced, specimens with flaws cannot be discarded.

Surface Finish   Surface finish has a marked influence on the strength of brittle materials.[4,7,9,10] Observe in Figure 11 that the strength of the pressed and fired alumina at 70°F decreased from about 37,000 psi at 20 rms to 23,000 psi at 300 rms.

Figure 12 shows that surface finish can totally mask other effects, in that the pressed and fired alumina had a decreasing strength with temperature at 20 rms but an essentially constant strength (at a lower absolute value) as a function of temperature at 120 rms. This same masking was observed under volume earlier, where 120 rms negated most of the volume effect primarily by decreasing the strength of the smaller volumes more than the larger ones.

Surface finish can also hide the stress-rate effect, as shown in Figure 13 where a higher stress rate gave a higher strength at 20 rms but had no effect at 120 rms where all values were lower.

Hence, all studies of conditions and properties should select surface finishes that permit the detection of the condition and property of interest and are consistent with the end use of the results.

Notches   Notches probably belong under stress concentration (behaviors) or in analysis but to some extent are an extension of the thoughts of surface finish and are discussed here until a spot for them becomes better defined. Notches

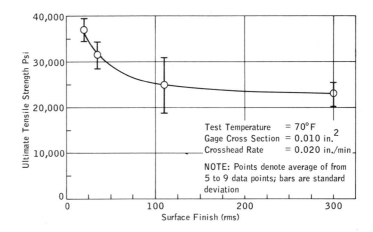

FIGURE 11. The effect of surface finish on the ultimate tensile strength of unnotched alumina at 70° F and one stress rate (Source: Pears and Digesu, "The True Stress-Strain Properties of Brittle Materials to 5000° F, AEC ORO 461, 1961).

about 30 mils deep and 4 mils wide with a 2-mil notch root radius reduced the nominal fracture stress of the hot-pressed alumina discussed previously[7] from about 39,000 to 15,000 psi. This latter value is obtained by dividing the load on the specimen by the area of the unnotched portion. However, by applying the Neuber analysis, the stress at the root of the notch is theoretically determined to be about 80,000 psi at failure or approaching the value that Weibull analysis predicts for the strength of that volume. See Figure 14 for a plot of the Weibull strengths and Neuber stresses. The point is that volume accountability brings sense into the analysis of stress intensification. This notch influence is reported in detail in forthcoming literature.[20] Similar work has been reported on "brittle metals."[21]

Stress Rate   The strength of brittle materials does vary with stress rate at room temperature and even more dramatically at higher temperatures. Figure 13 indicates that for a 20-rms surface finish the influence of stress

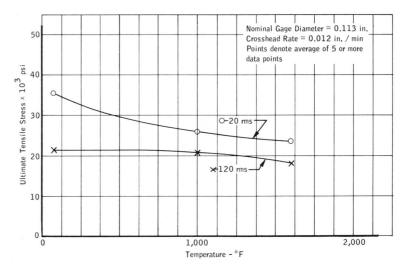

FIGURE 12. Influence of surface finish on strength of pressed and fired alumina as a function of temperature (Source: Pears et al., "Evaluation of Tensile Data for Brittle Materials Obtained with Gas-Bearing Concentricity," ASD-TDR-63-245; Pears and Digesu, "The True Stress-Strain Properties of Brittle Materials to 5000° F," AEC ORO 461, 1961).

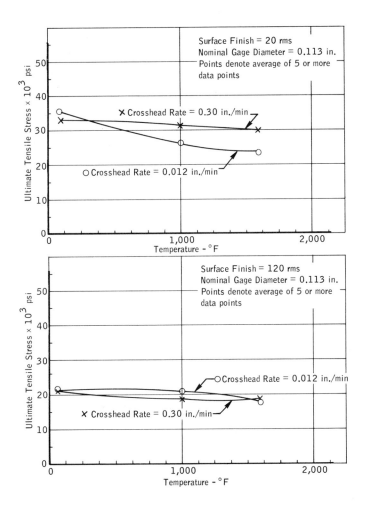

FIGURE 13. Influence of strain rate on strength of pressed and fired alumina as a function of temperature for two different surface finishes (Source: Pears et al., "Evaluation of Tensile Data for Brittle Materials Obtained with Gas-Bearing Concentricity," ASD-TDR-63-245; Pears and Digesu, "The True Stress-Strain Properties of Brittle Materials to 5000° F," AEC ORO 461, 1961).

rate over the small range investigated was quite small at 70° F but significant at 1,000 and 1,600° F. Other work on this same material, shown in Figure 15 and reported in the literature,[11] indicates that a much larger range of stress rates could introduce a range in fracture strength of from 24,000 to 34,000 psi.

Here again, stress rate is a significant controlled condition in the mechanical response of brittle materials and, therefore, must be controlled in studies of behaviors.

Environment   The influence of the environment (gas chemistry and density) of the test specimens on results undoubtedly is critical. Considerable information is available in the literature on glasses[22] and on some single crystals. A first search of ceramic abstracts back to 1961 revealed no information for polycrystalline magnesia or alumina. Dramatic effects are reported, such as a 20% strength increase for glass with removal of moisture at, say, 1,000° C and 10^{-5} torr. Stress-rate effects may be invalidated here; that is, many observed stress-rate effects may be masked by environmental effects, particularly

204

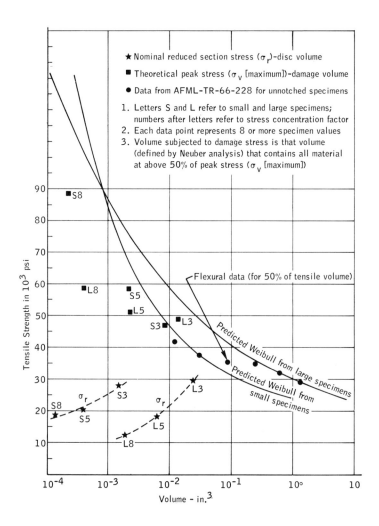

FIGURE 14. Stress-strength of notches in hot-pressed alumina (Source: Starrett and Pears, "A Study of Notches in Brittle Materials by Relating Stress Intensification and Volume," AFML-TR-67-254).

in fatigue and creep. This is because studies that have time as a variable may be permitting the environment to become operative. For polycrystalline structures the information is not so complete. This "condition" is not discussed further here other than to say that for a given material and program a total and complete definition is necessary.

Number of Specimens   The number of specimens that must be tested is quite important. Experience with graphites and aluminas[7] has indicated some consistencies; for example, 5 to 10 specimens may provide good mean strengths and perhaps 10 to 20 may provide meaningful standard deviations. In the same example, 40 or more specimens were necessary for Weibull's material constant such as m and σ_u.

Three points are often used to obtain mean strengths for screening purposes, with five points for engineering design and more, as indicated above, for statistical analysis. The tester must be cautious in agreeing to or recommending the number of specimens to provide meaningful conclusions.

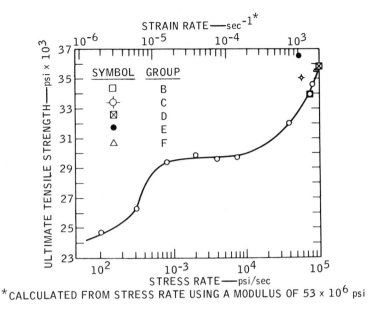

FIGURE 15. Effect of stress rate and gage volume on ultimate tensile strength of alumina (Source: Sedlacek, "Tensile Strength of Brittle Materials," AFML-TR-65-129).

Variability   Variability is that feature of a material that has to do with its inherent response and contributes to data scatter. The scatter of the test machine is not inferred here. This variability affects the number of specimens that must be tested, particularly for a meaningful statistical analysis. This condition is interwoven in the studies of all properties and conditions.

Anisotropy   Anisotropy refers to the different mechanical behaviors of a material on different axes. This effect on brittle materials such as metal oxides made by cold-pressing has been reported to vary from zero to over 20%, and for other refractory materials it may be as high as a factor of 30.[23,24]

Geometry   Geometry relates to the configuration of the specimen that must be used in a given testing apparatus, particularly if it may introduce variables unique to geometry or anisotropy. For example, in a controlled experiment[20] on ATJ graphite, with grain, a round cross section gave 22-1/2% higher ultimate strength than a square one and one-half the standard deviation (4% for the coefficient of variation for the round one). The surface finish was 30 to 50 rms.

Time at/to Temperature   Most brittle materials have residual stresses and/or undergo structural changes at temperature. As a result, the time at/to temperature must be defined in obtaining the property.

Residual Stress   Since it is quite difficult to anneal brittle materials and/ or define the residual stress that remains upon cooling, property studies must consider this effect in terms of specimen size, heating condition, and surface treatment.

Amenability to Analysis   "Amenability to Analysis" relates to the confidence in relating the numbers obtained to the actual stress, or property, calculated and of interest. For example, the Brazil test permits easy alignment, but the determination or definition of the stress field is quite uncertain.[1] Or as another example, in most shear tests, it is relatively simple to measure the total strain but quite difficult to determine the volume influenced and hence the unit strain.[17] For the uniaxial rod and the pressurized ring, this condition is no problem when the test is performed properly.

Thus it has been demonstrated that controlled and observed conditions do influence values obtained for tensile properties. The argument remains whether or not even those properties and conditions obtained on uniaxial rods and pressurized rings relate to the constitution of the material. This answer can only be inferred from the consistency in results and in theory testing. Certainly the evidence is mounting that "properties" are obtained. For examples: Weibull predicts a volume effect and there is one[7]; Neuber stresses and Weibull strengths show reasonable agreement[20]; relations between elastic modulus, Poisson's ratio, and shear modulus are in quantitative agreement even for anisotropic materials[17]; the predicted triaxial strains[27] are obtained experimentally and recorded in plastic deformations[17]; calculations of the shift of the force centroid from the area centroid for beams permit an explanation of beam (flexural) responses from tensile and compressive data; and the existence of a "damage" or threshhold stress at perhaps 50% of ultimate is appearing in tensile, fatigue, and flexure separately. Thus, we proceed with some confidence.

Now consider, but in less detail, the influence of conditions on other behaviors and/or properties of interest.

Influence of Conditions for Flexure

The major conditions that influence values obtained in flexure involve quality of influence, fractology, temperature, volume, surface finish, variability, anisotropy, geometry, and amenability to analysis. Most of these effects are obvious; however, a few deserve specific mention. Quality of influence is related to the large stress gradient and the uncertainty in such things as flaw orientation, blunting of the peak stress at the surface, biaxial strain effect, and departure from plane strains. The volume of the material under stress is ill defined. The maximum stress occurs at the surface, emphasizing the surface finish and probably precluding rigid volume studies, and an analysis of the results demands some questionable assumptions such as elastic behavior, anisotropic accommodations of the elastic constants, shear deflections, and the equivalence of compressive and tensile moduli. This latter assumption is quite dangerous at higher temperatures. There are other pitfalls. In the flexural specimen, only the surface is subjected to the peak stress, and the gradient falls rapidly. In a specimen with a height of 1/2 in., only the surface of 25 mils is subjected to stresses within 10% of the peak value. Thus, for example, studies of grain-size effect would have to recognize that a grain 1/32 in. in diameter transgressed the entire area of "peak stress." Finally, strength values obtained are a function of the specimen size and geometry in a fashion still rather ill defined.

Influence of Conditions for Compression

The major conditions related to compression involve fractology, variability, geometry, anisotropy, and amenability to analysis.[15,17] Most failures include an axial plane and a shear plane; the originator of fracture is difficult to determine. Anisotropy of the material demands accommodation of elastic constants. Amenability of analysis is subject to doubt from column buckling, squashing of the material thus changing the area, and determination of the actual failure mechanism, whether total strain, lateral tensile strength reduction, or shear failure.

Influence of Conditions for Shear

The major conditions related to shear involve quality of influence, fractology, stress rate, variability, anisotropy, and amenability to analysis.[17] It is practically impossible to define the gage volume (in other than torsion) and thus determine the modulus. Anisotropy again demands triaxial treatment of the elastic constants. Shear failures are practically impossible to obtain; fractology almost always indicates superimposed tension.

Influence of Conditions for Dynamic Modulus

The conditions related to dynamic modulus include quality of influence, stress rate, variability, anisotropy, and amenability to analysis. Quality of influence can be obtained with considerable experimental care. Stress rate and peak stress are invariably high and low, respectively, limiting the results to the material response at these levels; anisotropy demands triaxial treatment of elastic constants, and amenability to analysis requires equivalent tensile and compressive modulus.[26,27]

Influence of Conditions for Combined Stresses

The development of combined stress theories for the fracture of isotropic brittle materials has been studied by a number of investigators, and reasonable progress has been made theoretically. Experimental studies are badly needed. For anisotropic materials almost no work is available. Some information is available.[28]

Influence of Conditions for Thermal Conductivity

The conditions related to thermal conductivity include quality of influence, structure, temperature, variability, anisotropy, time at/to temperature, and amenability to analysis. Many accepted test methods demand a relatively large temperature gradient in the gage section so that the property varies, though assumed constant; that is, the average of a variable is detected. For a given chemistry, the property varies with structure. There are phase changes at different temperatures, giving discontinuities. Anisotropy defies thermal definition in some orientations. Amenability to analysis is confounded by uncertainties related to heat-flow patterns, anisotropy, and subtle structural changes. The problems related to refractory materials are well discussed in the literature.[17,29,30,31]

Influence of Conditions for Thermal Expansion

The conditions related to thermal expansion include structure, variability, anisotropy, and amenability to analysis. Inflections in expansion often occur from structural changes related to both additional sintering and phase changes.[4,29,30] Anisotropy leads to physical restraint (or assist) of free thermal expansion. Since the unit expansion usually is measured and the coefficient is required in, say, thermal-stress analysis, the analytical procedure in going from unit expansion to the coefficient is critical and adds to the uncertainty in the value.

Influence of Conditions for Heat Capacity

The major conditions related to heat capacity include quality of influence, structure, temperature, variability, and amenability to analysis. Quality of influence is important in that phase changes and other endothermic and exothermic events related with many materials are uncertain and result in a measure that truly is not heat capacity. As more information is gained on the refractory materials this problem will diminish. A final condition involves amenability to analysis in that the heat capacity usually is obtained by the slope of the enthalpy - temperature plot, thus introducing uncertainties in instantaneous values, particularly where inflections occur. These aspects are well reported in the literature.[29,30,32]

Influence of Conditions for Thermal Diffusivity

This quantity can either be measured directly or calculated from the specific heat, thermal conductivity, and density; the direct measurement requires great care. For the calculated value, other conditions seem secondary to the problems involved in the determination of instantaneous heat capacity and the analysis. For literature, see the references used in the following discussion of test methods.

Influence of Conditions for Emittance

The conditions of concern include quality of influence, structure, temperature, surface finish, variability, anisotropy, time at/to temperature, and amenability to analysis.[30,33,34] The major problems involve measurement of surface temperature and spectral variations introducing major problems at over 2,000°F and on a surface that will not accept a welded thermocouple. At lower temperatures the problems become those of degree.

TEST METHODS, THEIR DESCRIPTION, CAPABILITY, AND LIMITATIONS

Once the material processor, designer, or one interested in the response of materials selects a property and the conditions of interest, the next step is to select a suitable test method that is capable of isolating the behavior and property. This section describes these methods, their capabilities, and their limitations for the different properties shown in Table 4.

Since the ultimate tensile strength (with a homogeneous stress field) is a property of major interest, a detailed discussion of this property and the ability to isolate the conditions with different test methods will provide a better appreciation of the considerations for the other properties or test methods where more general discussions are employed.

Homogeneous Tension

There are several types of "tensile" tests, including a rod or bar with uniform tension, an internally pressurized ring, and several other configurations such as the disk (Brazil test) or thick-walled ring in which a specimen is loaded on a diameter and a theoretical tensile stress exists on one plane. The flexural test is included elsewhere as a behavior rather than one that provides a reasonably uniform stress field and thus a tensile property.

There are several vital factors involved in selecting the tensile test for use. The tensile test is much more useful if it is amenable to axial stress - strain, lateral strain, temperature scans, and studies of the other parameters mentioned in addition to the ultimate tensile strength. These elastic constants, temperature effects, and other considerations are vital to design and also to process control for material development for all applications where the property must be optimized. Certainly these measurements should be accommodated where the total test is not seriously hindered by the accommodation.

There is another aspect that requires some philosophic understanding. This aspect concerns the degree to which one tries to control all variables in a test, such as parasitic or bending stresses. There are at least three levels of performance advocated. One level involves "rough process control," whatever that is—perhaps engineering screening programs in which the "relative strengths" of material or the strength profile across a billet is desired. The inference is that comparisons can be obtained even with "bad" data. The second level involves obtaining "good" data with a minimum scatter attributable to the testing technique. The inference is that one knows the degree of uncertainty within reasonable limits. The third level involves precision testing in which uncertainties of such things as parasitic stresses are limited to 1 or 2%, and the data actually are correlatable with volume, surface finish, strain rate, and other conditions.

The third test probably is the only one acceptable for significant studies. Investigators have used precision guides, chains, adjustable platens, and other devices and find that parasitic stresses can be controlled one time and the next time they cannot.[12] Hence, every separate test becomes an experience in making fine adjustments.

Within this general framework there are a few tensile test methods for brittle material that have demonstrated an ability to detect properties and conditions.

Gas-Bearing   One method of tensile testing that can adequately detect the properties and conditions and that provides a defined stress field is the gas-bearing system. Its capabilities are discussed in the literature[9,10,13,17,20] and are described briefly as follows:

A typical tensile facility is shown schematically in Figure 16. The primary components are the gas-bearings, the load frame; the mechanical drive system, the furnace, the optical-strain analyzers, and associated instrumentation for measurement of load and strain.

The gas-bearings are positioned at each end of the load train on the crossheads. Each gas-bearing has a diameter of about 9 inches, which is sufficient to provide the design-load capacity of 15,000 pounds. The purpose of the gas-bearings is to eliminate parasitic stresses in the specimen by accommodating the misalignments that usually occur at the crosshead attachment and inevitably occur as the crosshead moves, and by permitting detection and elimination of "kinks" in the load train by virtue of the ability to rotate the load train before each run and check its "run out" with dial indicators.

The load train must be designed and fabricated to insure alignment of the specimen and extension rods between the crossheads. All members are machined true and concentric to 0.0005 in. and the entire load train is checked to insure over-all alignment within about 0.001 in. following assembly of the individual members. The load-train assembly is statically balanced and all leads are routed through the center of the top extension rod and fixed at the pivot point of the spherical gas-bearing.

A schematic of the precision tensile grip (part of the load train) also is shown in Figure 16. The design is much like the jaws of a lathe head or the chuck of a drill motor made with precision. Observe from the figure the long surface contact of the mating parts and the close fits to establish precise alignment with the specimen. As the load is applied the wedges maintain alignment to fracture.

Some acceptable configurations of the tensile specimen are shown in Table 5. This specimen provides a straight shank for measuring strength, axial strain (modulus), and lateral strain (Poisson's ratio). The flags for the measurement of axial strain are positioned 1 in. apart so that unit strain is recorded directly. The flag attachment for measurement of lateral strain is positioned between the flags for axial strain (see Figure 17).

Strain measurement consists of measuring optically the elongation between two flags, or targets, which are mounted on the specimen and separated initially by a predetermined gage length. The travel of the targets is measured by

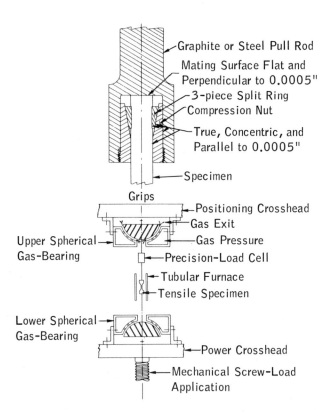

FIGURE 16. Schematic arrangement of gas-bearing universals, specimen, load train, and grips (Source: Pears and Starrett, "An Experimental Study of the Weibull Volume Theory," AFML-TR-66-228).

sensing the displacement of the image of the edge of the targets and then electromechanically following the image displacement. The relative travel of the two targets provides the strain. Readout is continuous and automatic on a millivolt recorder.

The precision of the strain measurement is to 0.000020 in., and the parasitic stress introduced in a tensile specimen is about 0.1%.

Now consider the capabilities and limitations of the gas-bearing system in terms of the conditions of the test.

Suitability for quality of influence. The uniaxially loaded rod is excellent in terms of "quality of influence" because a homogeneous stress field can be applied to a circular specimen and the stress level can be defined at any point in the cross section within about 0.1% uncertainty (with the gas-bearing).

Suitability for reproducibility. The uniaxial rod has demonstrated the ability to detect variations in reproducibility.

Suitability for fractology. The uniaxially loaded rod is excellent on fractology because it provides a well-defined tensile fracture face.

Suitability for volume. The uniaxially loaded rod is good in volume studies because it is amenable to different-sized specimens and it has demonstrated the ability to isolate the volume effect.

Suitability for surface finish. The uniaxially loaded rod has a well-defined surface and has demonstrated a good ability to isolate surface finish.

Suitability for notch. The uniaxially loaded rod is a specimen that receives grooves nicely and is amenable to notch studies.

Suitability for stress rate. The uniaxially loaded rod is adequate as a tool to study stress-rate effects, but there is a limit to the stress rates obtainable

Table 5. Typical Specimens for Collect Grip and Configuration of Gage Section for Split Sleeve Grip (adapted from Reference 7)

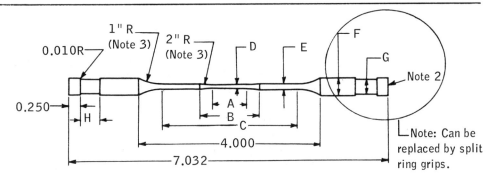

Specimen Type	A, Length ± 0.002	B, Length ± 0.002	C, Length ± 0.002	D, Diameter ± 0.002	E, Diameter ± 0.002	F, Diameter ± 0.002	G, Diameter ± 0.002	H, Length ± 0.002	Gage Volume, in.^{3}
1	0.500	0.910	3.070	0.250	0.271	0.500	0.453	0.516	0.0240
2	1.000	1.410	3.070	0.250	0.271	0.500	0.453	0.516	0.0491
3	0.894	1.252	2.952	0.187	0.203	0.500	0.453	0.516	0.0246
4	2.000	2.296	3.052	0.125	0.136	0.375	0.347	0.438	0.0246
5	1.000	1.296	3.052	0.125	0.136	0.375	0.347	0.438	0.0120
6	1.400	1.722	3.104	0.150	0.163	0.375	0.347	0.438	0.0247
7	1.334	1.588	2.992	0.094	0.102	0.375	0.347	0.438	0.00926
8	1.000	1.410	3.070	0.250	0.271	0.500	0.453	0.516	0.0491
9	0.188	0.440	2.992	0.094	0.102	0.375	0.347	0.438	0.00130
10	3.000	—	5.000	0.750	0.815	1.000	—	—	1.3300
11	2.5000	—	5.000	0.562	0.610	1.000	—	—	0.6180

Notes: 1. All diameters are true and concentric to 0.0005 in.
2. Both ends are flat and ⊥ C_L to 0.0005 in.
3. Do not undercut radii.
4. All dimensions are in inches.

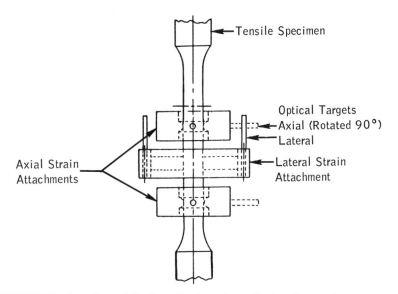

FIGURE 17. Location of the flag attachments on the tensile specimens (Source: Pears and Digesu, "Gas-Bearing Facilities for Determining Axial Stress-Strain and Lateral Strain of Brittle Materials to 5500°F," Proceedings of Annual Meeting of ASTM, 1964; Digesu and Pears, "The Determination of Design Criteria for Grade CFZ Graphite," AFML-TR-65-142).

in this system while still maintaining uniaxiality. The limit is unknown but the maximum stress rate demonstrated to date is about 10,000 psi per second.

Suitability for environment. The uniaxial rod as used in the gas-bearing is only fair for environment because of practical limitations. That is, performance in a vacuum has not been integrated in the system yet.

Suitability for number of specimens and variability. The uniaxially loaded rod is good in studies of variability because it permits a study of this variable with minimum parasitic stresses.

Suitability for anisotropy. The uniaxially loaded rod is good in studies of anisotropy and limited only by the ability to remove a specimen from a billet to the desired orientation.

Suitability for geometry. The uniaxially loaded rod is good for geometry because it will accommodate almost any length and cross-sectional configuration in the gage section.

Suitability for temperature and time to/at temperature. The uniaxially loaded rod is limited in temperature only by the furnace technology for the environment involved and is limited in time to/at temperature only by the ability to transfer heat to the specimen in an acceptable way.

Suitability for residual stress. The uniaxial rod is sufficiently precise to permit isolation of residual-stress effects if meaningful specimens could be made.

Suitability for amenability to analysis. The uniaxially loaded rod is easy to analyze because the stress in the gage section is uniform and known with certainty.

Pressurized Ring   Another method of testing that has been demonstrated for some parameters is the pressurized ring. The reader again is invited to review open literature and find a description of the bladder type.[11] A brief description follows.

This method has been developed over recent years for the purpose of avoiding, in tensile testing of brittle materials, the generation of parasitic stresses caused by misalignment, gripping, and various other stress-concentration factors.

The method employs basically a modified hoop stress and takes advantage of the intrinsic properties of hydrostatic pressure, i.e., the fact that this force is always normal to the confining surface and absolutely uniform at every point of contact. The test specimen is a short thin-walled cylinder against whose inner wall hydrostatic pressure is applied through a rubber bulb. This pressure, pushing radially, creates in the wall of the specimen a tangential tensile stress whose magnitude can be computed exactly from the value of hydrostatic pressure applied and the geometry of the specimen.

The experimental arrangement is very simple and can be seen in Figure 18, which shows the specimen holder. The apparatus consists of two steel plates provided with cavities of exactly the same diameter as the inside diameter of the specimen. In the assembled unit the cavities face each other, being aligned by three sturdy dowel pins. The bottom cavity, which is conical in shape, opens to the outside and contains a matching conical steel plug provided with a canal connected to the pressure line. When the rubber bulb is slipped over the plug, the latter is pushed down in the bottom cavity and a leak-tight seal is made. Next, the specimen is slipped over the rubber bulb and made to rest on the face of the bottom plate. Then, three spacers are placed symmetrically around the specimen and the upper plate is lowered into position. The spacing of the two plates is very important. If done properly, the specimen is free-floating and absolutely free of any compressive constraint. The gap between the specimen and the adjacent steel plates must, however, be kept small enough to prevent the rubber from extruding into the gap. In practice, this is easily achieved by using spacer blocks 0.001 or 0.002 in. higher than the specimen. Since the

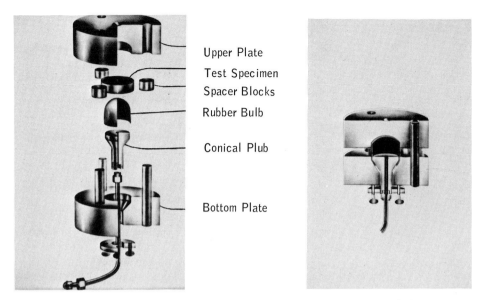

Upper Plate

Test Specimen

Spacer Blocks

Rubber Bulb

Conical Plub

Bottom Plate

FIGURE 18. Tensile test specimen holder: (a) exploded view, (b) assembled unit (Source: Sedlacek, "Tensile Strength of Brittle Materials," AFML-TR-65-129).

hydrostatic pressure would push the confining plates apart, the entire assembly is clamped together in a steel frame rigid enough to withstand the applied force and to maintain the proper width of gap between the specimen and the two steel plates. The rubber bulb is then inflated by the working fluid causing it to push against the inner wall of the specimen. Hydrostatic pressure is constantly monitored up to the point of failure. The ultimate tensile strength is computed from the value of hydrostatic pressure at the moment of failure, and the geometry of the specimen from the formula

$$\sigma_{t(max)} = \frac{Pr_i^2}{r_o^2 - r_i^2} \left(1 + \frac{r_o^2}{r_i^2} \right),$$

where P = hydrostatic pressure in psi, r_i = internal radius in inches, and r_o = external radius in inches.

By placing strain gages on the outside wall of the specimen, simultaneous measurements of strength, Young's modulus, and Poisson's ratio can be made.

Another type of internally pressurized ring (floated ring) has been developed as shown in Figure 19. In this apparatus, the specimen ring is floated between two conical end pieces that permit a controlled gas leakage from the gap between the ring and end pieces. Thus there is no end restraint on the specimen. The advantage of this floated ring is that it permits the possibility of operation at high temperatures since an internal bladder is not required. A disadvantage is that the specimen material must be nonpermeable and that the gas preheater will require large power inputs and relatively complicated operation.

Now consider the capabilities and limitations of the bladder-type of pressurized ring in terms of the conditions of the test.

Suitability for quality of influence. The pressurized ring is good from the standpoint of quality of influence, but less than excellent because a small stress gradient does exist and because a round specimen cannot be used and the influence of a rectangular one on the stress distortions in the corners is uncertain. Concerning the small stress gradient, it is known and subject to easy analysis.

Suitability for reproducibility. The pressurized ring is excellent as a monitor of reproducibility and has demonstrated good sensitivity to this variable.

214

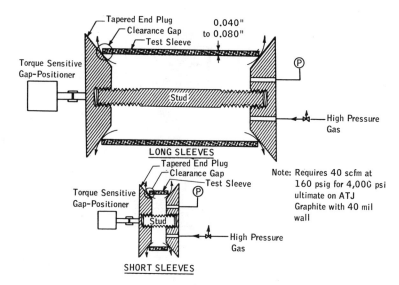

FIGURE 19. Schematic: gas-floated sleeves tensile test rig (Source: Starrett and Pears, "A Study of Notches in Brittle Materials by Relating Stress Intensification and Volume," AFML-TR-67-254).

Suitability for fractology. The multiple fractures obtained with the pressurized ring make it uncertain which fracture face occurred first on many of the specimens. Hence, fractology studies may suffer.

Suitability for volume. Over the range of volumes studied no volume effect has been observed with the pressurized ring.

Suitability for surface finish. The pressurized ring probably has a good ability to isolate surface finish but has not demonstrated this capability yet.

Suitability for notch. The usefulness of the ring for notches has not been investigated. The stress gradient would make the analysis of the stress intensification in the notch quite difficult.

Suitability for stress rate. The pressurized ring is quite amenable to the immediate application of all but very high (explosive) stress rates.

Suitability for environment. The pressurized ring is only fair for environment because it has some practical limitations such as, say, performance at high vacuum or in some corrosive environments.

Suitability for number of specimens and variability. The pressurized ring is good in variability studies in that it permits a minimum of confounding by contributions of the test apparatus itself.

Suitability for anisotropy. The ring is limited in studies of anisotropy since the weaker plane in the ring (for one orientation) will initiate fracture, and it often is impossible to get a typical ring with a single orientation entirely around the circumference.

Suitability for geometry. The ring has limitations for, say, a round cross section.

Suitability for temperature and time to/at temperature. The pressurized ring is temperature-limited to about 600°F using the bladder and fluid and is only fair for time to/at temperature because it will not handle extremely rapid heating rates; however, it would be good for normal heating rates to 600°F.

Suitability for residual stress. The ring is sufficiently precise to permit isolation of residual-stress effects if meaningful specimens could be made.

Suitability for amenability to analysis. The pressurized ring is easy to analyze because the stress in the gage is known with certainty except for the small gradient that exists from inside to outside.

<u>Monitoring System</u>   It seems reasonable that another method of testing could be developed, if necessary, by one who did not want to copy the gas-bearings or one of the pressurized rings. This method would involve a rod specimen and sufficient monitoring (and perhaps adjustment) on each run to insure that the bending stress was no more than about 2%.

The solution to the problem of providing a uniform tensile field on a rod specimen without using a gas-bearing involves six different areas: (a) the specimen configuration, (b) the grips, (c) the flexible load train, (d) the attachment to the crosshead, (e) the crosshead, and (f) monitoring of parasitic stress. The requirements in each area are influenced by what is occurring in the other areas, so a brief discussion of the over-all idea seems mandatory. Consider the schematic of a tensile system as shown in Figure 20.

The only two real requirements are that the specimen have an identifiable geometry and that the centerline of force be coincident with the centerline of the specimen. In order to accomplish this latter condition though, there must be precision alignment (to within 1/2 mil for most typical specimen lengths and diameters of, e.g., 3/8-in. diameter by 4 in. long) at the grips, in the extension rods from the grips to the machine crossheads, at the attachment to the crossheads, and in the travel of the crossheads if their attachment to the extension rods is rigid. Another way of thinking of the problem is that the specimen and extension rods must not have any "kinks" and that the action of the crossheads must pull on the centerline of the assembly—not at some angle nor with a lateral force component such as is necessary to pull a heavy crosshead laterally into position.

Within this general framework the different areas can probably be discussed in the same order in which one should attempt to resolve the problems.

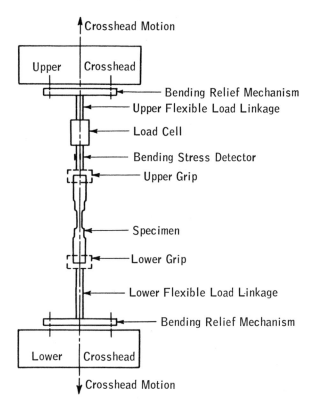

FIGURE 20. Schematic of a proposed tensile facility with monitored bending.

The specimens should be round in cross section and have a uniform diameter over the gage length of, e.g., 1 to 2 in. The reasons for selecting a round specimen are obvious. Machining is simple and the corner effects are by-passed. The uniform gage length has the obvious advantage of providing a defined volume and the ability to provide a desired surface finish over an appreciable area. Also, the specimen is amenable to the measurement of the elastic constants and other parameters. In addition, a geometry of the total system is provided over which one can monitor the specimen motion laterally during the test and thus detect bending stresses. At least 95% gage breaks can be anticipated for a homogeneously loaded rod even though one must use fillets in specimen design.

The attachment between the specimen and the extension rods is called the grips in this discussion and can involve a threaded end, a button, a tapered shoulder, a split sleeve with concentric grooves, or a collet. Any one probably can be made with sufficient precision. However, the collet-type grip probably is the only one that repeatably and reliably holds the alignment necessary. Other techniques will on quite a few occasions result in parasitic stress that must be detected by the monitoring process and will require reassembly or run rejection.

The load train includes the grips, the flexible extension rods (chains) from the grips, a load cell of some type for measuring load, a connection necessary to permit the installation of the specimen, and a way to monitor kinks. Chains are flexible and have been used with satisfaction[35]; but remember that a chain must transmit its force to the specimen on the centerline and this is not easy at all in terms of 1/2 mil. Also, the bending monitor must be on the specimen side of the chain.

Several methods can be used to monitor the parasitic strains in a specimen. Strain gages on the specimen are often adequate. Some laboratories use this technique and use the peak circumferential stress as the ultimate. The problem here is that the entire gage volume is not subjected to a uniform stress; information on volume effects, surface-finish effects, notch effects, and such variables is lost. The only way to retain the additional information on the variables is by holding the parasitic stress to, say, 1 or 2%. (This discussion concerns induced parasitic strains; there are inherent strain variations where the modulus varies across a specimen.[35])

Strain gages can be mounted on a link in the load train so that they do not have to be mounted on each specimen. This procedure is cheaper and has both the advantages and disadvantages of mounting the gages on the specimen. It does require a careful correlation to specimen bending stress.

Another way of monitoring the parasitic stresses is to relate them to the "swing out" that occurs when rotating the load train or to the straightening (dekinking) that occurs during loading. For the gas-bearings, this tolerable swing out for less than 1% parasitic stress is about 1 mil for a specimen about 1/4 in. in diameter. This, of course, is a function of the particular arrangement but is a reasonable guide for other systems.

Considering the problem of measuring strains, one must "hold the specimen still" to within 1 mil and not let it move laterally in optical systems. If it moves, all known optical-strain systems give readout error of perhaps 10% of the lateral motion.[13] Other strain-measuring systems are available,[1,24] but it is doubtful their sensitivity is sufficient for most ceramics except, of course, for strain gages at near room temperature.

Flexure

The first decision involving the selection of a flexural test involves the use of three- or four-point loading. For extremely small specimens, three-point loading is almost mandatory from geometric considerations. If a specimen of sufficient size is available, four-point loading with three-axis rotation of three of the load points as shown in Figure 21 is preferable.[37] The four-point system permits an inspection of more of the material and a better definition of the surface area and volume under inspection. That is, the moment is uniform between the shorter load span rather than just a line transversely across the specimen. The use of load points with three-axes freedom (properly implemented) eliminates the effect of friction at the bearing points and superimposed torsion in the specimen. The first gives an erroneously high (typically 10%) indication of strength and the second, an erroneously low indication (typically 5 to 15%). Alignment of the load applicators is important. Transverse displacement on the specimen by 1 mil gives typically a 3% parasitic stress. These typical values are for specimens nominally 1/2 in. x 1/2 in. x 5 in.

Now consider the capabilities and limitations in terms of the conditions of the test: a homogeneous stress field is not applied; fractology studies are of little consequence; volume definition cannot be made as yet; surface-finish effects are amplified; and notch studies involve a large stress gradient. There are some capabilities: stress rate can be controlled; anisotropy can be handled; geometry cannot be varied in a satisfying fashion; and the test is cheap.

Compression

The compressive test appears deceptively simple but requires as much care as others. The major test requirements are that a dumbbell-type specimen be selected, the force application be on the precise axial centerline of the specimen, and extremely "free" universals preferably be inserted in the load ram to permit the ram to rotate about a center falling at the end of the specimen.[17] Obviously, buckling must be prevented. These points are usually begged so that parasitic or column stresses of 10 to 50% are introduced. For example, cheap small imprecision universal joints are used that do not have much freedom after the load is applied. Further, such a universal cannot truly accommodate misalignments in a fashion to keep the forces applied on the specimen axis.

Shear

There is no good shear test for brittle materials.[17] The torsion test provides a measure of shear modulus but is poor for ultimate because most materials

Dimensions:	Size A	Size B	Size C
Specimen Height, d	1/2	1	2
Specimen Length, l	4	8	16
Support Span, L	3	6	12
Load Span, l/3	1	2	4

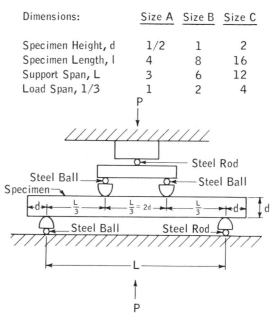

FIGURE 21. Beam with four-point loading (ASTM Test C-75-64).

fracture in a tensile mode at less than the shear strength. This has led investigators to conclude that shear strength is less than tensile and related by factors
such as 0.58 in a way traceable to theoretical expectations. About the only
meaningful shear specimen found to date seems to be a notched tensile one in
which "V" notches are machined on the centerline of a specimen pulled in tension so that the load is resisted by shear between the points of the "V".[17]
Invariably, these specimens provide higher shear strengths than ones with
small round holes where failure starts at the edge of the circular hole, undoubtedly from superimposed tension. Unfortunately, this test for shear ultimate is
poor for shear modulus because the gage volume is difficult to analyze even
when the shear zone between the notches is recessed.

Dynamic Modulus

There are at least two general types of tests referred to as dynamic modulus.
One involves the use of longitudinal-wave velocity and the other the excitation
of a laterally vibrating reed or beam. The first is discussed in detail in the
literature[17,26]; a precision of elastic modulus of a few percentage points is
claimed for several brittle materials. The latter technique also is discussed
in detail in literature, with claims of good precision.[7,15] These test techniques
produce numbers that, without extremely careful analyses, are dependent on
specimen geometry and size and too often depart from values obtained from a
stress - strain curve obtained by direct loading and strain measurement.

Combined Stresses

No good tests for combined stresses have been demonstrated and proofed with
relation to specimen work by an accepted theory. See the literature[28] for some
initial studies.

Thermal Conductivity

Some type of comparative rod, axial rod, or similar apparatus[17,38] seems
simplest and best for thermal conductivity to 2,000°F (within the range of
thermocouples and precision guarding where radiation is not excessive). A hot-
plate method has also been developed.[39] Uncertainties of 2 to 5% can be expected. In the "rod" method a cylinder of the specimen material is stacked in
series with either cylinders of known conductivity or in series with a rod (or
rods) that has been calibrated as a heat meter. The axial temperature gradient
is measured and the conductivity calculated. In addition to the rod techniques,
different types of stacked disk techniques[40] using radial heat flow either from
a hot wire on the axis or to a cold sink on the axis (such as length of tubing
with internal water flow) are used and are perfectly adequate to 2,000°F.

Above 2,000°F, the uncertainty in this measurement increases rapidly[29,30,31]
(to perhaps 10 to 15%) as guarding becomes difficult and thermocouples more
uncertain. The stacked-disk methods[29,30,40] seem preferable at the higher
temperatures from the standpoint of better guarding.

Thermal Expansion

Up to 1,800°F, thermal expansion probably is best measured by dilatometers
(quartz and others).[17,29,30,41] Above 1,800°F, direct optical viewing of the
elongation of a gage length is preferred by some over dilatometers, although
there are considerable difficulties in maintaining a sharp reference mark on
the specimen and in eliminating refraction errors of the optical line of sight
proceeding from the hot interior of the furnace to the colder one in the vicinity
of the tracking telescopes. Uncertainties of 0.001 in./in. can be expected.

Heat Capacity

Heat capacity can be determined by the drop-type calorimeter (cup or ice)[17,29,30,42] with an uncertainty of 2 to 5% at temperatures up to 5,000°F. One main limitation is that the apparatus gives the enthalpy between a drop and a cup temperature and hence is not as sensitive as some others to endothermic or exothermic events that occur at discrete temperatures and may be of interest. Up to 2,000°F, good precision and sensitivity for these heat spikes have been obtained by transient methods in which the heating or cooling curve of a specimen is monitored[43,44] so that either the heat input or heat output from the specimen is monitored.

Thermal Diffusivity

Thermal diffusivity usually is determined directly by exposing one face of a disk of material to a known heat-flux density, monitoring the temperature change at some location through the thickness of the disc, and analytically resolving the parameter (diffusivity) involving heat capacity, density, and thermal conductivity. The actual techniques vary so much that the reader must go to the literature.[45,46,47,48] It appears that the use of a quite uniform heat field such as a laser, attached thermocouples, and a detailed analysis that considers all conditions is resulting in far better results than were apparent a few years ago.

Emittance

Emittance can be measured in many ways. The most direct is to compare the irradiance from a surface of the specimen to the irradiance from a blackbody cavity maintained at the same temperature. Spectral information is obtained by the use of a spectrophotometer to inspect the signals at different wavelengths. Normal and hemispherical values can be obtained by geometry considerations. The major concern is in knowing the surface temperature of the specimen, which means that ingenious methods are necessary to attach thermocouples where direct spot welding is not possible and values above 2,000°F are suspect. Emittance also is adequately measured by observing the temperature-time relation while heating or cooling in a known environment or in a calorimeter. Uncertainties of 0.01 to 0.05 can be expected where surface thermocouples can be used. At high temperatures the uncertainties are higher. This subject also demands an extensive review of the literature by one seeking understanding.[33,49,50,51]

Nondestructive Testing

Nondestructive testing could be a major device in assisting both the processor and the designer if sufficiently sensitive techniques could be developed and the results correlated with properties and behaviors. There is interesting work proceeding in this correlation.[26] All studies of materials' response should consider this tool and, as often as possible, use it, if only to generate data to permit an accumulation of information on its actual correlation. The various methods include x ray, sonic, laser, and an infinite list of others as discussed in more detail elsewhere in this report. There is considerable difference in opinion on the state of this art.

CONCLUSION

The quantitative influence of conditions on properties has been demonstrated in some detail and test methods and their amenability to the control of conditions have been discussed more thoroughly.

As a final thought, it should be emphasized that these test methods were selected as ones that could produce property values related to the constitution of the material if sufficient care were exercised. It is perfectly obvious that there are other tests that will be used by the processor, the designer, and others as screening devices or in detecting differences. These other tests include the concentric ring test, the Brazil test, the thick-walled cylinder, and many, many others. Their use is absolutely proper so long as it is understood that the value obtained may not be a property and may not be responsive to conditions.

The best insight to the probable performance of a test method can be obtained by an inspection of the ability to control the conditions as exemplified for uniform tension. Use Table 4 as a guide in making this inspection.

Interaction among Properties, Structural Design and Analysis, Environmental Behavior, and Quality Assurance

INTRODUCTION

An attempt is made in this section to describe the continuum mechanics point of view with respect to the structural utilization and testing of ceramic materials. In a completely general vein, the fields of structural design and structural analysis are reviewed to indicate to materials and testing engineers how requirements for material properties arise and how the various response models give rise to testing guidelines. At the same time, we expose the naivete of the structural engineer who attempts to control the behavior of materials by understanding only their "macro" features. Our general remarks are followed by a number of subjective observations, which are directed specifically to polycrystalline ceramics at both room and elevated temperatures.

STRUCTURAL DESIGN

The problem of structural design is the disposal of material in such a way that it will, within some level of reliability, equilibrate given systems of loading under appropriate environmental conditions without exceeding permissible amounts of deflection. Formulated in this way, the solution to the design problem is not unique and merely represents a synthesis which satisfies the functional requirements within the confines of existing limitations. There are other additional requirements, such as weight and cost, that can be taken into account.

The conventional approach is for the most part concerned with stress or deflection analysis of given structures. This means that in practice it can only be used in design by a process of trial and error in which the structural layout and sizes are first guessed or very roughly calculated and are then subjected to as complete analysis as theory will permit. The results of these calculations are compared to some performance yardstick, and on this basis the various parts of the structure are judged to be adequate or inadequate. The design is then modified and the detailed analysis repeated as a check. In the case of a ceramic structure, the material might be approximated as linear, elastic, isotropic, and homogeneous, and a thorough analysis would result in a description of the stresses, strains, and deflections throughout the structure. The integrity is then established by applying fracture theories to determine the probability of fracture occurring under the imposed stress distribution. If this probability is sufficiently low, one can accept the design or modify it to lower its weight or cost. If the fracture probability is too high, the design is unacceptable and modification is required. The initial guess at the dimensions of a trial component is a matter of art, and many of the dimensions will be set by functional requirements on the structure.

In addition to establishing the geometry of a component, the design engineer is charged with the responsibility of selecting the best material from a finite number of candidates. To fulfill this responsibility, the designer must consider the many qualitative and quantitative aspects of successfully producing a component based on the state of the art for both the material and the associated design concepts, which account for the combined effects of thermal, mechanical, and chemical stability.

The complex interactions of the many variables involved requires the designer to draw upon many disciplines for his tools.

The design process for high-performance components typically includes:

1. Analytical methods
   a. Loads
   b. Thermal
   c. Stress
   d. Economic
   e. Chemical
   f. Electrical

2. Mechanics of materials
   a. Properties
   b. Deformation behavior
   c. Fracture behavior

3. Experimental techniques
   a. Environmental behavior evaluation
   b. Analytical verification
   c. Hardware verification

4. Quality assurance
   a. Raw-material control
   b. Process control
   c. Product control
   d. Proof-testing

Integration of the various procedures requires the exercise of engineering judgement based upon experience and a certain amount of black magic.

While the design process outlined above is equally applicable to ductile and brittle materials, the care required in each step of the process is much greater when brittle materials are used. Those topics pertinent to the design-properties interface will be expanded in subsequent discussions.

ANALYSES

Quite generally, the purpose of analysis is to determine the response of a given component, that is, one whose material, geometry, and loading are specified. It is the function of the engineer to conduct such analyses with efficiency, which usually means that he strives for minimum cost. Three approaches can be identified for evaluating a component. The first of these deals with the simulated testing of full-scale prototypes; the second, with the testing of small scale models; and the last with behavior theories that utilize small specimens to establish the associated theoretical parameters.

At the outset, let us dispel any notion that the engineer operates under any scientific constraint that motivates him to describe behavior in terms of first principles; that causes him to seek out those intrinsic properties that form the common denominators of all structures; or that inclines him to the analytical rather than the empirical. Indeed, his constant allegiance is to practicability, and only when the scientific goals promise also to be the most pragmatic will he adopt this viewpoint. Several examples may help to clarify these observations.

In the manufacture of wire, the processing produces different materials on the surface and in the interior of the wire. This makes the specification of wire strength in terms of unit stress quite meaningless, since no useful number can be found that will reflect the change in wire strength as we go to different wire diameters. The problem is economically circumvented by recording the fracture and/or yield load for each wire product. On the other hand, complete homogeneity is achieved with respect to the elasticity of the constituent wire materials. Here, the modulus of elasticity provides a useful common denominator for the determination of the stiffness of wire of any size.

Another example may be found in the field of fiber-reinforced plastics, where two distinct approaches can be recognized for predicting the strength and stiffness of composites of various size. One of these attempts is to describe behavior in terms of the properties of the matrix material, the reinforcing material, and the matrix-fiber interface. The other, called the phenomenological approach, uses the behavior of a particular composite as the building block for composites of different geometry and loading. The latter approach is presently the more accurate and less versatile of the two and is usually the more economical. In reinforced concrete analysis, the first approach is the less expensive. We note that the data required for the phenomenological approach is entirely different from that needed to predict behavior from individual constituent properties.

We observe that only one of the three analysis methods mentioned is substantially uninfluenced by theoretical considerations—full-scale simulated testing. In the other cases the required data is specified by the prediction scheme contemplated by the designer. Furthermore, the type of tests used to obtain this data is highly dependent upon the analysis method adopted. Specifically, such methods provide necessary conditions for the design of the tests. To be sure, these conditions are not sufficient, and many other considerations may be introduced by the testing engineer, which form additional necessary conditions on the proper design and conduct of a testing program.

The procedure for establishing a mathematical model for approximating the behavior of a material involves a sequence of steps of ever-increasing refinement, which demand greater and greater ingenuity and skill. Beginning with either exploratory experiments or a preliminary hypothesis, the sequence alternates between hypothesis and experiment as it proceeds to a satisfactory description of the material response.

The following discussion is presented to outline the general functions, limitations, and requirements of the various analytical methods that might be used in predicting the response of a structural component for any application or environment. Similar analytical procedures and techniques must be employed in evaluating material response and properties from a laboratory test sample. In this sense, the analytical treatment required for the simple laboratory sample is analogous to the detailed analysis applied to the structural component, and, based on the complexity of the problem, it is obvious that the designer, theorist, experimentalist, and material developer cannot work effectively alone.

Loads

The analysis of any component begins with the specification of mechanical and thermal loadings. The mechanical loadings may take the form of body forces and tractions. Body forces act throughout the body, such as gravitational forces; tractions act on the surfaces of the body and may be concentrated or distributed. Residual- and thermal-stress loadings generally are classified as self-equilibrating forces. Since stresses, and hence the integrity of a component, are directly related to loading, it is clear that these loads should be defined as functions of time in either an exact or a conservative manner. However, inefficiency results from the latter approach.

Loadings induced by both environmental conditions and installation must be considered, and often statistical definition of such loads is necessary.

Thermal

The detailed knowledge of the thermal history of all points in a component may be a requirement of the design analysis for any one or all of the following purposes:

1. To establish the magnitude of the self-equilibrating forces if a thermal gradient exists, i.e., evaluate thermal stresses.

2. To account for the time-independent influence of temperature on the material constants used in analysis.

3. To account for property variations due to microstructural changes that might occur in a material under the combined influences of time and temperature for the prescribed "use cycle" of the component.

Heat-transfer analyses based on numerical computing techniques are available for calculating thermal histories of complex shapes. The material properties are required as functions of temperature and include thermal emittance, thermal conductivity, and specific heat and density. Density variation with temperature is generally of secondary importance and is usually neglected.

While the uncertainties in predicting the externally applied heat flux from environmental conditions are great, once the applied heat flux has been defined the major inaccuracies in the predictions from the heat-condition analyses arise through the uncertainties in defining thermophysical properties.

Chemical and Electrical

From the standpoint of structural analysis, chemical or electrical effects are considered only in terms of their influence on mechanical or thermal properties of the material at all points in the component. If changes in chemical or electrical reactivities are evident throughout the "use cycle" of the component, successive analyses must be performed using the appropriate mechanical properties for several intervals of time.

Thermal, electrical, and chemical variations that affect one portion of the component more than another seriously complicate the problem of analyses, since this behavior must be accounted for analytically through the provisions for handling heterogeneity and/or anisotropy. For example, thermochemical reactions at one surface of a body acting for a period of time will change the material properties at and near the surface. The magnitude and location of these changes must be identified in terms of changes in mechanical properties for input into the stress analysis. It may be difficult or impossible to obtain the mechanical test samples needed from the proper location in the billet. In addition, the stress analysis employed must be capable of handling these complications.

A variety of analytical techniques are used for studying the thermal - electrical - chemical behavior of materials. Investigations of these effects are usually conducted independent of the structural evaluations except in cases where the combined effects, including stress, are known to produce gross variations in behavior. Stress corrosion is one example of this type of behavior, and, due to the complexity of the phenomenon, empirical laboratory evaluations are used to study the problem. Often the laboratory experiment is not capable of producing an appropriate environmental condition and one must resort to subscale simulation testing. However, the uncertainty of scaling these results to the end-item hardware imposes the need for extensive verification testing of full-scale hardware. Simulation, verification, and qualification testing is employed extensively throughout aerospace industry in the development of rocket engines, reentry vehicles, and other high-performance hardware that must withstand severe thermochemical - mechanical environments.

Structural Analysis

General Objectives   To determine whether a given component will do its job, it is usually sufficient to examine the component's deformations and integrity. In both cases a stress analysis is required; in the latter, a theory of fracture must also be used. The general structure of these analysis methods is described in this subsection in order to illustrate how the various material constants and parameters arise in the prediction process.

Stress - strain analysis. The normal approach to the problem of stress analysis is to adopt the methodology of continuum mechanics. This carries with it the tacit assumption that one's material can be approximated as having a continuously distributed mass. As the mass of a continuum is continuously distributed, so any force or displacement stemming from the mass is also continuously distributed. Generally speaking, the continuum hypothesis accurately describes gross phenomena such as deflections and redundant forces. As we address ourselves more to pointwise behavior such as the displacements at grain boundaries or the stress at the tip of a crack, the reliability of continuum predictions is open to serious question.

Some of the physical considerations that give rise to the equations that determine the states of stress and strain in a body are described in the following brief remarks:

Equations of motion. The requirement that every part of a body in equilibrium remain at rest leads to three partial differential equations involving six unknown stresses or stress rates at every point in the body. The equations hold for any continuum, and, consequently, they do not require any information concerning the mechanical properties of the material. If the body is in motion, the equations will also contain terms for the density and time derivatives of the three unknown displacements. Thus, for heterogeneous materials subjected to accelerations, the structural engineer will require a density profile for the component.

Kinematics. Using purely geometric arguments, relationships can be established among the six strain components at every point in a continuum and the associated three displacements or among the corresponding strain rates and velocities. If we expect a continuum to remain continuous after loading, i.e., if all the infinitesimal elements are to fit together perfectly after they have been strained, we must maintain certain relationships among the six strain components. Mathematically, we have six strains that can be expressed in terms of only three displacements, and, consequently, they cannot be taken arbitrarily. Specifically, for any continuum, six differential relations among the components of strain must be specified. Since these compatibility conditions hold for any continuum, they do not contain any information regarding the mechanical properties of the material.

Constitutive relationships. So far, we have six stress components, six strain components, and three displacement components, which are unknown. We have only three equilibrium equations and six compatibility or six strain-displacement relationships. For most solid materials the required six additional equations are furnished by the constitutive equation; this is a tensor equation, which establishes a relation between statical and kinematical tensors, for instance the stress or the stress rate and the strain or rate of deformation. The coefficients in this tensor equation are properties of the material and will, as a rule, depend on temperature. However, since the temperature field is usually regarded as known beforehand, this temperature dependence does not introduce any new unknowns into our system of equations.

The most familiar example of a constitutive equation is provided by the general linear elastic material,

$$\epsilon_{ij} = C_{ijkm}\,\sigma_{km}\,, \tag{1}$$

where the indices take on the values 1, 2, and 3, and the repeated subscript indicates summation over the index that is repeated. Here, σ_{km} is a component of the stress tensor, ϵ_{ij} is a component of the strain tensor, and C_{ijkm} represents 81 material constants that are independent of the deformation history. For an isotropic solid, only two of the 81 constants are independent, say, the modulus of elasticity, E, and Poisson's ratio, μ. In this case we have the following relationships based on linear infinitesimal strain theory:

$$\epsilon_{11} = \frac{\sigma_{11}}{E} - \frac{\mu}{E}(\sigma_{22} + \sigma_{33}) \tag{2}$$

$$\epsilon_{12} = \frac{2(1 + \mu)}{E}\sigma_{12} . \tag{3}$$

In the temperature range where a material is linearly elastic and isotropic, E and μ must in general be determined as functions of temperature.

The elastic-perfectly plastic material furnishes an example of a constitutive equation that relates strain rates to stresses and stress rates. A basic assumption of plasticity theory is that the total strain rate $\dot{q}_{ij}$ can always be decomposed into an elastic strain rate $\dot{\epsilon}_{ij}$ and a plastic strain rate $\dot{p}_{ij}$, where dots indicate differentiation with respect to time. The elastic strain rate may be obtained by differentiating equation 1; it then follows that

$$\dot{q}_{ij} = C_{ijkm}\dot{\sigma}_{km} + \dot{p}_{ij} . \tag{4}$$

Now, if the stresses σ_{km} remain sufficiently small, the behavior is elastic and no yielding or flow can occur ($\dot{p} = 0$). The criterion for defining the elastic range is given by a functional representation, f, called the yield condition, which generally depends upon the stress components and the previous stress history. When f is less than some preassigned number the material is elastic. For the particular case of a perfectly plastic material this yield condition, f, is by definition independent of the stress history and depends only upon the stress. Therefore, defining f in a suitably normalized fashion, we may write a condition for elastic behavior as

$$f(\sigma_{ij}) < 1 . \tag{5}$$

Further, it follows from the definition of perfect plasticity that f can never be greater than 1, i.e., no increase in resistance at a point can occur once yielding begins.

For the remaining case, f = 1, we must generalize the role played in simple tension. When the applied stress remains at yield, flow takes place (f = 1). However, if we begin to unload we experience elastic behavior, $\dot{f} < 0$. Now, we can write the constitutive equation for an elastic-perfectly plastic material:

Elastic: f < 1 or $\dot{f} < 0$

$$\dot{q}_{ij} = C_{ijkm}\dot{\sigma}_{km} , \tag{6}$$

Plastic: f = 1 and $\dot{f} = 0$

$$\dot{q}_{ij} = C_{ijkm}\dot{\sigma}_{km} + \lambda\frac{\partial f}{\partial \sigma_{ij}} , \tag{7}$$

where $(\partial f)/(\partial \sigma_{ij})$ is the gradient to the yield surface formed by f = 1, and λ is an undetermined but nonnegative number.

If we know C_{ijkm} and $f(\sigma_{ij})$, equations 6 and 7 provide six relationships between the stress rates and strain rates in either the plastic or elastic conditions. Before we discuss how material properties enter into f, we shall comment on the implications of the observation that "energy put into plastic deformation can never be recovered." First, this implies that f is convex and second, that at a smooth point on the yield surface, the plastic strain rate $\dot{p}_{ij}$ is in the direction of the normal to the yield surface. Thus $\dot{p}_{ij} = \lambda \partial f/\partial \sigma_{ij}$ where the magnitude of this strain-rate component may be any positive quantity. This is called the flow law.

In two dimensions, five different forms for f may be represented by the appropriate yield surfaces. The tensile yield stress, σ_{ys}, is the only material property entering the <u>maximum-stress</u>, <u>maximum-shear</u>, and <u>distortion-energy</u> theories. For the <u>maximum strain</u> and the <u>maximum-strain-energy</u> theories we must also have Poisson's ratio. For example, the two-dimensional yield surface for the maximum-strain-energy theory is

$$\left(\frac{\sigma_{11}}{\sigma_{ys}}\right)^2 + \left(\frac{\sigma_{22}}{\sigma_{ys}}\right)^2 - 2\mu\left(\frac{\sigma_{11}}{\sigma_{ys}}\right)\left(\frac{\sigma_{22}}{\sigma_{ys}}\right) = 1 . \tag{8}$$

<u>Boundary conditions</u>. For the most solid continua, the constitutive equations and the field equations represented by the equilibrium and compatibility relationships are sufficient for the complete determination of the stresses, strains, and deformations, provided that the proper boundary conditions are specified. In an elasticity problem, for example, we might specify the tractions or forces acting at every point on the surfaces of a component. We might also have specified the three displacements at each boundary point. When our problems deal with stress rates and velocities rather than stresses and displacements, the resulting boundary-value problems presuppose that a certain time t the displacements and stresses are known throughout the body, and stress rates and velocities are prescribed on the surfaces of the components. In such cases, the problem is to determine the stress rates and velocities throughout the interior of the component. These may be used with the specified stresses and displacements at time t to establish the stress and displacement histories.

<u>Failure analysis—excessive deformations</u>. We have seen that the analysis of stress, strain, and displacement gives rise to material-property requirements through the constitutive equations. Once these properties are known, a component may be anlayzed as the first step in its structural evaluation. The displacements that result from the stress analysis may be used directly to judge whether the deformations of the component exceed the functional limits imposed by the application. If these are tolerable, we pass into the next stage, which concerns itself with the component's integrity. Here, either the stress or the strain history will provide the required input to a strength analysis.

<u>Failure analysis—structural integrity</u>. The integrity of a component will be taken as its ability to equilibrate a given load system. A loss in this ability may come about in two ways: the component may fracture into two or more separate parts, or the component may flow or continuously deform (become a mechanism) under the loading. To examine these failure modes in more detail we shall consider a basic element of finite volume in a structural component. Two factors are involved in the determination of the component's integrity: the behavior of a basic element and its influence on its neighboring elements. We shall consider three distinct behavior patterns.

In the first situation an ultimate resistance will be achieved in the basic element, followed by a complete loss of strength caused by a crack penetrating the unit. Having been mobilized, the crack continues to propagate through the material until over-all fracture is accomplished and the component can no longer equilibrate the applied loading. These characteristics may be called perfectly brittle behavior or series fracture. We observe that fracture at any point in a material necessarily constitutes over-all failure of the component.

In our second case, we again experience a complete drop in the resistance of our basic element, only here the propagating crack will be arrested. For a homogeneously stressed component, this type of behavior enables the applied stress to break all the weak elements while it continues to equilibrate the applied loading with the strong ones. The fracture-arrest type of behavior may be characterized as a series-parallel fracture mechanism to reflect the idea that, after fracture, alternative or parallel load paths are available to redistribute the loads that were carried by the basic element. We note that the removal of weak basic elements causes the stiffness of the over-all system to decrease. The load-deflection diagrams for such materials gradually bend toward the horizontal, producing a sort of pseudoductility such as we experience in fiber-reinforced composites.

Our third behavior pattern involves yielding in the basic element, which produces a maximum constant resistance that does not diminish. The unit can no longer equilibrate loads larger than those causing incipient flow. Yielding in the basic element does not affect the adjacent elements. As the external load on the component is increased, more and more elements will be brought to the yield state until the array of these elements forms a mechanism. We will then experience unconstrained plastic flow of the entire component.

For yielding failures, the methodology-of-plasticity theory provides a powerful tool for predicting component strength. Unfortunately, this high state of development is not shared by the other disciplines used for predicting incipient fracture. These are primarily represented by the fields of fracture mechanics and statistical-fracture theory. Fracture mechanics is basically a deterministic theory that establishes the stress field necessary to propagate a crack of given size. Statistical-fracture theory attempts to correlate the strength of large components under combined stresses with the strength of small specimens under simple stress states.

The development of fracture mechanics began with the work of Griffith,[1] who assumed a brittle solid such as glass would contain tiny cracks of various dimensions. Examining the largest of these, he reasoned that crack propagation would occur when, with increase of tensile load, the strain-energy release rate became greater than the solid-state surface tension. Although his theory adequately described the behavior of amorphous brittle materials, it left aside the large dissipation of strain energy in the plastic flow that normally accompanies crack extension in metals. A new viewpoint was introduced by Irwin[2] and by Orowan,[3] who recognized that unstable crack extension would develop regardless of plastic flow if the plastic strains tended to localize near the boundaries of the crack. In the Griffith theory thus modified, work expended in plastic deformation replaces surface tension as the factor controlling fracture toughness.

The applicability of the fracture-mechanics theory to polycrystalline ceramic materials has not been successful. Conversely, for both amorphous brittle materials and ductile materials the technique has considerable merit. In either case the analysis of integrity requires a description of the flaw sizes and locations and their associated stress environments. In addition to the elastic constants, a new material property is specified in fracture mechanics—the total energy required to create new cleavage surface. For amorphous materials this is usually taken as the solid-surface tension energy; ductile materials add to this quantity the energy of plastic deformation. In this latter case, another concept has been introduced by Irwin,[4] which utilizes a property called the crack-extension-force for rapid crack extension.

The approach of statistical-fracture theory, which is described in Appendix 1, is considerably broader than that of fracture mechanics. This theory does not examine the details of the fracturing process; it does not specify the nature of a flaw; and it does not attempt to characterize the exact state of stress in the neighborhood of cracks or crystals. Instead, it regards the imperfections of a material as one of its fundamental properties. It attempts to correlate the response of the imperfect material with the nominal or average stress states predicted from continuum mechanics. The input to this theory is a set of fracture test data obtained from nominally identical specimens drawn from a representative batch of material of interest. These tests result in a cumulative distribution curve, which usually must be fit with some analytical expression containing two or more parameters. When properly done, these statistical parameters become constants of the material, i.e., they are independent of geometry or stress state. The statistical parameters are normally determined for static conditions at room temperature, and when we deviate from these conditions, as we do in elevated-temperature and high-strain-rate applications, we should anticipate a change in the values of the parameters. Indeed, the parameters will become meaningless when new phenomena are introduced by differing environments.

The classical formulation of statistical-fracture theory was intended for perfectly brittle materials - series-fracture behavior. This is also true of classical fracture mechanics, which assumed that the onset of crack propagation was tantamount to complete failure of the component. Both these theories now recognize explicitly the possiblity of crack arrest mechanisms.

Property Requirements   A laboratory test to determine properties is governed by the same analytical models used in describing the stress-strain-failure behavior of a component. Test conditions and environments again are defined by the preceding constitutive relationships, boundary conditions, and equations for equilibrium and compatibility. Thus the complexity of the test situation requires varying degrees of experimental sophistication and the corresponding analytical complications. Historically, property tests have been defined by the simplest sets of loading, geometry, and boundary conditions. Test data taken from simple elements have the advantage of economy and reliability in meeting the specifications dictated by analysis.

Occasionally, the applicability of assumed constitutive relationships can be deduced from the simple test results. More often, however, a more complicated environmental-behavior test is required to examine the design parameters from the constitutive relationships. In general, the material constants from these tests must be obtained indirectly through detailed analysis, since the test would be designed to prove some specific analytical point. Thus, it is intended that environmental tests will suggest improvements in the analytical techniques through refinement in the constitutive relationships. In this sense, the environmental-behavior test forms the link in the hypothesis-test loop.

The following information is to be expected from property tests on a given material:

1. A basis for establishing the appropriate constitutive relationships. In general, these data will reflect the influence of inhomogeneity, anisotropy, temperature, strain rate, and stress state.

2. The determination of materials constants that enter into the constitutive relationships. These data can also be a function of temperature, strain rate, and anisotropy, for example.

3. A definition of the load-redistribution mechanism such as: the form of fracture-strength-distribution curves for various stress states, the constants entering into a statistical fracture theory, and the constants pertinent to a theory of fracture mechanics. Based on these requirements, it is evident that property data must be obtained with a specific application in mind, and very often the type of application will dictate the analytical approach to be followed. However, in general, most analytical requirements are for mechanical-property test data obtained in uniaxial tension or compression.

CERAMICS

Elastic Behavior

The first part of this chapter has addressed itself to the task of outlining the role of structural analysis in the material development - property testing - design cycle. Although this has been done in a very general way, many specific recommendations for properties have grown out of these discussions. In this subsection, our comments and recommendations will be directed toward poly-crystalline ceramic specimens. In particular, suggestions will be tendered that arise from the requirements for structural analysis of ceramic components.

Reproducibility   Perhaps the most serious shortcoming of ceramic technology, from the analysis point of view, is the difficulty of consistently producing exactly the same material. This is a problem not only when relating the materials in laboratory specimens to those in full-scale prototypes, but when obtaining the same laboratory materials from time to time and from batch to batch. It is a major goal of characterization efforts to identify those differences in materials that affect their functional behavior. When ceramic materials cannot be reproduced, it is the job of the material-testing engineer to communicate this problem to the designer. We hasten to point out that the number of samples that must be studied to assure a consistent manufacturing capability may greatly exceed the number required to determine various statistical parameters accurately. Care must be taken to draw specimens from different batches and production runs before accepting a material.

Homogeneity   The problem of heterogeneity in a ceramic component is not fundamentally a troublesome problem in structural analysis. As the structural engineer moves from point to point in a component, he only requires that he can identify the material at each location and that its basic properties are available to him. When more than a few distinct materials are present in a component, it is very costly to identify and characterize them.

When a specimen is chosen to measure a property, it is highly desirable that it be homogeneous. In no case should one accept more than two materials in a specimen. We are, unfortunately, forced into such a situation when the surface material differs from the interior material. This will always happen if the material reacts chemically with the testing environment. Even when such effects are absent, however, the surface finish may change the behavior of the surface material so that it is effectively a different material.

The response of a ceramic specimen may depend very sensitively on the "microgeometry" of its surface. At present, there is no way to describe or measure the topography of a surface so that the microgeometry effects can be separated from the surface-material behavior. The macrogeometry effects are, of course, accommodated in stress analysis and failure theories. It may be useful to define a pseudomaterial on the surface of a component to account for surface finish; however, no attempt is currently underway for doing this. In any event, if the behavior of the surface is unknown it will be necessary for the structural engineer and testing engineer to devise some combined theoretical and experimental scheme for defining the properties of the interior material.

Residual Stresses   For linearly elastic materials, the structural engineer can account for residual stresses by merely superimposing them on his standard-elasticity solutions for the applied stresses. This presupposes, of course, that the residual stresses are known. Clearly, this is seldom the case, and, furthermore, statistical means may be required to define them.

The rational evolution of a design must anticipate the residual stresses that can arise in a ceramic component. For a specimen, every effort must be made to eliminate this condition.

Strength   For polycrystalline ceramic materials it is recommended that the procedures of statistical-fracture theory be adopted for fracture analysis when plasticity effects are absent or negligible. As input to this theory, we require that fracture tests be conducted on a sufficiently large number of nominally identical finite volumes of homogeneous materials subjected to a homogeneous stress state. These data are used to establish the form of the cumulative-distribution function that characterizes the material strength. It also provides an estimate of the associated statistical parameters. This information will enable the structural engineer to predict the reliability of a series-fracture material or to estimate the reliability of a series-parallel material conservatively. To deal more efficiently with behavior of the nonseries-type materials, it will be necessary to establish the applicable load-redistribution mechanism. This latter problem has never been tackled in ceramic materials. The need for doing so can rapidly be determined from fracture data obtained from two different-size specimens of similar geometry and under similar loading.

A number of guidelines arise from theoretical considerations that should influence the selection of test specimens:

1. The applied stress state should be related to the loading and support conditions by a simple formula.

2. The cumulative distribution function for the specimens should be represented by a simple formula.

3. Parasitic stresses in the specimens should be held to a low value; otherwise, we will greatly underestimate the strength of our material and our designs will be overly conservative.

4. If the cumulative-distribution formula for this specimen describes only a portion of the specimen, which we shall call the gage section, we must establish how the data will be handled for fractures outside the gage section.

5. For combined-stress specimens, only homogeneous stress states in the gage section are acceptable. Furthermore, the same gage section should be used for all the stress states examined.

6. For series-parallel materials, the smaller the specimen, the more conservative will be the theoretical predictions (based on the series model).

At present, statistical-fracture theory cannot account for anisotropic behavior. The effects of temperature and perhaps strain rate may, however, be accommodated by accumulating fracture data at each temperature and for each strain rate of interest.

Number of Specimens   It is customary to choose the number of specimens for a property determination on the basis of convenience, economy, or whimsy. Indeed, it is possible to predict the reliability of a component regardless of the specimen sample size; however, both the accuracy and the confidence in this prediction are directly influenced by the number of specimens. Once a particular statistical theory has been chosen, the confidence - accuracy -sample-size relationship for a component can be established analytically. This makes it possible to select the required number of specimens in a rational manner.

Constitutive Relationships   The stress - strain relationship for most ceramic materials can be accurately represented by Hooke's law. This linear behavior usually persists over a substantial range of temperatures. However, the elastic constants will, in general, change with the temperature and must, therefore, be determined as functions of this quantity. As the temperature increases, the response of most ceramics becomes increasingly more sensitive to strain rate. It may be necessary, after a certain temperature has been reached, to adopt new constitutive equations that will reflect this strain-rate sensitivity. These remarks are equally applicable to creep.

Thermal Properties   One of the most important thermal characteristics of a material is its thermal strain - temperature relationship. Unfortunately, it usually does not remain linear at elevated temperatures, and measurements must be made at all temperature levels of interest. Furthermore, since thermal stresses often depend sensitively on the exact shape of the curve, this property determination places great demand on the testing engineer and his ability to monitor high-temperature strains. If the temperature distribution in a component is to be predicted, rather than measured, several other thermal properties must be determined as functions of the temperature. These may include thermal conductivity, thermal diffusivity, emittance, and heat capacity. The minimum accuracy required for each property determination must be established through analysis for each application.

Screening or Material Evaluation   The predicted behavior of components in complex environments depends in a complicated manner on the various material properties entering into the analysis. It is often necessary to run the properties of candidate materials through an entire computational algorithm to rate them for a particular application. It is shown in Appendix 1 that the selection of a material for a simple tension member can be rather sophisticated when its strength must be described statistically.

Plastic Behavior

At high temperatures (1,500 °C), in the range employed for hot-forming ceramics, the stress - strain characteristics of most materials depart from linear elastic. When an application calls for duty cycles in this temperature range, one must consider the inelastic features of the constitutive relations. In the preceding discussion of the constitutive equations an additional plastic-strain term was added to the stress - strain relationship to mathematically account for plastic behavior. This additional strain term greatly complicates the problem of stress analysis and reduces the selection of alternative analytical solutions to those which are based on numerical procedures. Since most of the theories of plasticity require a yield criterion to describe the plastic flow, additional material constants must be obtained from the stress - strain curve, and it is necessary to measure the complete stress - strain curve with more care and precision. An example of these requirements is given in Appendix 2, along with the description of a thermoelastic-plastic stress analysis. A similar procedure might be followed if the material of interest was found to be non-linear elastic. Again, different mathematical models would be used to describe the stress - strain behavior. Probably the most important consideration in utilizing any behavior model is to verify its applicability in describing the response of the particular material of interest. This must be done experimentally for each class of materials to determine if the model applies. If correlation between theory and experiment does not exist in a given situation, modifications to the mathematical model may be possible to obtain a more realistic representation of the real materials behavior. Appendix 2 deals with materials testing with these objectives in mind rather than the routine gathering of property data.

Reproducibility   In general, the preceding remarks addressed to elastic behavior apply to inelastic behavior, with a few exceptions. For example, when dealing with plasticity one usually is concerned with deformation rather than fracture as a mode of failure. However, in a thermal-stress problem one might consider both deformation and fracture: deformation in the hottest portion of the body and fracture at a cooler surface. Generally both types of behavior are dealt with concurrently.

In considering deformation, one is concerned more with the shape of the stress - strain curve than the point at which it terminates with fracture. Thus, reproducibility and scatter become less of a problem in describing the deformation behavior of a ceramic body, since the shape of the stress - strain curve demonstrates less variability than the fracture strength. It will probably still be advisable to treat the data statistically, since the transition from brittle to ductile behavior will be subtle and the magnitude of plastic strain in ceramics will be small.

The magnitude of strain and strain rates that one would consider will depend greatly on the application. For example, large strains may accompany creep loading, although it appears unlikely that plastic behavior in tension comparable to metallic ductility can be expected from any ceramic material. However, small plastic strains in compression may play a significant role in reducing the thermal stresses in tension for components subjected to a thermal-shock environment. This is true, since the maximum thermal strain ($\alpha \Delta T$) is small, amounting to only several percent from room temperature to melting for most materials. In addition, the thermal strain is divided between tension and compressive components, which further reduces the maximum resultant mechanical strain acting in any direction.

At high temperatures the effect of strain rate becomes more significant due to the rate-dependent processes which govern plastic flow. Every effort should be made to obtain property data consistent with the rate of load application to the component. In the thermal-stress problem the effective strain rate may vary as a function of time during the duty cycle, based on the temperature difference and material stiffness from point to point in the component.

Homogeneity   In measuring the elevated-temperature properties of a ceramic material, the test environment may produce unwanted changes in the material structure of the specimen. Thus, it is important to choose a test condition that will not affect the chemistry of material during handling or testing. Although the chances for surface contamination are greater in an elevated-temperature test, the resulting influence on behavior will probably be less than for a room-temperature test. This follows, since plastic flow provides a force-redistribution mechanism to reduce the effect of concentrated stresses from inhomogeneity which might otherwise cause fracture when the material is in a brittle state.

As stated previously, the prerequisite for analyzing the behavior of a component fabricated from a nonhomogeneous material is that the variation in the material, along with its properties, be described as a function of location in the component.

Residual Stresses   Similar arguments may be made regarding other effects such as surface residual stresses from machining, internal stresses from processing and local stresses from attachments. It is not implied that residual stresses pose no problem; it is suggested only that the problem is much less severe at high temperatures. Moreover, by understanding the nature and behavior of residual stress, which is possible through the application of a realistic stress analysis, one may control residual stresses through processing and force them to act in a favorable direction to enhance the integrity of a ceramic component. Prestressing is an example of this concept, although composite structures of several different materials are usually employed.

Anisotropy   The effects of anisotropy can be handled with the elastic - plastic stress analysis. The greatest difficulty is in obtaining the appropriate property data. This problem arises most often because of the size limitations in the part from which the test samples must be taken. The use of several different specimen configurations may reduce this problem but may produce widely varying results in terms of fracture strengths. Again, the variations in the high-temperature stress - strain behavior based on data from different specimen configurations should not be as significant. In treating the anisotropy of small-diameter rod material, it may be efficient to obtain the transverse properties using a ring specimen and the longitudinal properties using a straight tensile bar.

An example of the requirements for mechanical-property data needed in treating the effects of anisotropy in a thermoelastic-plastic stress analysis is given in Appendix 2.

Porosity   In predicting stresses and strains using the stress analysis, one assumes that the volume of strained material remains constant after yielding begins and during plastic deformation, i.e., $\mu = 0.5$. The influence of this assumption on analytical predictions may be significant in evaluating ceramics whose densities are less than theoretical. Errors in this regard may be checked using the uniaxial tension or compression tests by making before and after test volume measurements on the sample. It is advisable to unload the sample before cracking occurs. Having noted whether or not the constant-volume assumption is valid, one may proceed to make corrections in the stress - strain relationships to account for the observed variation, if necessary.

The materials-test engineer should familiarize himself with the theory used in designing his experiments and assume the responsibility for observing and reporting anomalies in behavior to the designer and theoretician.

QUALITY ASSURANCE

Since satisfactory service performance of a component is the objective of design, it is logical to expect the designer to be intimately concerned with quality assurance; that is, the guarantee that each fabricated component will, in fact, perform its intended function. The production drawings of the component serve as the vehicle for specification of not only the over-all geometry but also for dimensional control, the construction material, and the inspections to be performed. Deviations from this total specification, which might be identified during the quality-control operation, are reported to the designer, who then decides the disposition of the affected component—rejection, rework, or acceptance.

Basically, the designer is interested in providing components whose service performance is not compromised by dimensional inaccuracies, defects, or material-property variations. Since performance requirements will vary from one application to another, it seems logical to expect the objectives and scope of the quality-control effort to vary for each specific application.

A detailed discussion of quality control is provided in Appendix 3. It is sufficient here to identify the designer's interest in assuring quality and to note the differences in procedure that might be expected when ceramic materials rather than more conventional structural materials are used.

The type of construction material should have no effect on the method of defining dimensional requirements, despite the fact that ceramic materials may require closer tolerances in some areas, notably attachment points, than ductile materials. Specification of surface finish is expected to be more difficult, however. For conventional construction materials, various industrial and government specifications are available to define inspection procedures, while extensive experience permits the establishment of acceptance and rejection standards. Furthermore, conventional material can be defined by available specifications that define chemical composition, processing, and heat treatment in sufficient detail to assure a minimum guaranteed level of properties. In contrast, for ceramics, meaningful inspection procedures are not well defined, acceptance and rejection standards are practically nonexistent, and specifications do not insure reproducible material properties. This lack of definitive specifications for the control of ceramic structural components requires the designer to take a more direct interest in all phases of hardware production, including raw-material control and process control as well as inspection and control of the final product. It seems apparent that the fullest cooperative efforts of the material producer and the designer are necessary if efficient structural ceramic components are to be produced.

CONTRIBUTIONS TO SCATTER OF DATA

As pointed out earlier in this report, the properties of ceramics of most interest to the Committee are those related to their use for structural applications at elevated temperatures. Therefore, the Panel on Evaluation has addressed itself primarily to the task of determining the sources of the scatter of strength data for ceramics. Since this panel has been concerned with characterization, testing, and character - property and behavior relationships, it has been in a unique position for obtaining a broad-scope view of the various interrelated factors that have been responsible for the apparent variability in ceramics. The background thus obtained has emphasized the fact that much of the data upon which ceramic variability has been based were obtained under conditions where neither the test nor the material was adequately described or characterized and therefore do not aid in determining the source of variability of these materials. However, a few programs were found in which sufficient characterization of the material was performed and such care in testing was exercised that confidence could be placed on the property data obtained and where the scatter in data might be related to the material rather than the test procedure itself. This was possible only in cases where the test was properly used and the test specimens were properly prepared, machined, and surface-finished. The results of these programs have also shown that the ceramic processor tends to overestimate his ability to provide the same product from day to day and batch to batch. This has been observed with respect to research processors as well as production processors. This appears to be based on the assumption that he is aware of the ceramic process parameters that determine the character of his product, and that he has these under adequate control. However, as a result of sophisticated testing of certain of these products, it has been possible to uncover character features that were not controlled and as a result were directly responsible for variability in property data. Therefore, one of the objectives of this report is to communicate the need for adequate characterization and precisely controlled testing to reduce a major source of variability and therefore aid in developing and controlling the processing of ceramics for critical structural applications.

Since so many factors contribute to the scatter in strength data of ceramics, and since they generally have not been considered in the vast majority of the work reported in the literature, it is not surprising that charges of lack of reliability have been made against these materials. In fact, under these circumstances it is rather more surprising that there has been as much reliability observed as there has. This would suggest that, through the proper application of existing characterization and testing techniques, ceramic reliability could immediately be raised to a higher level than is now being achieved. One example was reported in which the allowable design strength of a particular ceramic material was doubled just through the application of a suitable proof test. Therefore it is not necessary for the designer to wait until the ceramic processor develops some new material, or radically alters his processing, in order to consider these materials for structural applications. What is required, however, is a better understanding by the ceramic processor of how to apply the knowledge already available to aid in upgrading his product. This is primarily a problem of communication.

The extent to which ceramics will find application in the more severe structural applications of the future will depend upon the ability of the processor to provide ceramic products with the maximum desired properties and maximum reliability. Since this section is concerned with the sources of the scatter of data, and since there are so many interrelated factors, it will not be possible to discuss the independent contribution that each factor may make to the scatter of data. It is just this situation that has confounded the work of so many investigators who have attempted to study the effect of a certain character feature on property data but who failed to control testing conditions, surface finish, or other more subtle character features. Therefore, this discussion will deal briefly with the more important factors that have been found to contribute to the scatter of data.

Test Methods and Techniques

The ideal test device for obtaining strength data should provide a uniform stress distribution in the specimen for all sizes and under all environmental conditions of interest. The accuracy of the data will vary as the stress distribution departs from uniformity. The scatter of data will be related to the ability of the test device to reproduce a given stress field from test to test.

TENSILE STRENGTH

It has been demonstrated that tensile test devices may introduce bending stresses that vary from 20 to 90% of the uniform tensile stresses and that it is as likely to be 90 as 20%. Such stresses are considered as parasitic and are present to some degree in all test devices. Therefore, parasitic stresses, unless measured and reported, will represent uncertainties in the data obtained from all test devices. Such stresses will contribute to the scatter of data if they are not reproducible, as in the case referred to above. Since parasitic stresses will cause a specimen to fail at a lower applied load than if no parasitic stresses existed, such conditions will result in lower apparent strength values. These lower-strength values coupled with data scatter due to poor testing itself could well disqualify an otherwise satisfactory material. Precision tensile test devices are available in which parasitic stresses may be as low as 0.1%.

FLEXURE STRENGTH

The same general comments apply for flexure testing as for tensile testing. Four-point loading is to be desired over three-point loading in order to provide a more definable surface area and volume under stress. Fixed-load points impose frictional forces and torsion on the specimen. These conditions provide parasitic stresses that would not be expected to be constant from test to test. Uncontrolled parasitic stresses will likewise arise from any misalignment of the load when using fixed-load points. For example, in a specimen 1/2 in. x 1/2 in. x 5 in., a displacement transversely on the specimen by 1 mil gives typically a 3% parasitic stress.

CONCLUSIONS

The use of tensile or flexure test devices for which parasitic stresses have not been determined and which are of unknown reproducibility may be expected to contribute significantly to the scatter of data. Typically, such values would range from 10 to 20% of the mean strength.

Loading rate would also be expected to have some influence on the scatter of data for ceramic materials, as would the testing atmosphere.

Variability in Body-Character Features

The test specimen itself is a critical factor in determining the quality of the property data obtained for a ceramic material. It should be recognized that extreme care must be taken in the design and preparation of the test specimen. It is particularly important that the surface condition of the test specimen be of sufficient quality to allow other character features to influence the property measurements. Assuming that this is done and that the test method used provides a known and reproducible stress field, some confidence can be given to identifying character features that may be responsible for scatter in data.

DEFECTS AND PORES

It is recognized that pores, microcracks, and cracks affect the strength of ceramics. However, it appears that the size, shape, location, and distribution of these defects, rather than quantity, are responsible for the scatter in data. Such anomalies are difficult to identify by existing characterization techniques and are usually found through postmortem examination of the fracture surface.

GRAINS

The effect of grain size on the strength of ceramics has been studied by many investigators. But, as in the case of defects, it would be expected that variations of grain size and geometry within the structure would be the primary source of scatter of data. One study of a polycrystalline alumina of 98 to 99.5% of theoretical density and 1 to 3 μ average particle size provided tensile strength values that ranged from 20,000 to 50,000 psi. Fractography revealed that strength differences were probably more related to grain-size variations within a specimen and to other microstructure anomalies than to slight changes in total density and average grain size. These tests were carried out using precision testing equipment with a minimum of parasitic stresses. Surface finish was controlled so that the major source of the scatter in data could be attributed to the ceramic body and that, in turn, to microstructure variability.

CONCLUSIONS

Variations in body-character features can be a major source of scatter of data. It would be misleading to assign any range of values to this scatter since the sensitivity of a ceramic body to such variation would depend upon the body itself. An aluminum oxide body of moderate density and containing silica as a second phase would probably exhibit a different sensitivity to a given variation in grain size, porosity, and microcracks, for example, than a 99.9% alumina body of near theoretical density.

Variability in Surface-Character Features

The condition of the surface of a ceramic test specimen has a major influence on the strength of the specimen. This is particularly significant when the specimen is stressed in tension and flexure. Therefore, any variability in surface finish, surface-flaw concentration, or distribution would be expected to have a direct effect on the scatter of data.

SURFACE FINISH

The need for a high-quality (low-rms) surface finish can be compared to the need for high-quality testing methods. Both are mandatory if the data are to be indicative of the true strength of the material. A poor surface finish does not necessarily yield scatter in data but will result in lower apparent-strength values. However, if the surface finish is not uniformly "poor," scatter in data will result. It might be expected that surface-finish variations would be more critical with respect to scatter of data as the average surface finish becomes of higher quality. For example, a given alumina composition exhibited a drop in tensile strength from 37,000 to 32,000 psi when the surface finish increased from 20 to 35 rms. A change in surface finish from 120 to 300 rms resulted only in a change in strength from 25,000 to 23,000 psi.

SURFACE DEFECTS

The use of root-mean-square surface-finish indices at best provides only a measure of surface consistency for comparative purposes. They do not describe the integrity of the surface with respect to its ability to withstand stresses nor identify surface or subsurface microcracks or cracks. These flaws would be expected to be a major source of scatter of data and are not easily detected by current characterization techniques. Their contribution to the scatter of data can vary depending upon the size of the specimen and the size of the flaw. One example was given where microflaws in the form of 1/64- to 1/32-in. cracks reduced the tensile strength of 1/8-in. diam specimens of a hot-pressed alumina body by 25 to 30%, but the same defects reduced the strength of 3/4-in. in diameter specimens of the same body by only about 5%.

CONCLUSIONS

Variability of surface-character features is probably a major source of the scatter of data for ceramics. The criticality of the problem lies in the fact that this condition represents an inconsistency in or near the surface, and, therefore, in the area of maximum stress when exposed to tensile or flexure loading. Any defects in this area serve as stress risers and may be considered the weak link in the system. They are also critical because they are difficult to identify and may be associated with residual strains resulting from differences in expansion between grains, hot-forming operations, or heat treatment, for example, or may be due to the finishing operation itself. As such, these defects not only contribute to scatter in data but often confuse or mask other factors that may be under investigation.

Variability as a Character of Brittle Materials

The previous discussions have illustrated the fact that there are numerous factors that contribute to the scatter of data. These may be related to material defects as well as to the test procedures themselves. Until each of these factors has been systematically studied, with adequate attention given to controlling all the other potential sources of variability, it will not be possible to answer the question, "How much scatter in data may be attributed to the intrinsic nature of brittle materials?" It is possible that the question may never be answered completely but will depend upon the quality of the product of the ceramic processor and the ability of characterization procedures to characterize that product adequately, particularly with respect to surface defects and other less obvious sources of scatter of data. One case has been reported where an aluminum oxide body was carefully machined into specimens that were exposed to uniaxial tension with a minimum of parasitic bending. The average tensile strength of 8 specimens was 23,680 psi with a standard deviation of 2.6%. It is highly unlikely that these specimens were free of surface microflaws, strains in grains, strains at grain boundries, or many of the other potential sources of variability. Therefore, it would be reasonable to assume that some of the scatter in the data for this particular material was due to microstructural anomaly. Thus it appears likely that the great majority of the scatter in data may be related to defects in the body and in the surface that may be eliminated, or at least their effect reduced, through improved ceramic processing.

DEVELOPMENT OF RECOMMENDATIONS

The primary objective of the Panel on Evaluation is to examine that part of the Committee's activities that deals with the coupling of processor with user. Evaluation is considered to be made up of character determination and property determination, followed by analysis of their relevance to processing and to design. The examination of evaluation procedures for ceramics for structural and/or high temperature uses is directed toward recommending measurements and analysis procedures to constitute a minimum evaluation based on present knowledge, and recommending areas of study that should lead to improved evaluation. It has become apparent that significant improvement in control of ceramic processing is possible through proper application of current evaluation techniques. In addition, this combination of improved process control and optimum use of present evaluation techniques should lead to more effective utilization of ceramics for structural and/or high-temperature applications.

The first section of our recommendations is directed toward the development of improved evaluation techniques and study of character-property relationships. These recommendations are organized into two groups. The first group offers a high probability for immediate payoff. The recommendations of the second group are of a long-range continuing nature. The second section of our recommendations is directed toward encouraging the wider use of present evaluation procedures. This section will include minimum evaluation procedures.

Improvement of Evaluation Techniques

This committee emphasizes the linkage of processor to user through evaluation. As pointed out previously, character and property determinations are included in evaluation, but it is emphasized that the development of the science of ceramic processing is dependent upon the capability of relating controlled ceramic processing to the production of a characterized material or product. The properties and behavior of a ceramic, in turn, are related to its character. This relationship is shown in Table 3 (p. 186). The critical character parameters of Table 3 are listed again in Table 4 (p. 192) together with analytical techniques for determining these parameters. The limits of resolution of these analytical techniques are given in Table 2 (p. 185). A review of these tables will show that many character features have some influence on the properties of ceramics. The practical use of these tables is restricted by the fact that analytical techniques are not yet capable of providing complete characterization and by the fact that the relative importance of some character parameters is not fully established. The limitations on characterization techniques require some reliance on properties in addition to the available characterization in order to provide an adequate coupling between processor and user. As discussed previously, this combination of character and properties is called description (D) and may be written as $D = XC_T + (1-X)(P+H)$, where C_T is total character, P is properties, and H is sample history. Therefore, adequate description of ceramics for structural and/or high-temperature use requires judicious selection of good character determination and good property measurements.

The user of ceramics desires both optimum properties and minimum variability of properties consistent with the economics of the application. Although substantial progress in this direction can be made by the application of currently available techniques, future development of ceramics for high-performance applications will be seriously limited unless characterization and property-measurement techniques are improved. A better understanding of character-property relationships must be developed—such understanding will be assisted by the improved techniques and will in turn support the development of the techniques themselves. The recommendations in this section are directed toward improving these techniques and developing this understanding. They are organized along the lines of the five objectives set forth in the Introduction to the Report of the Panel on Evaluation.

OBJECTIVE 1

The first objective is to assess the capability of current characterization techniques to determine the character of ceramic products adequately and to recommend areas for research.

Research That Offers High Probability for Immediate Payoff

Recommendation 1: Improved techniques for the characterization of surfaces are needed. These should be able to detect residual microstrain, defects including surface cracks (transgranular and intergranular), and composition (including phase distribution). This area has been identified by the Panel as one of the most critical areas of need. The traditional use of root-mean-square surface-finish indices at best provides only a control of surface consistency for comparative purposes.

Recommendation 2: Standard materials are necessary both as a means of communication concerning character features and for calibration. Character features for which standard materials would be helpful in communication are microstructure and surface condition. Specific examples of standard materials needed for calibration purposes are materials of controlled impurity content in the ppm range and materials of controlled surface finish.

Long-Range Programs

Recommendation 1: Improved methods for measuring residual microstrain are required. Present methods using x-ray diffraction are limited because the volume for which the average strain is determined is relatively large and because variation in composition (including departure from stoichiometry) affects the result.

Recommendation 2: Improvement in the resolution of the electron microprobe or the development of some other fine-scale analytical tool is needed.

Recommendation 3: Statistical measures of grain shape, relative orientations (other than crystallographic orientation), and description of the morphology of a second phase are wanted.

Recommendation 4: Improved techniques for the characterization of grain boundaries are desired. In particular, the distribution of impurities, defects, and microstresses is a character feature generally assumed to influence physical properties, including mechanical properties. Chemical and physical events occurring at grain boundaries are directly related to ceramic processing. Improved characterization would substantially improve our understanding of ceramic processing.

Recommendation 5: Improved techniques for using high-resolutions instruments to examine areas substantially larger than the field of view are necessary. Continuous recording and computer analysis of the area scanned should be considered.

Recommendation 6: Nondestructive testing techniques are wanted that can be used to characterize ceramics. Particularly, equipment and techniques should be developed that would allow in-process characterization of ceramics.

OBJECTIVE 2

The second objective is to review and evaluate the capability of property test methods and associated analysis of data in order to determine the properties of ceramic materials quantitatively and to recommend areas for the improvement of test methods and procedures.

Research That Offers High Probability for Immediate Payoff

Recommendation 1: Mechanical tests should be improved to permit attainment of uniform stress distribution in the specimen over a wider range of environmental test conditions and specimen size. One source of variability of the strength of ceramics results from the lack of control of stress (e.g., bending moment in tensile tests) during testing. Better control of mechanical testing is urgently needed to permit the determination of other sources of variability.

Recommendation 2: A comprehensive program incorporating experimental testing and analytical studies of different test techniques should be undertaken to establish the criticality of the test conditions. This would be similar to the work being done for uniaxially loaded rods and the pressurized ring.

Recommendation 3: Stress analyses of mechanical tests should be evaluated, developed, and organized (extended if necessary) to provide comparison of different tests and assessment of how undesired variation in test equipment and operation affects stress distribution. In addition, such stress-distribution information should aid in selecting test procedures best suited for evaluating materials for a given end-use application. Many existing analyses assume linear elastic behavior. This consolidation of stress analyses should indicate limits of applicability and areas where analyses based on nonlinear elasticity or inelastic deformation are needed.

Recommendation 4: Other areas of mechanical testing that require development are related to methods for determining stress and strain in the microstrain region, fracture-surface energy, fatigue behavior, creep, and multiaxial stress-strain behavior.

Recommendation 5: Standard materials are needed for elastic moduli and for tests of behavior in tension, compression, and flexure.

Recommendation 6: Studies should be initiated to relate properties by destructive techniques. Surplus materials should be provided as a part of future material-development programs involving controlled processing, careful characterizing, and accurate property measurement. These samples would be stored for future characterization and testing as significant improvements in characterization and property-measurement techniques are realized.

Long-Range Program

Recommendation 1: A program of mechanical testing should be carried out to support improved flaw-characterization techniques (as they are developed) to help identify and determine the significance of those flaws controlling strength. Consideration should be given to means of introducing controlled flaws.

OBJECTIVE 3

The third objective is to examine means of relating the property data available from these test methods to the character of ceramic products, with special reference to the sources of variability, and to recommend areas for study and improvement.

Research That Offers High Probability for Immediate Payoff

Recommendation 1: Study of the mechanisms of crack initiation and propagation is needed. One source of variability of the strength of ceramics is attributed to brittle behavior on a macroscopic scale, which reflects the behavior on a microscopic scale taking place at the end of a crack and permitting it to propagate. Such studies should aid in assessing the degree to which this source of variability is intrinsic.

Recommendation 2: Study of processing variables that are responsible for character features which in turn control properties, is necessary. One source of variability of the strength of ceramics results from inadequate control of processing. The purpose of this study is to evaluate their source of variability. Although this recommendation falls within the service of the Processing Panels it is also recommended by the Evaluation Panel in order to stress the importance of the interface between processing and evaluation.

Long-Range Program

Recommendation 1: Studies of the dependence of mechanical and thermal properties on character features are needed. In its broadest sense this recommendation points out the need for progress in the general area of physical ceramics as a basis for understanding the character-property relationship. Progress in understanding is interrelated with progress in characterization and property measurement; the three areas should receive balanced attention to insure simultaneous and mutually helpful progress.

Recommendation 2: Study of the mechanism of mass transport of ceramics is required. Both bulk and boundary transport should be included. Creep of ceramics is thought to be influenced by mass transport acting directly (e.g., diffusional creep) or indirectly (dislocation creep). This study should provide information relating processing to control of character.

Recommendation 3: Study of solid solutions, including their range of occurrence and the kinetics of precipitation, is necessary. Many attempts to control properties are based on variation of trace components. Such studies would provide a more scientific basis for these efforts.

Recommendation 4: Study of the mechanism of inelastic deformation and the quantitative development of constitutive equations for mechanical behavior is needed. Improved knowledge of mechanisms is needed to understand which are the controlling character features. Improved constitutive equations are needed for design and application.

OBJECTIVES 4 AND 5

Objective 4 is to review special procedures required for quality control and procedures to evaluate the environmental behavior of ceramics for specific applications.

Objective 5 is to review properties that will provide the data that are required in the design of ceramic hardware.

Objectives 4 and 5 were included as part of this Panel's activities in order to assure the Committee that the needs of the user, as represented by designers, were being adequately considered. The results of our examination of this area indicate that the requirements of the designer will be largely satisfied if the recommendations under Objectives 1, 2, and 3 are carried out. Any recommendation of test methods and environmental test procedures necessarily depends upon the specific design and mission for which the material is being considered. This observation has focused attention on the critical roles that the designer and materials analyst play in the application of ceramics for advanced DOD applications. The use of ceramics for these applications is limited not only by

242

the state of the art of ceramic processing but also by the state of the art of design with brittle materials.

Recommendation 1: A program to advance the state of the art of design with brittle materials should be undertaken. This program should make maximum use of the results of the report by the Ad Hoc Committee on Ceramic Processing. Particular attention should be given to the use of realistic models to describe the behavior of ceramic materials.

Use of Current Evaluation Techniques

Although the state of the art of ceramic processing may be improved substantially by developing better evaluation techniques, it has become apparent that significant improvement in control of ceramic processing is possible through the proper application of currently available techniques. These recommendations are made in the hope that they will encourage the wider use of existing evaluation technology by the processors and thereby improve communications with the user.

Recommendation 1: Character features influencing properties of interest should be determined and recorded as part of any meaningful physical test program. For example, tests of tensile strength, compressive strength, or transverse strength should be accompanied at least by determination of chemical composition, grain size, second-phase, porosity, surface finish, and as many other relevant character features as practical.

Recommendation 2: Property test procedures should be carefully evaluated to determine the sensitivity of the test method to the properties of the material and scatter in the results caused by the procedure itself. In particular, tests of tensile, compressive, or transverse behavior should be evaluated with respect to parasitic stresses and specimen configurations, and the results should be reported. The number of specimens measured and the test data should also be reported.

Recommendation 3: Character features as well as physical properties should be determined and recorded as part of any meaningful material program. In particular, in any program in which material properties are to be optimized for critical DOD applications, Recommendations 1 and 2 should be adhered to as minimum requirements.

ACKNOWLEDGMENTS

The Panel wishes to express gratitude to Henry P. Kirchner and Vladimir E. Wolkodoff, who were guest contributors at a meeting of the Panel on Evaluation. Winston H. Duckworth and Alfred Rudnick contributed to the state of the art of evaluation as guests at a meeting of the Ad Hoc Committee.

BIBLIOGRAPHY

Properties of Ceramic Materials and Methods to Detect Them

1. Proceedings of Seminar on Mechanical Testing Procedures for Brittle Materials; sponsored by IITRI-AMRA on March 28, 29, 30, 1967; publication under preparation.
2. C. D. Pears, "The Strength of Materials of Brittle Materials as a Guide to the Tester," to be published in the Proceedings of Reference 1.
3. S.C. Carniglia, "On the Brittleness of Refractory Compounds and the Ductility of Metals," 67th ASTM Annual Meeting, 1964.
4. E. G. Kendall and J. D. McClelland, "Nonmetallic Materials for High-Temperature Structural Applications," Annual Meeting for Aerospace Vehicles, 1964.

5. Stephen W. Tsai, "Mechanics of Composite Materials," AFML-TR-66-149.

6. Hayne Palmour III, "Raw Materials for Refractory Oxide Ceramics," ML-TDR-64-110.

7. C. D. Pears and H. Stuart Starrett, "An Experimental Study of the Weibull Volume Theory," AFML-TR-66-228.

8. J. Pask (private communication).

9. C. D. Pears, F. J. Digesu et al., "Evaluation of Tensile Data for Brittle Materials Obtained with Gas-Bearing Concentricity," ASD-TDR-63-245.

10. C. D. Pears and F. J. Digesu, "The True Stress-Strain Properties of Brittle Materials to 5000°F," AEC ORO 461, 1961.

11. R. Sedlacek, "Tensile Strength of Brittle Materials," AFML-TR-65-129.

12. N. M. Parikh et al., "Studies of the Brittle Behavior of Ceramic Materials," ASD-TR-61-628, Parts I, II, and III.

13. C. D. Pears and F. J. Digesu, "Gas-Bearing Facilities for Determining Axial Stress-Strain and Lateral Strain of Brittle Materials to 5500°F," Proceedings of Annual Meeting of ASTM, 1964.

14. S. C. Carniglia, "Grain Boundary and Surface Influence on Mechanical Behavior of Refractory Oxides—Experimental and Deductive Evidence," Materials Science Research, Vol. 3; Plenum Press, New York, 1966.

15. C. D. Pears (private communication).

16. Fred B. Seely and James O. Smith, "Advanced Mechanics of Materials," 2nd ed., John Wiley & Sons, New York, 1952.

17. F. J. Digesu and C. D. Pears, "The Determination of Design Criteria for Grade CFZ Graphite," AFML-TR-65-142.

18. C. D. Pears, J. E. Shoffner, and F. J. Digesu, "The Tensile and Compressive Ultimate Strengths and Moduli of Beryllium Oxide," presented at Ceramic Society Meeting in Seattle, Washington, in October 1962.

19. Ralph L. Barnett, James F. Costello, and Paul C. Herman, "The Odds Against Fracture," Machine Design, November 1966.

20. H. Stuart Starrett and C. D. Pears, "A Study of Notches in Brittle Materials by Relating Stress Intensification and Volume," AFML-TR-67-254.

21. V. Weiss, A. Takimote, and G. Nash, "A Study of the Effect of Superimposed Stress Concentrations and Fracture of Inhomogeneous Brittle Solids," AFML-TR-66-235.

22. R. E. Mould, "Strength and Static Fatigue of Abraded Glass under Controlled Ambient Conditions: IV, Effect of Surrounding Medium," Journal of the American Ceramic Society, Vol. 44, October 1961.

23. Jack E. Hauck, "Boron Nitride: High Cost Material with a Promising Future," Materials in Design Engineering, February 1967.

24. W. V. Kotlensky and H. E. Martens, "Tensile Properties of Pyrolytic Graphite to 5000°F," NASA Technical Report No. 32-71.

25. A. E. H. Love, "The Mathematical Theory of Elasticity," Dover Publications, 4th Edition, New York, 1927.

26. G. E. Lockyer, F. M. Lenoe, and A. W. Schultz, "Investigation of Nondestructive Methods for the Evaluation of Graphite Materials," AFML-TR-66-101.

27. M. E. Fine, "Dynamic Methods for Determining the Elastic Constants and Their Temperature Variations in Metals," ASTM Special Technical Publication No. 129, 1952.

28. H. W. Babel, "Biaxial-Fracture Strength of Brittle Material," AFML-TR-66-51.

29. D. S. Neel and C. D. Pears, "High Temperature Thermal Property Measurement to 5000°F," Second Symposium on Thermophysical Properties, ASME, 1962.

30. D. S. Neel and C. D. Pears, "The Thermal Properties of Thirteen Solid Materials to 5000°F or Their Destruction Temperatures," WADD-TR-60-924.

31. "Development of High Temperature Thermal Conductivity Standard," AFML-TR-66-415.

32. Richard Pawel, "Critique on the Analytical Representation of Specific Heat Data," WADC-TN-57-308.

33. C. D. Pears, "Some Problems in Emittance Measurements at the Higher Temperatures and Surface Characterization," Proceedings of Symposium on Measurement of Thermal Radiation Properties of Solids, AFML, 1962.

34. B. E. Walker, C. T. E. Wing, and R. R. Miller, "Instability of Refractory Metal Thermocouples," MRL Report 6231.

35. B. L. Greenstreet, et al., "Room-Temperature Mechanical Properties of EGCR-Type AGOT Graphite," ORNL 3728.

36. Leon Green, Jr., "High Temperature Stress-Strain Measurements on Polycrystalline Graphites," Instron Publication C-2.

37. American Society for Testing & Materials Standards, Phila. Pa., C78-64.
38. T. W. Watson and H. E. Robinson, "Thermal Conductivity of Some Commercial Iron-Nickel Alloys," ASME Paper No. 60-WA-47.
39. "An Instrument for Measuring the Thermal Conductance of High Temperature Structural Materials," ASD-TDR-63-359.
40. T. G. Godfrey et al., "Thermal Conductivity of Uranium Dioxide and Armco Iron by an Improved Radial Heat Flow Technique," ORNL 3556.
41. American Society For Testing & Materials, Phila. Pa., ASTM B95-39.
42. Leonard S. Levinson, "High Temperature Drop Calorimeter," Review of Scientific Instruments, Vol. 33, June 1962.
43. C. P. Butler and E. C. Y. Inn, " A Radiometric Method for Determining Specific Heat at Elevated Temperatures," U. S. Naval Radiological Defense Laboratory TR-235.
44. M. Hoch and S. M. Gary, "Determination of the Specific Heat of Al_2O_3 by a Transient Technique," AFML-TR-66-97.
45. George Sonnenschain and Robert A. Winn, "A Relaxation Time Technique for Measurement of Thermal Diffusivity," WADC-TR-59-273.
46. H. M. Childers and J. M. Cerceo, "Electron Beam Technique for Measuring the Thermophysical Properties of Materials," WADD TR 60-190.
47. W. A. Plummer, D. E. Campbell, and A. A. Comstock, "Method of Measurement of Thermal Diffusivity to $1000°C$," Journal of the American Ceramic Society, Vol. 45, June 1962.
48. W. J. Parker et al., "A Flash Method of Determining Thermal Diffusivity, Heat Capacity, and Thermal Conductivity," USNRDC-TR-424.
49. Joseph C. Richmond and William N. Harrison, "Total Hemispherical Emittance of Coated and Uncoated Inconel and Types 321 and 430 Stainless Steel," Journal of Research of USNBS, Vol. 66C, September 1962.
50. Howard E. Clark and Dwight G. Moore, "Method and Equipment for Measuring Thermal Emittance of Ceramic Oxides from 1200 to $1800°K$," NASA SP55 (1965).
51. S. Katzoff, ed., "Symposium on Thermal Radiation of Solids," NASA SP55.

Interaction among Properties, Structural Design and Analysis, Environmental Behavior, and Quality Assurance

1. A. A. Griffith, Phil. Trans. Roy. Soc., London, Ser. A, Vol. 221, 163, 1920.
2. G. R. Irwin, "Fracture of Metals" (ASMS, 1947); ASM, Cleveland, 1948.
3. E. Orowan, "Fatigue and Fracture of Metals" (MIT Symposium 1950); John Wiley & Sons, New York, 1950.
4. G. R. Irwin, "Fracture Mechanics," Proceedings 1st Symp. Naval Struct. Mech., Structural Mechanics, Pergamon Press, New York, 557-594, 1960.

APPENDIX 1 TO CHAPTER 5

STRUCTURAL ANALYSIS AND DESIGN IN CERAMICS USING STATISTICAL-FRACTURE THEORY

The problems associated with the structural analysis and design of brittle-state materials, such as ceramics at moderate temperatures, are explored in this appendix. Adopting the methodology of statistical-fracture theory, a capability is described for predicting the integrity of complex prototype components from information obtained with laboratory specimens or small-scale models. The analysis method is illustrated by a detailed example of the reliability calculations for a circular brittle disk. A brief introduction to direct design methods is included, which is based on statistical behavior.

The Behavior of Brittle Materials

THE STRENGTH PROBLEM

According to the classical theory of elastic structures, the ultimate strength of a body is determined by the stresses acting at a point, assuming that by a suitable combination of the three principal stresses or strains, a characteristic value may be computed for the material considered. This value is supposed to be definitively decisive in judging whether or not the ultimate strength has been reached. It is, of course, implied in the theory that materials can be obtained with mechanical properties that are perfectly reproducible. Indeed, few real materials approximate this property; however, examples may be found in the case of ductile materials.

An investigation involving 30,000 tons of structural steel showed only two out of 3,124 specimens to yield below the minimum specified value of 33 ksi, and these fell no lower than 31 ksi. Such reliability is unprecedented in ceramic materials where fracture strengths are characteristically spread over a very wide range of values, which appears to broaden as more and more elements are sampled. To the designer, the significance of such scatter is to preclude the prediction of individual component strength and the associated development of a deterministic design theory.

When no useful one-to-one correspondence can be established between a sample and a prototype, it is reasonable to ask if there is not some relationship between a group of samples and a group of prototypes. In fact, the entire foundation of statistics depends on the existence of just such a relationship. One would hope, for example, that the average strength of a sample group would be reproduced in subsequent groups of specimens. To be really useful it would be desirable to predict the entire distribution of strengths in subsequent groups of tests. This point of view is depicted in Figure 1, which contrasts the deterministic problem with that of the statistical. Figure 1A shows a one-to-one correspondence between measured and predicted strength values; Figure 1B indicates only a group-to-group correspondence.

The distribution of fracture strengths is described by a cumulative probability function such as that shown by the solid line in Figure 2. For any stress value along the abscissa, the ordinate to the curve gives the probability of fracture. The solid curve has been limited on the left and right at values of stress corre-

MEASURED STRENGTH	PREDICTED STRENGTH	COMMENTS
		i) Deterministic
		A ii) Insignificant Scatter
		iii) Excellent Mfg. Control
		iv) Conventional Design Theory
		i) Statistical
		B ii) Large Scatter
		iii) Ordinary Mfg. Control
		iv) Statistical Design Theory
		i) Mixed Populations
		C ii) Large Scatter
		iii) Poor Mfg. Control
		iv) No Theory Available

FIGURE 1. The prediction of strength (Source: Barnett and McGuire, Amer. Ceram. Soc. Bull., 45, 595-602, 1966).

sponding to the zero and the 100% probability strengths, respectively. For stress levels below the zero-probability strength no failures can occur; for stress levels above the 100% probability strength there can be no survival. For many brittle materials it appears that the zero-probability stress approaches its physical lower bound, zero. In the case of the 100% probability stress there does not appear to be an obvious upper bound; however, it may be conjectured that strengths as high as the theoretical molecular strength are possible in view of recent evidence that single-crystal filaments approach such stress levels.

For a deterministic material, the strength of a specimen can be specified using a single number; for a brittle material, a different strength value is given by the distribution curve for every level of reliability. For convenience, the distribution function is usually described analytically. This requires an expression containing a minimum of two parameters to account for both a central measure of strength and for scatter. The Gaussian distribution, for example, is characterized by its mean and its standard deviation. The famous Weibull distribution[1] for fracture strength is described by the three parameters m, x_o, and x_1, where x_1 represents the zero-probability strength.

In spite of the fact that the strength of a specimen is precisely defined by its

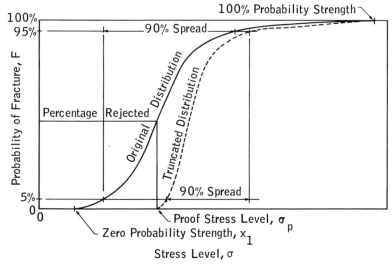

FIGURE 2. Typical cumulative probability curve for the strength of a brittle element (Source: "The Behavior and Design of Brittle Structures," AFFDL-TR-65-165).

distribution parameters, it is not necessarily simple to relate them to our conventional concept of strength specification. To illustrate this point, consider two materials whose fracture strengths are normally distributed with the following means and coefficients of variations:

Mean: $\quad\quad\quad\quad\quad\quad \bar{\sigma}_1 = 50$ ksi $\quad\quad \bar{\sigma}_2 = 40$ ksi

Coefficient variation: $\quad V_1 = 10\%$ $\quad\quad V_2 = 7\%$.

From the information given, it is not clear which of these materials is the better. In general, low scatter is the more important property for structures of very high reliability, and, consequently, the second material is the better in these applications. At low reliability, the average strength or mode becomes the predominant material characteristic and here the first material excels. Materials developers will note from this example that superior candidate materials may inadvertently be excluded from further consideration when they are evaluated on the basis of average strength alone.

To compare materials in a rational manner, the modern approach is to consider their optimum usage in a given application of interest. For example, when a tension member of length L is designed with a reliability (1-F), its weight is a minimum when its resistance is precisely equal to the applied load, P. Using a Weibull material in which $x_1 = 0$, the minimum weight W of the member becomes[2]

$$W = \frac{1}{\left[x_o^{m/(m-1)}/\rho \right]} \frac{(PL)^{m/(m-1)}}{\left[-\log(1-F) \right]^{1/(m-1)}} , \tag{1}$$

where ρ is the weight density. When the load, length, and reliability of a tension member are specified, one can readily evaluate various materials by comparing their associated W's. This procedure is illustrated in Table 1, using three materials. Because $m/(m-1)$ is approximately unity for reasonably large values of m, the loading index term (PL) in equation 1 does not greatly influence weight comparisons among materials. Furthermore, when $m \to \infty$, the weight approaches $W = PL/(x_o/\rho)$ where x_o/ρ is the specific tensile strength of a classical material.

In the statistical approach to the description of strength, the tacit assumption is made that a capability exists for the consistent production of material from the same universe. Stated in another way, a distribution function must exist for the material. Unfortunately, there is considerable doubt concerning this capability for many of the cermets and ceramics of current interest. Much of the data on fracture strength of ceramics leads one to suspect that the populations studied are mixtures of several different materials in spite of the fact that their chemical composition and superficial appearance are the same.[2] Since the ratios of the various components in the mixtures are random, the problem of prediction is extremely complicated. This situation is illustrated schematically in Figure 1C where we are trying to predict the behavior of a collection of populations of differently behaving materials which, nevertheless, have something in common. The statistics for such a cast are not well developed, and, consequently, many currently manufactured ceramics are beyond the state of the design art.

Table 1. Tension Member Weights (P = 1,000 lb, L = 20 in., F = 0.01)

Material	m	x_o (psi)	W (lb)
Plaster	7.7	1,680	3.1
Beryllium oxide	7.25	7,800	0.66
Porcelain-white glazing	16.2	13,220	0.176

STATISTICAL-BOUNDARY CONDITIONS

In a generalized sense, the normal procedure in "ductile design" is to proportion a structure in such a way that the assumed stress distribution nowhere exceeds the yield stress. When this is done, our plasticity theorems tell us that our design is safe because we have designed in such a way that the final structure has a statistically admissible state of stress. The fact that the actual state of stress may be different than the assumed one is of no concern to the designer. Conversely, in brittle design it is mandatory that the designer know the exact stress conditions throughout the structure. Failure to assess these stresses is certainly one of the major reasons that brittle design has been unsuccessful.

Recognizing this problem, many investigators have strongly advocated the use of very exact methods of stress analysis. Unfortunately, one suspects that the problem is more complicated than this recommendation reflects. It is our contention that the exact boundary conditions are significantly statistical in nature and that they can critically influence the state of stress in a ceramic component. A preliminary investigation of this hypothesis was conducted by instrumenting a single ceramic-dogbone tension specimen to study the percentage of bending introduced into the specimen through the grips. The dogbone was placed carefully in a set of grips, loaded to some level, and the total stress was compared to the nominal tensile stress. The specimen was then removed from the grips and carefully replaced again to repeat the procedure. The resulting rectangular distribution of "percent bending stress" is shown in Figure 3. We observe that bending stresses are obtained that are greater than 90% of the uniform tensile stresses and that they are just as likely to occur as the lower stress values. In view of these parasitic bending stresses, it is not surprising that the simple tension test has fallen into disuse as a means of determining statistical-fracture-strength parameters.

The statistical-boundary conditions that gave rise to the variable stress state in the dogbone specimen of Figure 3 are of the traction type. Similar manifestations are perhaps more frequently encountered when the boundary conditions are of the displacement type. Current design, fabrication, and maintenance practices for flight structures allow for rather sloppy tolerances, and this, in turn, requires "forced fit" of many component sections. For example, it is a common practice to pull mating components into place with mechanical fasteners. For ceramic elements, the resulting mismatch stresses will generally be substantial because of high component stiffness and the lack of ductility.

The variability in the applied-stress state caused by statistical-boundary conditions presents a very thorny complication. There appear, however, to be several approaches for attacking the problem. It is, for example, possible to measure the variability in the applied stress, as was done for the dogbone speci-

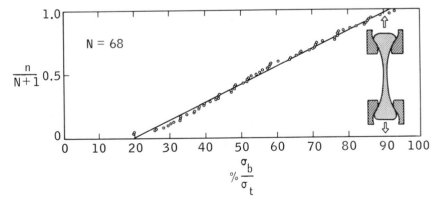

FIGURE 3. Cumulative distribution of bending stress in a tension specimen (Source: "The Behavior and Design of Brittle Structures," AFFDL-TR-65-165).

men, and to account for it analytically. If the fracture strength of an element is denoted by x and the applied stress by X, fracture will occur whenever the quantity y = x - X is negative. The frequency distribution f(y) can be found from the known distributions of x and X and then a simple integration of f(y) over the region y < 0 yields the probability of fracture for the element. For cases other than Gaussian distributions for x and X, the distribution of "strength minus load" will probably not have a simple closed-form expression, and recourse to numerical schemes will be required.

Various ideas have been proposed for controlling the forces and stresses occurring at the boundaries of ceramic structures. Nonredundant attachments have been used so that the loads at the junctures are unaffected by differential displacements.[3] In certain types of attachments it may be possible to use ductile inserts that limit the loads transferred to the yield of the inserts. Here, as long as the transfer forces are bounded, it may not be necessary to know their exact distribution. Sometimes it is possible to use the techniques of prestressing to impose compressive stresses in a component of sufficient magnitude to guarantee that all spurious forces will result in net compressive stresses.

TEST SPECIMENS FOR BRITTLE MATERIALS

To obtain the stress-strain relationship for a material, it is necessary to have some method of relating the load on the specimen to the stress at some point. In general, the determination of the relationship between load and stress in a solid body requires a knowledge of the material properties—precisely what we are trying to find. Fortunately, there exist some special combinations of loading and geometry that enable one to relate load to stress by appealing only to equilibrium considerations. Examples of such situations are provided by thin-walled cylinders under torsion of internal pressure and odd-shaped solids under hydrostatic pressure and prismatic rods under uniformly applied axial end loads. Certainly, in this group the prismatic rod would seem to be the least involved method of producing tension. However, it is extremely difficult to insure a uniform end pressure, and it is here that we must make an appeal to a physical assumption called Saint-Venant's principle. This principle essentially states that all stress distributions on the end of the bar, which are statistically equivalent to the uniform pressure, will produce a uniform stress in the central regions of the bar if the bar is sufficiently long.

Saint-Venant's principle enables us to produce any number of varieties of grips and flanged ends and still get stress = force/central area. However, any moment transmitted to the ends of the rod disqualifies the application of the principle, since the presence of end moments makes it impossible to have a stress distribution at the ends that is statistically equivalent to a uniform pressure. In practice, it is an exacting feat to eliminate the terminal moments. The seriousness of the problem is clear from our previous consideration of Figure 3.

Recognizing the difficulties of performing reliable tension tests even at room temperature, many investigators have proposed other tests for studying material behavior, which make use of the assumption that the stress is a linear function of the strain. An evaluation of various specimens for measuring room-temperature strength is given in Figure 4. For materials which obey Hooke's law, any of the specimens shown can be considered; for nonlinear materials, only the "equilibrium specimens" can be used for unit-strength determinations.

Ideally, specimens and loading conditions are sought that exhibit the proper combination of low variability in applied stress and a simple formula for the statistical distribution of their strengths. This latter property makes it possible to establish statistical parameters from ultimate fracture-strength data. A further attribute of a specimen and its loading apparatus would be its adaptability to elevated-temperature testing. (See p. 208, Test Methods, Their Description, Capability, and Limitations.)

Specimen Type	Stress Determination	Stress Gradient	Variability in the Applied Stress	Weibull's Statistical Distribution F^n	Comments
tension	Simple Formula Uniaxial Tension	H O M O G E N E O U S S T R E S S	Very High	Simple Formula	Very Poor Specimen; Stress State Highly Statistical, Parameter Determination Simple
thin ring	Simple Formula Uniaxial Tension		Low	Simple Formula (Same as Tension)	Has The Greatest Potential; Parameter Determination Simple
thin-walled cyl	Simple Formula Pure Shear		High	Simple Formula (Generalized Stress Req'd.)	Poor Specimen; Actual Stress State Highly Statistical; Expensive
odd-shapes	Simple Formula Hydrostatic		Almost None	No Failure Possible	Useless Specimens; Only Compression is Possible
sphere	Simple Formula Biaxial Tension		Low	Simple Formula (Generalized Stress Req'd.)	Very Expensive

EQUILIBRIUM SOLUTIONS→   ←ELASTICITY SOLUTIONS

Specimen Type	Stress Determination	Stress Gradient	Variability in the Applied Stress	Weibull's Statistical Distribution F^n	Comments
pure bending	Simple Formula	Through Depth- (small)	Med.	Simple Formula	Support Friction Must Be Minimized To Reduce Systematic Errors
three pt. bend	Simple Formula	Through Depth- Across span (small)	Med.	Series Solution	Must Minimize Support Friction; Parameter Determination - Difficult
ring test	Series Solution	Very High Under Load	Low-Med.	Numerical Solution	Parameter Determination- Difficult if Not Impossible; Self Aligning; Simple Loading
theta specimen	Numerical (photoelastic solution)	Low-Med.	Med.	Numerical Solution	Parameter Determination - Difficult if Not Impossible; Self Aligning; Simple Loading

FIGURE 4. Various specimens for determining strength (Source: "The Behavior and Design of Brittle Structures," AFFDL-TR-65-165).

ESTIMATION OF STATISTICAL PARAMETERS

With few exceptions, the vast body of work in the field of statistical-fracture theory has been based on the idea that an infinite amount of data is available for describing the strength of a material. In other words, investigators have assumed that the distribution curve shown in Figure 2 can be precisely determined from experiments. Their design procedures reflect this assumption since they all begin by fitting the distribution curve with an assumed analytic expression in which the parameters are taken to be well-defined constants of the material.

Unfortunately, real materials must be described using a finite amount of data, and under this condition the parameters associated with the hypothesized distribution function can only be estimated. Indeed, when various finite samples of fracture data are drawn from the same infinite population, the distribution curves for each sample will be different. It turns out that these parameter estimates are themselves statistical variants and possess a frequency distribution that is related in a nontrivial way to the original distribution of fracture strengths.[4]

Four typical probability density curves for a parameter estimate m are shown shown in Figure 5. Consider, for example, the curve in Figure 5(a), which represents samples of size 10. One could imagine that this curve is constructed along estimates of the parameter, m, obtained from an infinite number of samples of size 10. True values of this parameter μ are shown to coincide with the mode, as is frequently the case. Because large samples give more reliable parameter estimates than small ones, we would expect the scatter of such estimates to diminish with increasing sample size. Since the total area under a frequency curve must be equal to unity, the curves representing the large sample sizes are taller and more constricted.

There are usually many methods available for estimating the parameters in a given type of distribution function. One can, for example, estimate the mean of a normal distribution by taking the arithmetic average or by finding the most frequently occurring value of the data—there are at least a dozen methods used to obtain Weibull parameters. Each estimation method will lead to a different frequency distribution for the parameter estimates and, in general, the superior method will lead to the least dispersion around the true value of the estimate. For example, Figure 5 clearly shows that for the same sample size, Estimation Method 2 is the better.

Specification of a sample size and a method of estimation leads to a particular probability density curve for the parameter estimate. The probability that an estimate will fall between any two values can then be found by integrating the area under the frequency curve f(m) between these values. In particular, we can find the probability P that our estimate is accurate to within -a and +b of the true value of μ. Formally, we have

$$P\left[(\mu - a) \leq m \leq (\mu + b)\right] = \int_{\mu-a}^{\mu+b} f(m) \, dm. \tag{2}$$

This probability is called the confidence level. For a given method of estimation we have a trade-off among sample size, accuracy, and confidence level. It is clear from Figure 5 that the larger sample size leads to a higher confidence of obtaining an estimate within a specified accuracy. For a fixed sample size the problem resolves itself to a trade-off between accuracy and confidence. We can have higher confidence of a lower accuracy and vice versa.

Once the parameters have been determined, the assumption of the particular form of the distribution function can be checked. Essentially, this is a go or no-go situation. Using a chi-square test one can determine the credibility of the assumption and then decide whether or not it warrants being used as a working hypothesis. This procedure is satisfactory for attempts to find a distribution function that fits observed data. Granted that a sufficiently good fit is obtained, we will then presume that the population is characterized by the parameters.

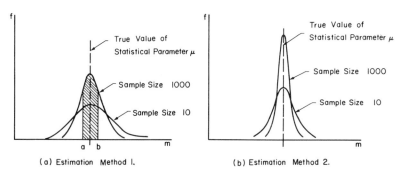

FIGURE 5. Estimation of a statistical parameter (Source: Barnett and McGuire, Amer. Ceram. Soc. Bull., 45, 595-602, 1966).

The Analysis of Brittle Components

RELIABILITY PREDICTIONS BASED ON FULL-SCALE TESTING

Three approaches are available for predicting the strength of frangible structural components. The first deals with full-scale prototypes, the second with small-scale models, and the last with small specimens. In each case the respective structures are fracture-tested in sufficient number to assure a well-defined cumulative distribution function in the sense of accuracy and confidence. In the first case, this leads directly to the relationship we seek between reliability and strength for the full-size component as shown in Figure 2. The use of such a curve in design differs from the usual statistical applications, which are concerned with the values of the variant close to the mean value. Here, the demand for structural components of high reliability forces the designer to deal with the low failure probabilities associated with the lower portion of the distribution curve.

Unfortunately, because of the rarity of extreme events, a suitable definition of the lower-distribution tail will require an enormous amount of data. The conventional and more economical alternative to such a prospect is to embrace the procedures of the previous section, i.e., to find an analytic expression of a distribution function that closely describes the available data and then to extrapolate to find the stresses that correspond to low-failure probabilities. Indeed, this is the only possible procedure for defining the zero-probability stress. We hasten to point out, however, that regardless of the goodness of fit obtained for the existing data, the behavior at the lower-distribution tail will always remain a mystery.

The establishment of a distribution curve based on prototype testing is generally impractical in view of the costly procedures involved in the manufacture and testing of ceramic components. On this basis it seems reasonable to explore the possibility of basing performance predictions on either small models or small specimens. In both cases a scaling law will be required. This brings us to the second significant difference between conventional statistics and statistical fracture theory. Here, a load redistribution model is utilized to reflect the effect of size on the strength of components.

SCALING—LOAD REDISTRIBUTION MODELS

When fracture occurs in some element in a brittle body, two possibilities arise. First, the resulting crack may be arrested and the loading on the body may be increased until this crack or some other finally propagates throughout the body, causing complete failure. In the second case, no crack-arrest mechanism exists, and the first crack to form propagates through the body, causing over-all failure. The lack of a load-redistribution mechanism in this latter situation can be depicted by the model shown in Figure 6A. This weakest link or series model, first proposed by Peirce in 1926,[5] has received more attention than any other statistical model. Referring to Figure 6A, a relationship can be derived between the reliability of the entire chain and that of its links. Since the probability that the chain will survive, $1 - F_s$, is equal to the probability that the various links will simultaneously survive,

$$1 - F_s = (1 - F_1)(1 - F_2) \ldots (1 - F_n) = \prod_{j=1}^{n} (1 - F_j), \qquad (3)$$

where F_j is the failure probability of the jth link and n is the total number of links.

Since its introduction there have been two extremely important advancements

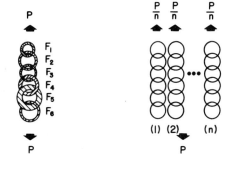

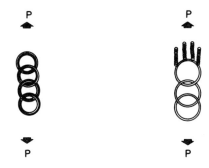

FIGURE 6. Various types of load-redistribution models (Source: "The Design and Behavior of Brittle Structures," AFFDL-TR-65-165).

in the development of the weakest-link theory. The first of these was due to Weibull, who proposed an extremely simple form for the distribution curve of a unit volume of material. He proceeded to use this distribution function to describe the behavior of many simple and important load-carrying elements. For a tension member or specimen his theory takes the form

$$F(x) = 1 - \exp\left[-\frac{\nu_g}{\nu}\left(\frac{x - x_\ell}{x_o}\right)^m\right] \quad x \leq x_\ell$$
$$= 0 \qquad\qquad\qquad\qquad x < x_\ell \qquad (4)$$

where x is the tensile stress, ν_g is the volume of the tensile member or the gage volume of a specimen, ν is a unit volume in the same dimension as ν_g, and x_ℓ, x_o, and m are assumed to be constants of the material. Units should be chosen so that the argument of the exponential function is dimensionless. In order to maintain the consistency necessary to compare different geometries and materials, it is good practice to retain the units adopted for the tension data.

Following Weibull's theory in 1939,[1] many different weakest-link theories were proposed without any apparent unification. The second important development of the series model came with the recognition by Epstein[6] in 1948 that the series model represents a special case of extreme value statistics. Among other things, this theory concerns itself with the distribution of the smallest value in k independent observations. Referring to the series model illustrated in Figure 6A, Epstein provided the tools for establishing the strength distribution of a chain based on the knowledge of the strength distribution of the individual links.

A great deal of effort in the field of brittle design has been devoted to the verification of specific statistical-fracture theories, e.g., the Weibull theory. It cannot be overemphasized that the specific form of the fracture theory is not nearly as significant as establishing the statistical model that governs a material's behavior. Extreme value statistics furnish us with an important necessary condition for a series material that does not require the specific form of the distribution function nor a knowledge of the combined-stress theory appropriate for the material. Specifically, when the loading and geometry of two different-size components are similar, their distribution function $F(x)$ must scale according to the following relationship when the material obeys the series model.

$$1 - F_2 (P_2) = [1 - F_1 (P_1)]^{V_2/V_1} , \qquad (5)$$

where F_i is the fracture probability of the ith structure, V_i is the volume of the ith structure, and where

$$P_2 = (V_2/V_1)^{2/3} P_1 . \qquad (6)$$

The statistical variants designated by the letter P can be taken as any load, load magnitude, or combination of loads on the member. We could also choose the stress σ acting at any point as our variate in which case the arguments of F_1 and F_2 are each σ. To demonstrate the application of equation 5, two different-size circular plates in plaster* were fracture-tested using simple edge supports and a concentrated central load. The distribution curves for these experiments are shown in Figure 7, where we observe that the performance of the large plates differs from that predicted from the small plates using the volume ratio $V_2/V_1 = 125$. We conclude that the plaster is not a series material.

If the distribution function for the strength of a link in a series model has a zero strength x_ℓ, this will also be the zero strength of the chain regardless of its length. Recognizing the possibility that a material has a strength level below which no failures can occur, many investigators have proposed that a deterministic design theory be based on this zero strength. This is, of course, impractical

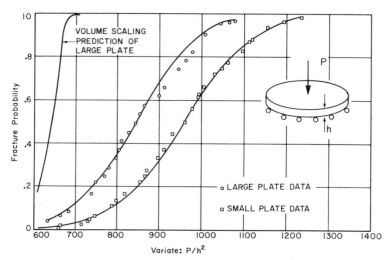

FIGURE 7. Distribution functions for the fracture strength of small and large hydrostone plaster plates (Source: "The Design and Behavior of Brittle Structures," AFFDL-TR-65-165).

*Hydro-Stone Super Strength Gypsum Cement; United States Gypsum Company, Chicago.

when x_ℓ is very small or zero. Even when this is not the case we must remember that the true value of x_ℓ can only be determined from a population of infinite size. Using a finite sample size we can only estimate the value of x_ℓ and, as we have seen, such an estimate is itself a statistical quantity. Consequently, we are faced again with a statistical design problem.

The parallel model illustrated in Figure 6B has received only a fraction of the attention that has been devoted to the series or weakest-link model. Oddly enough, Peirce, who introduced the series model, was also first to consider the parallel model, and, furthermore, he did so in the same paper.[5] In this model, we observe that fracture at a point (or link) may not constitute fracture of the specimen. That is, alternate-force paths are available to the axial load. It should be pointed out that the parallel model seems appropriate for describing the strength of filamentary ceramic elements and perhaps for reinforced composites that derive their strength primarily from parallel ceramic fibers.

Daniels[7] has shown that the fracture load S for a bundle of n strands will normally be distributed for large n if S is always divided equally among the unfractured strands. This result is independent of the distribution function $F(x)$ governing the strength of the individual filaments. Specifically, the mean strength of the bundle is given by

$$S_{mean} = nx \left[1 - F(x)\right] \qquad (7)$$

and the variance by

$$\sigma^2 (S) = nx^2 F(x) \left[1 - F(x)\right], \qquad (8)$$

where x maximizes the quantity $x[1 - F(x)]$. When the load, S, is not equally distributed among the strands, the problem is a great deal more complicated, and a considerable amount of research is needed in this area.

The actual behavior of most real materials is probably best represented by a statistical model that involves both series and parallel elements. Typical of such models are those shown in Figure 6, C and D. Many of their properties can be inferred from results obtained for the pure series and parallel models. For example, if we observe in Figure 6C that each link is actually a parallel model, we know from the work of Daniels that the strength distribution of the links must be normal regardless of the properties of the individual hoops. Thus, we have a chain composed of Gaussian links, and we can appeal to the work of Epstein[6] for its strength distribution.

The series-parallel model shown in Figure 6D represents a physical situation where some cracks are arrested in a body and some propagate undisturbed. Our previous discussions would indicate that a minimum of two parameters is required to describe the series regime of the model, and two for the parallel regime. Furthermore, an additional parameter is needed to define the ratio of series to parallel elements. This, of course, results in a five-parameter theory which should be very demanding in its data requirements and awkward in its analytical versatility.

Experimental investigations in statistical-fracture theory have primarily concerned themselves with the verification of specific weakest-link theories without trying to establish the underlying statistical models. Attempts to verify specific theories quantitatively have in general been inconclusive. Usually, too few tests were used to estimate the distribution parameters properly. Where great numbers of specimens were used, either the programs considered only one size of specimen or a distribution function did not exist for the materials considered. Typically, these experimental efforts support the predicted size-strength trends from a qualitative standpoint. Such verifications are not useful in selecting a statistical theory since almost every reasonable model shows decreasing unit strength with increasing size.

RELIABILITY PREDICTIONS BASED ON SMALL-SCALE MODELS

Because direct methods are not presently available, the discovery of the appropriate statistical model for a given material is an arduous task that requires the testing of many alternative model hypotheses. However, if we are willing to forgo an exact description of material behavior and accept instead a conservative prediction of component strength, a suitable compromise can be effected by reinterpreting the series model. We recall that this is the only model that provides no load-redistribution mechanism upon fracture initiation at a point. Consequently, predictions based on this model will underestimate the strength of materials that can redistribute stresses after a local fracture. More specifically, if the fracture probability of a component is scaled according to equation 5, the true fracture probability will be less than or equal to this prediction. This far-reaching result provides the basis for a conservative general-analysis capability that is applicable to any brittle material. This theory is applied to the plaster plates in Figure 7, where we observe that the data for the large plates fall to the right of the predictions based on the small-plate data. Similar demonstrations of this conservative scaling technique can be found in Reference 4 for beams, cylinders, and leading edges.

We see then that equation 5 provides a means for determining the distribution curve for a full-scale component by merely testing small-scale models. A significant feature of this technique is that it does not require an analysis of the stress distribution; nor does it require the use of a multiaxial-fracture stress theory. Finally, it does not depend on the form of the distribution function obtained from the small models. However, the material must all come from the same statistical population, and there must be no variation in the applied stress from such sources as statistical-boundary conditions, random loads, or residual stresses.

If the design material costs too much for scale-model trials, tests can sometimes be run on cheaper materials.[8] The reliability of a prototype component, $1 - G_p$, can be expressed as a power function of the reliability of a model component, $1 - F_m$, when the geometry and loading are identical. The validity of this relationship requires that both materials be of the weakest-link type and that their fracture distributions under combined stresses be related through the equation

$$[1 - G(S_1, S_2, S_3)] = [1 - F(S_1, S_2, S_3)]^k, \qquad (9)$$

where k is a constant found by plotting the tension reliability log $[1 - G(S)]$ of the prototype against log $[1 - F(S)]$ for the model, with S as a parameter. The slope of a straight line fitted to this plot and passing through the origin is taken as k. This determination of k is illustrated in Figure 8. After k has been established, the component reliability can be found by the volume-scaling criterion

$$[1 - G_p(\sigma)] = [1 - F_{sm}(\sigma)]^{k(V_2/V_1)} \qquad (10)$$

where $(1 - F_{sm})$ is the reliability, determined from tests, of a small model. The stress, σ, appearing in the arguments of G_p and F_{sm} can be associated with any location in or on the component. If a load P_{sm} is taken as the statistical variate for the scaled model, the argument of $G_p(P_p)$ is simply $P_p = (V_2/V_1)^{2/3}P_{sm}$.

RELIABILITY PREDICTIONS BASED ON TEST SPECIMENS

Analysis Algorithm

When it is impossible or uneconomical to investigate the integrity of a component through tests on small models, the analysis can be based on data obtained from

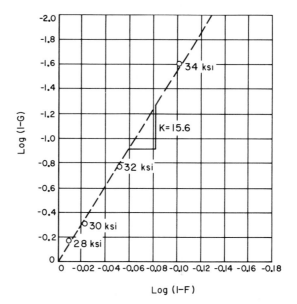

FIGURE 8. Scaling factor K obtained from logarithmic plots of the reliabilities of the design material (ordinate) and test material (abscissa). The data must plot as a straight line through the origin for the scaling law to be valid. These particular data are for an Al_2O_3 prototype and a TiB_2 test material (Source: Barnett et al., Machine Design, 38, 184-191, 1966).

simple test specimens. For this method, a combined-fracture stress theory is needed to relate the behavior of a unit volume under a complicated stress state to the behavior of the test specimen.

Development of such an approach is far from complete; however, a simple theory has been proposed.[4]

If S_1, S_2, and S_3 are three principal stresses acting on a uniformly stressed unit volume ΔV_i, the reliability of the volume, $1 - F_u$, is

$$1 - F_u = [1 - F(S_1)][1 - F(S_2)][1 - F(S_3)], \qquad (11)$$

where $F(S)$ is the fracture probability of a unit volume under a pure tensile stress, S. This equation can be used for any homogeneously stressed basic unit for which $F(S)$ has been established, including, for example, infinitesimal volumes.

The simplest way to determine the reliability-strength trade-off is to test full-scale prototypes. This method requires neither a stress nor strength analysis. The big drawback is expense. The testing of scale models costs less than full-scale tests, but still avoids the need for an accurate stress analysis. However, this technique requires knowledge of the strength-volume relationship. Neither of these approaches provides basic information about the material being tested. Therefore, subsequent designs with the material must be developed from scratch.

The most sophisticated approach—the theory of which is explained above—requires not only data from test specimens but also requires a detailed stress analysis. Small, relatively inexpensive specimens are tested to determine the reliability characteristics of small volumes. A conservative algorithm, based on a series model, then is used to predict prototype behavior. The entire analysis requires six steps:

1. Obtain the tensile-strength distribution $F_{vg}(x)$ using a tension specimen with gage volume v_g.

2. Perform a complete stress analysis of the component.

3. Divide the component into n convenient volumes, V_1, V_2, ..., V_n. No volume should be smaller than the gage volume of the test specimen. Choose volumes with approximately homogeneous stress states.

4. Determine the "worst" stress condition in each volume V_j and assume that the corresponding principal stresses S_1, S_2, and S_3 act uniformly throughout the volume.

5. Determine the reliability of each volume $(1 - F_V)_j$ by first finding the reliability of the gage volume under the principal stresses through application of equation 11,

$$[1 - F_{vg}(S_1, S_2, S_3)] = [1 - F_{vg}(S_1)][1 - F_{vg}(S_2)][1 - F_{vg}(S_3)].$$

Then scale gage-volume reliability to find $(1 - F_V)$ by using equation 5,

$$(1 - F_V)_j = (1 - F_{vg})^{Vj/vg}.$$

6. Use equation 3 to establish the reliability of the entire structure, $1 - F_s$, from the reliabilities of the volumes V_j.

$$1 - F_s = \prod_{j=1}^{n} (1 - F_V)_j.$$

Example - Circular Disk

Calculate the reliability of a circular plate (Figure 9) loaded by uniform tensile stresses S_o on the outside edge and S_i on the inside edge. Use the tensile-strength distribution in Table 2.

The curve in Figure 10 was constructed from fracture data for typical brittle-tension specimens (Table 2). To construct such a curve:

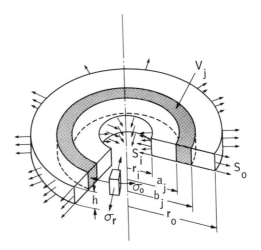

FIGURE 9. Sample problem: circular plate containing a hole is loaded by inside and outside tensile stresses (Source: "Fracture of Brittle Materials under Transient Mechanical and Thermal Loading," AFFDL-TR-66-220).

1. Order the data from smallest to largest. This will yield a sequence of numbers, $x_1 \leq \ldots \leq x_i \leq \ldots \leq x_n$.

2. Estimate the cumulative distribution function, $F(x)$, by calculating $F_n(x_i) = i/(n + 1)$ for each value. This is a function commonly used in statistical work

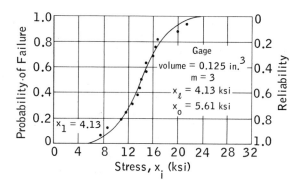

FIGURE 10. Failure-distribution curve for typical brittle tensile specimens (Source: Barnett et al., Machine Design, 38, 184–191, 1966).

Table 2. Failure Strengths of Typical Brittle Tensile Specimens

Ordered Fracture Stresses, x_i (ksi)	Rank, i	Failure Probability, $F = i/(n+1)$	x_i^2	x_i^3
7.55	1	0.0625	57.00	430.37
8.55	2	0.1250	73.10	625.03
10.91	3	0.1875	119.08	1298.60
11.60	4	0.2500	134.56	1560.40
12.44	5	0.3125	154.75	1925.13
13.50	6	0.3750	182.25	2460.38
13.65	7	0.4375	186.32	2543.30
14.00	8	0.5000	196.00	2744.00
14.75	9	0.5625	217.56	3209.05
14.83	10	0.6250	219.93	3261.55
15.96	11	0.6875	254.72	4065.36
16.41	12	0.7500	269.29	4419.02
16.60	13	0.8125	275.56	4574.30
20.00	14	0.8750	400.00	8000.00
21.50	15	0.9325	462.25	9938.38

$\Sigma x_i = 212.25$

$x_a = \frac{1}{n}\Sigma x_i = 14.15$

$m_2 = \frac{1}{n}\Sigma(x_i - x_a)^2 = \frac{1}{n}\Sigma x_i^2 - (x_a)^2 = (213.49) - (14.15)^2 = 13.26$

$m_3 = \frac{1}{n}\Sigma(x_i - x_a)^3 = \frac{1}{n}\Sigma x_i^3 - \frac{3x_a}{n}\Sigma x_i^2 + 2(x_a)^3$

$= (3403.69) - 3(14.15)(213.49) + 2(14.15)^3 = 7.24$

$A_3 = m_3/(m_2)^{3/2} = 7.24/(13.26)^{3/2} = 0.15$

$\Sigma x_1^2 = 3202.38 \quad \Sigma x_1^3 = 51055.34$

to estimate the failure probability at a stress x_i (i.e., the percentage of samples that will fail below a stress x_i).

3. Plot $F_n(x_i)$ against x_i as shown in Figure 10.

It is possible to use a smooth curve passed between the points as an estimate of reliability in the range for which test data are available. This is a good approximation for central values of x. For extreme values, however, the fit becomes questionable, especially when the number of test samples is small. Also, a purely graphical curve offers no information about failure probabilities in the regions beyond the maximum and minimum fracture strengths obtained in the test. An analytical approach, analogous to curve fitting, is necessary to carry the curve into these regions.

The Weibull distribution function described in Equation 4 is used to fit the data of Table 2. This requires that we estimate the values of the three statistical parameters, x_ℓ, x_o, and m. One method for doing this, called the method of moments, requires that the first three moments of $(dF)/(dx)$ and the data be equated. The first three statistical moments, x_a, m_2, and m_3, and the parameter A_3 are evaluated at the bottom of Table 2. Using Figures 11 through 13, which have been reproduced from Reference 9, one can solve the three equations:

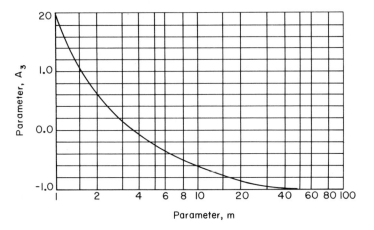

FIGURE 11. Parameter m as a function of A_3 (Source: Gregory and Spruill, "Structural Reliability of Re-entry Vehicles Using Brittle Materials in the Primary Structure," IAS Aerospace Systems Reliability Symposium, 1962).

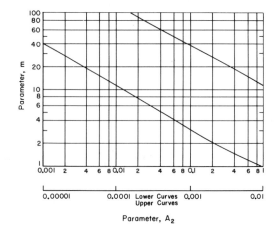

FIGURE 12. Parameter A_2 as a function of m (Source: Gregory and Spruill, "Structural Reliability of Re-entry Vehicles Using Brittle Materials in the Primary Structure," IAS Aerospace Systems Reliability Symposium, 1962).

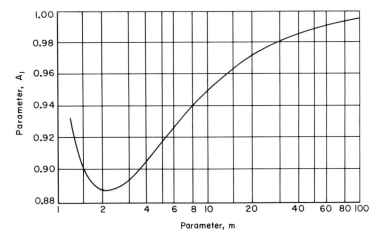

FIGURE 13. Parameter A_1 as a function of m (Source: Gregory and Spruill, "Structural Reliability of Re-entry Vehicles Using Brittle Materials in the Primary Structure," IAS Aerospace Systems Reliability Symposium, 1962).

$A_3 = m_3/(m_2)^{3/2}$ = function of m shown in Figure 11,

$x_o = (v_g/v)^{1/m} (m_2/A_2)^{1/2}$, where A_2 (m) is shown in Figure 12,

$x_\ell = x_a - A_1 (m_2/A_2)^{1/2}$, where A_1 (m) is shown in Figure 13,

to get estimates of x_ℓ, x_o, and m.

For the data in Table 2, $A_3 = 0.15$, so that m = 3 in Figure 11. Then, from Figure 12, $A_2 = 0.105$. Thus

$$x_o = \left(\frac{0.125}{1}\right)^{1/3} \left(\frac{13.26}{0.105}\right)^{1/2} = 5.61 \text{ ksi}.$$

From Figure 13,

$$A_1(3) = 0.893,$$

and

$$x_\ell = 14.15 - (.893) \left(\frac{13.26}{0.105}\right)^{1/2} = 4.13 \text{ ksi}.$$

The smooth curve shown in Figure 10 is the Weibull distribution with these parameters. Because of the small number of tests used for this illustration, the fit is not good at the extremes of the curve. Many more tests, sometimes hundreds, are required for practical problems. Sample-size requirements are discussed more fully in the literature.[4]

Now, using our analytical representation of the data given in Table 2, we may proceed with the reliability predictions for the disk. The numbered paragraphs that follow correspond to the numbered steps in the Analysis Algorithm.

1. The fitted Weibull curve in Figure 10 is

$$1 - F_{vg}(x) = \exp\left[-\frac{v_g}{v} \left(\frac{x - 4.13}{5.61}\right)^3\right]. \tag{12}$$

2. The material is assumed to be linearly elastic, and the radial and circumferential stresses are found from elasticity theory

$$\sigma_r = S_i \left(\frac{r_o^2 - r^2}{r_o^2 - r_i^2}\right)\left(\frac{r_i}{r}\right)^2$$

$$+ S_o \left(\frac{r^2 - r_i^2}{r_o^2 - r_i^2}\right)\left(\frac{r_o}{r}\right)^2$$

$$\sigma_\theta = - S_i \left(\frac{r_o^2 + r^2}{r_o^2 - r_i^2}\right)\left(\frac{r_i}{r}\right)^2$$

$$+ S_o \left(\frac{r^2 + r_i^2}{r_o^2 - r_i^2}\right)\left(\frac{r_o}{r}\right)^2$$

Given: S_o = 4.956 ksi, S_i = 4.460 ksi, r_o = 4.0 in., r_i = 1.0 in., and h = 1.0 in. The expressions then reduce to

$$\sigma_r = 4.99 - \frac{0.495}{r^2}$$

$$\sigma_\theta = 4.99 + \frac{0.495}{r^2} .$$

3. Arbitrarily divide the plate into five concentric rings with the dimensions indicated in Table 3. Note that each ring volume is greater than the gage volume v_g = 0.125 in.^{3} Also, the stress state becomes more homogeneous when the number of ring divisions is increased.

4. The largest radial stress in the jth ring occurs at its outside radius

$$\sigma_r = 4.99 - \frac{0.495}{b_j^2} .$$

The largest circumferential stress is at the inside radius,

$$\sigma_\theta = 4.99 + \frac{0.495}{a_j^2} .$$

These values are tabulated in Table 3.

Table 3. Plate Reliability Calculations

j	a_j (in.)	b_j (in.)	V_j (in.^{3})	σ_r (ksi)	σ_θ (ksi)	$\exp\left[-V_j\left(\frac{\sigma_r - 4.13}{5.61}\right)^3\right]$	$\exp\left[-V_j\left(\frac{\sigma_\theta - 4.13}{5.61}\right)^3\right]$	$1 - F_V$
1	1.0	1.5	3.927	4.76	5.48	0.99445	0.94673	0.94148
2	1.5	2.0	5.498	4.86	5.21	0.98796	0.96154	0.94996
3	2.0	2.5	7.069	4.91	5.11	0.97984	0.96026	0.94090
4	2.5	3.0	8.639	4.94	5.06	0.97434	0.96141	0.93674
5	3.0	4.0	21.991	4.95	5.04	0.93368	0.91054	0.85015

5. There are several steps required to determine the reliability of the V_j. The reliability of the gage volume under the biaxial stresses $S_1 = \sigma_r$ and $S_2 = \sigma_\theta$ is

$$(1 - F_{vg}) = [1 - F_{vg}(\sigma_r)][1 - F_{vg}(\sigma_\theta)].$$

If σ_r and σ_θ are assumed to be uniform throughout the ring, the reliability of the ring becomes

$$(1 - F_V) = (1 - F_{vg})^{V_j/v_g}$$

$$= \left[1 - F_{vg}(\sigma_r)\right]^{V_j/v_g} \left[1 - F_{vg}(\sigma_\theta)\right]^{V_j/v_g}.$$

The bracketed quantities are replaced by equation 12 to obtain

$$(1 - F_V) = \left(\exp\left[-\frac{V_j}{1}\left(\frac{\sigma_r - 4.13}{5.61}\right)^3\right]\right)\left(\exp\left[-\frac{V_j}{1}\left(\frac{\sigma_\theta - 4.13}{5.61}\right)^3\right]\right).$$

Each of these bracketed quantities is tabulated separately in Table 3 together with its product $(1 - F_V)$.

6. The reliability of the plate, $1 - F_s$, is simply the product of the ring reliabilities, $1 - F_V$.

$$(1 - F_s) = \prod_{j=1}^{5} (1 - F_V)_j$$

$$= (0.94148)(0.94996)(0.94090).$$

$$(0.93674)(0.85015)$$

$$= 0.670.$$

If the material in the plate is known to be a series material, V_j need not be greater than v_g. Then the rings may be infinitesimal and calculus can be used to obtain a reliability prediction of 0.696. Thus, in this example, the partitioning of the plate into five subvolumes produces a fairly accurate estimate of the over-all reliability.

The Design of Brittle Components

CONVENTIONAL OR ADEQUATE DESIGN

The problem of structural design is the disposal of material in such a way that it will, within some level of probability, equilibrate given systems of applied force under appropriate environmental conditions without exceeding permissible amounts of deflection. Formulated in this way the solution to the design problem is not unique, and the various possible designs are called adequate designs to indicate that they merely represent a synthesis that satisfies the functional requirements within the confines of existing limitations. If, in addition, designs are required to be minimum weight or minimum cost, we enter the more specialized fields of minimum-weight design or minimum-cost design.

The theory of adequate structural design is for the most part concerned with stress or deflection analysis of given structures. This means that in practice it can only be used in design by a process of trial and error, in which the structural layout and sizes are first guessed or very roughly calculated and are then subjected to as complete analysis as the theory will permit. The results of these calculations are compared to some performance yardstick, and on this basis the various parts of the structure are judged to be adequate or inadequate. The design is then modified, and the thorough-going analysis is repeated as a check. In the case of a ceramic structure, the material would be approximated as linear, elastic, isotropic, and homogeneous, and a thorough analysis would result in a description of the stresses, strains, and deflections throughout the structure. The integrity is then established by applying our statistical-fracture theories to determine the probability of fracture occurring under the imposed-stress distribution. If this turns out to be sufficiently low, we can accept the design or modify it to lower its weight or cost. If the fracture probability is too high, the design is unacceptable and modification is required.

The initial guess at the dimensions of a trial component is a matter of art. Many of the dimensions will be set by functional requirements on the structure. The remainder should be selected with a view toward minimizing stress concentrations. When the first component has been proportioned we can proceed to analyze it by the most appropriate method, outlined previously (p. 252). However, for definiteness we will describe the procedure for a very typical case, specifically, the multiaxial-stress problem in a material whose statistical fracture model is unknown.

After a component geometry is selected, the distribution curve for uniaxial tension is obtained. Then, the previous analysis algorithm (p. 256) may be applied to establish the component reliability. Now, if modification of the trial component is required to improve the reliability or to lower the weight, it will be very useful to have the maximum applied stress and the fracture probability F_{V_j} recorded for each basic unit, j. The critical units can be identified in this way, and modifications can be made that tend to balance the design. This procedure must be repeated until a satisfactory trial design results. Finally, we may check out this trial design by fracture-testing scale models in sufficient number to establish a satisfactory distribution curve. Using Equation 5, we obtain a conservative estimate of the reliability and, indeed, the entire distribution curve for the trial prototype.

If at this point the trial design is not satisfactory, it means that the assumed combined-stress theory is too unconservative and that the conservative weakest-link theory cannot compensate for it. Additional modifications may require further model testing.

MINIMUM-WEIGHT DESIGN

The proportioning of either ductile or brittle structures through the use of conventional design theory is at best a clumsy procedure producing many candidates which are all structurally adequate. If we wish to achieve a structure which is optimum, in addition to having adequate integrity, we must impose other conditions on our design procedures, such as minimum weight or minimum cost. This extra condition generally enables us to solve the design problem directly for one or more optimum dimensions. Solutions of this type are expedited by having simple analytical expressions for both the resistance and the applied stress for the classes of structures of interest.

To illustrate the minimum-weight design procedure in the setting of statistical-fracture theory, let us consider the problem of selecting the optimum width of a rectangular beam under terminal couples M when its length L, its depth d, and its reliability (1 - F) are specified. For a Weibull material the bending resistance can be specified implicitly in terms of the maximum fiber stress σ_r,

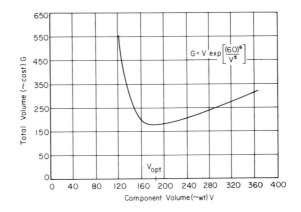

FIGURE 16. Variation in total volume with component volume (Source: "The Behavior and Design of Brittle Structures," AFFDL-TR-65-165).

Nomenclature

A_1, A_2, A_3 = Functions used in estimating Weibull parameters

a = Lower bound on accuracy of μ

a_j = Inside radius of subvolume V_j, in.

b = Upper bound on accuracy of μ

b_j = Outside radius of subvolume V_j, in.

d = Beam depth

$F(x)$ = Failure probability; the probability that failure occurs between 0 and x

F_j = Failure probability of subvolume V_j

F_m = Probability of failure of a model component of a model material

F_n = Fracture probability of nth link or volume

$F_n(x_i)$ = Estimate of the failure of the structure

F_s = Probability of failure of the structure

F_{sm} = Probability of failure of a small-model component of a model material

F_u = Probability of failure of a unit volume under multiaxial state of stress

$F_{vg}(x)$ = Probability of failure for a tension specimen of gage volume v_g

$1 - F(x)$ = Reliability

$1 - F_s$ = Reliability of the entire structure

$(1 - F_V)_j$ = Reliability of the subvolume V_j

F_V = Fracture probability of volume V

F_i = Fracture probability of ith element

$F_p(\sigma)$ = Truncated distribution function

F_{Vj} = Fracture probability of jth volume

$f(x)$ = Frequency distribution of x; strength of component

(f_2) = Strength of given component

G = Probability of failure of a unit volume of a prototype material

G_p = Probability of failure of a component made of a prototype material

h = Thickness of circular plate, in.

i = Rank number for individual observation

j = Subscript denoting j^{th} element

k = Material-scaling factor

L = Length

m = Parameter in the Weibull distribution

m_2 = Second moment about the mean

m_3 = Third moment about the mean

M = Terminal couple

n = Total number of observations; number of strands

N = Total number of specimens

P = Magnitude of the load acting on the component, lb

P_1 = Load on structure 1

P_2 = Load on structure 2

P_{sm} = Load on small element of a model material

P_p = Load on prototype element

r_i = Inside radius of the circular plate, in.

r_o = Outside radius of the circular plate, in.

r = Polar radius

S = Pure tensile stress, psi; load on bundle of strands

S_1, S_2, S_3 = Principle stresses acting at a point in a component under load, psi

S_i = Uniform tensile stress applied to inside radius of circular plate, psi

S_o = Uniform tensile stress applied to outside radius of circular plate, psi

V = Volume of component or specimen, in.^{3}

V_j = Convenient subvolume of the component, in.^{3}

V_i = Volume of ith element

V_n = n^{th} volume

V_{opt} = Minimum component volume

ν = Volume of the unit volume, in.^{3}

ν_g = Gage volume of test specimen, in.^{3}

W = Weight

x = Fracture strength (stress or load)

$\dot{x}$ = Maximum of quantity x $[1 - F(x)]$

x_i = Value of the ith smallest fracture strength

x = Largest stress at which failure will definitely not occur, also a parameter in the Weibull distribution

x_ℓ = Largest stress at which failure will definitely not occur, also a parameter in Weibull distribution

x_n = Largest fracture strength observed in tests

x_y = Smallest stress at which failure will definitely occur

x_1 = Smallest fracture strength observed in tests

x_o = Parameter in Weibull distribution

x_a = Average of strength measurements, psi

σ = Magnitude of the stress developed in the component, psi

σ_r = Radial stress developed in circular plate, psi; resistance stress

σ_θ = Circumferential stress developed in circular plate, psi

σ_a = Applied stress

σ_p = Proof-test stress

σ_b = Bending stress

σ_t = Tensile stress

μ = General statistical parameter

ρ = Weight density

REFERENCES

1. W. Weibull, "Statistical Theory of Strength of Materials," Ing. Vetenskaps Akad. Handl. 151, 45 pp., 1939.
2. R. L. Barnett, "Utilization of Refractory Non-Metallic Materials in Future Aerospace Vehicles: Part I," Flight Dynamics Laboratory, Air Force Systems Command, Contract No. AF33-(657)-8339, September 1964.
3. F. M. Anthony and A. L. Mistretta, "Leading Edge Design with Brittle Materials," (Paper No. 61-151-1845) presented at Joint IAS-ARS Meeting, Los Angeles, June 1961.
4. R. L. Barnett, J. F. Costello, P. C. Hermann, and K. E. Hofer, "Utilization of Refractory Non-Metallic Materials in Future Aerospace Vehicles," Flight Dynamics Laboratory, Air Force Systems Command, Contract No. AF33-(615)-1494, September 1965.
5. F. T. Peirce, "Tensile Tests for Cotton Yarns: V.," J. Textile Inst., 17, 1355-1368, 1926.
6. B. Epstein, "Applications of the Theory of Extreme Values in Fracture Problems," J. Am. Stat. Assoc., 43, 403-412, September 1948.
7. H. E. Daniels, "Statistical Theory of the Strength of Bundles of Threads: Part I," Proc. Roy. Soc. (London), 183, 405-435, 1945.
8. R. L. Barnett and K. E. Hofer, "Strength Analysis of Joints in Brittle Materials," SAMPE 9th National Symposium, November 1965.
9. L. D. Gregory and C. E. Spruill, "Structural Reliability of Re-entry Vehicles Using Brittle Materials in the Primary Structure," IAS Aerospace Systems Reliability Symposium, April 1962.
10. H. H. Hilton and M. Feigen, "Minimum Weight Analysis Based on Structural Reliability," Jour. Aero. Sci. 9, 641-652, September 1960.
11. E. K. Gumbel, "Statistical Theory of Extreme Values and Some Practical Applications," Natl. Bur. Std., Appl. Math. Ser., 33, 51 pp., February 1954.
12. R. L. Barnett and P. C. Hermann, "Proof Testing in Design with Brittle Materials," J. Spacecraft Rockets, December 1965.

APPENDIX 2 TO CHAPTER 5

ENVIRONMENTAL BEHAVIOR

The term "environmental behavior" is used here to define and catagorize experimental and analytical activities that have been established to evaluate the response of materials subjected to complicated test situations and environments. The term "environmental" is extended to include the influences of mechanical constraints in addition to those normally implied, such as electrical, chemical, and thermal. The experimental activities might include the familiar tasks of determining creep, fatigue, stress corrosion, or thermal shock resistance. Other activities could involve the development, refinement, or verification of analytical theories or techniques that would be used in predicting stresses, fracture, or oxidation resistance.

Very useful materials and design information, representing the interests of both the materials processor and user, often come from these activities, which are supported by both industry and governmental agencies. Much of this information contributes to the advancement of material and design technology for specific hardware applications. New tests as well as new experimental and analytical techniques are developed. Results from these tests may be presented in the form of newly defined properties or parameters (dimensionless groups of conventional properties) where much of the information reflects to a high degree the influences of an environment for a particular application. The precise conditions of the test and the environment should be presented with these data to avoid the possibility of misapplying the data in future applications. The danger of misapplication is more evident for data based on empirical analyses coming from complex test situations. For the sake of avoiding confusion, property data measured in an unconventional manner should be classified separately from the classically defined and well-established material properties. This is especially true for ceramics since it is recognized that the wide variability in property data may be the result of very subtle variations in testing techniques. Hence, the category of Environmental Behavior was established by the panel to permit classification of test data obtained by means difficult to analyze or by techniques other than those recognized for classical property determinations. It is not meant to be implied that the new test techniques or analyses may not be superior to the ones established; only time can tell, through the correlation of theory with experiment.

Most of the classical property tests are based on some fundamental analytical consideration; thus, the data from such tests must be interpreted in terms of the uncertainties, limitations, and assumptions of the analysis and the experiment. In the simple case of a uniaxial tension test, one expects to relate stress to strain but measures neither variable in the experiment. Instead, one measures load and displacement that must be equated to stress and strain. Stress may be related to load simply over a limited range of strain if a pure uniaxial stress state exists within the gage length of the specimen. The stress state will be affected by a number of conditions such as alignment of the loading fixture, the isotropy and homogeneity of the material, and the magnitude of applied strain. Thus, the problem of determining stress may not be as simple as the test implies. The number of variables affecting strain and the difficulty of its measurement is even greater. Two approaches may be taken in dealing with the prob-

lems of relating the measured variables to properties. The experimentalist may
be ingenious in providing a clean experiment where the data may be reduced by
simple analysis. Or, a comprehensive analysis may be applied to account for
the conditions of a complicated test situation. The first approach is recommended although the latter may be necessary when the environmental constraints
of the test situation are severe.

Modern computer technology is promoting significant advances in the development of analyses, which in turn emphasize the need for more meaningful and
reliable property data in order to verify the supporting theories. At the same
time the new and improved analyses provide a means for new property-measurement techniques. For example, a computer program designed to predict the
transient temperature response of the thermal history of a body from thermophysical property data may be adapted to work in reverse to determine the
thermophysical properties of the body in a thermal environment measured in
a definitive laboratory experiment. Before such a technique can be applied with
confidence, one must demonstrate that the properties derived from such a procedure are comparable to those obtained using the conventional methods. Determination of the elastic modulus using dynamic resonance techniques is another
example of property measurement by an indirect method. Although discrepancies
very often occur in comparing these data with the results from static tests, the
lack of correlation may be due to the poor experimentation techniques used for
both the static and dynamic determinations. An additional example is brought to
our attention by reviewing the methods used in evaluating the complex mechanical behavior of viscoelastic materials. For linear viscoelastic response, the
elastic effects are Hookean and the viscous effects are Newtonian. In the mathematical model describing this behavior there is a linear time-independent elastic
constant for each elastic effect that relates stress to strain and one constant for
viscosity for each viscous effect to relate stress to strain rate. In a tension test
one observes different stress-strain relationships for different strain rates
and is compelled to make measurements over a wide range of strain rates. For
small strain amplitudes one may perform this task more readily with greater
accuracy using dynamic techniques to obtain the time-dependent modulus over
a wide range of frequencies (a fraction to several thousand cycles per second).
Again, this is possible only when the assumed mathematical model (linear viscoelastic) is shown to describe adequately the behavior of the material in question.
This latter procedure gained rapid acceptance in dealing with the complex behavior of viscoelastic materials used as solid propellants where the conventional
uniaxial tensile properties were of limited value.

Problems in predicting the high-temperature thermomechanical response of
refractory materials offer the opportunity for similar approaches. Materials
that are heterogeneous or anisotropic, which vary with time at temperature,
require greater sophistication in the measurement of properties than can be
realized from tests based on empirical analyses. One should avoid tests for
properties that cannot be substantiated by a fundamental analysis, or where it
is known in advance that critical limitations in the analysis will be exceeded.
This is especially true when dealing with thermochemical, thermophysical, or
thermomechanical responses, since the test conditions and environments used
for measuring properties may vary greatly depending on the particular analytical prediction scheme followed in design. For example, the time-dependent
properties required for a particular thermal-stress analysis may be more useful when measured in a short-time creep- or stress-relaxation test than from
a uniaxial-tension test under conditions of varying strain rate. The best experimental and environmental conditions will often depend on the treatment of a
particular type of material behavior, assumption, or boundary condition used
in the analysis. Trial analyses using assumed property data may be employed
as a first approximation to establish the appropriate conditions for subsequent
property testing to be used in the final analyses.

The preceding examples point to the necessity of close coordination between design and analyses and the activities of property testing and materials characterization. The category of environmental behavior was defined to provide the means for coupling activities of property measurement with design. Analysis is the principal instrument for accomplishing this relationship, since materials are developed on the basis of character, and design on the basis of applications and hardware. Hardware must first be designed before it can be analyzed and then successively redesigned and analyzed for optimization. Properties must be measured before analysis can be applied and then remeasured and refined to optimize analysis. The scientific - engineering approach for making better use of existing materials appears to be an iteration process.

The practical problems of implementing new test procedures and analysis arise through difficulties in maintaining communication between the designer and the materials processors. The designer is pressed by schedules, budgets, and the qualification of hardware and is seldom able to support the materials-oriented analytical-design approach, which usually requires more time and money than is available. The materials supplier is dedicated to the process development of high-volume low-value articles. In the aerospace field the main support for environmental-behavior work is provided by government agencies directly or indirectly responsible for critical mission-oriented hardware. Much of the related research and analysis is conducted by industry, universities, and independent research laboratories, making communication difficult. Improved liaison between these performers and the various supporting agencies could result in better utilization of the available resources. Specialists in the related fields of materials, processing, analyses, and design could be more effective working as a team.

The category of environmental behavior may be divided logically into mechanical, electrical, thermal, and chemical responses and each response may be further subdivided for the sake of classifying environment in terms of the other responses. For example, one may be interested in mechanical responses as they are influenced by the complex interactions of thermal, mechanical, electrical, and chemical environments. The following brief outline gives some of the details for this example. Discussion of the many possible combinations of response and environments is beyond the scope of this activity.

1. Environments
    a. thermal—changes character and geometry and influences all properties
    b. electrical—influences chemical and thermal properties
    c. chemical—changes character and other properties
    d. mechanical—influences geometry and chemical properties
2. Loading (static—dynamic)
    a. traction forces—result in combined mechanical stresses
    b. body forces—result in combined mechanical stresses
    c. self-equilibrating forces—residual and thermal stress
3. Response to stress
    a. deformation—elastic, inelastic, plastic
    b. fracture—brittle, ductile
4. Material behavior
    a. time dependent
    b. temperature dependent
    c. isotropic—anisotropic
    d. homogeneous—heterogeneous

Since analysis is the means for predicting the response of a body by relating material behavior to the environment, it is necessary to describe response, behavior, and environment by the appropriate mathematical models. These models must in some way account for all the effects listed above. The properties of a material that relate its behavior to an environment are represented by the same form of analysis. The properties required for design, discussed in the section covering properties, usually are based on a simple definitive analysis and experiment. Past experience has shown these properties to be useful in analyses when predicting the response of simple elements. The more complex design problems often require supplementary data obtained from auxiliary experiments to support or justify the analytical procedures and results. Tests commonly used to study the effects of time, temperature, and loading for a simple stress state are: creep, stress relaxation, fatigue, and impact. The results from these tests provide information that is useful in evaluating the applicability of the constitutive relationships used in analysis. The effects of multiaxial stress states may also be evaluated when required for a specific design application of a given material. The accumulation of data, on a routine large-scale basis, for this type of behavior cannot be justified, owing to the high cost of specialized testing and the limited application of the results. Material behavior in these tests may be measured in terms of deformation and fracture, or both.

Numerous tests have been used to study phenomenological materials behavior when the complexity of environmental response was beyond the scope of detailed analyses. Many tests of this type are used to measure surface effects such as wear, erosion, hardness, and stress corrosion. The results from these tests provide a qualitative rating for comparing the behavior of one material with another. In general, both deformation and fracture mechanisms play important roles in determining the resistance of surfaces to these effects. However, for most structural applications, direct extrapolation can be made from the results of laboratory specimens to components of hardware.

A similar approach has not been successful in scaling the results from laboratory thermal-shock tests to full-scale hardware applications. In the past, numerous approaches have been taken to relate laboratory thermal-shock behavior of refractories to hardware, and the large variety of different tests correlates well with the large number of different investigations. A systematic review of the literature describing the many test techniques and analyses is reported by Boland and Walton.[1] Actually the thermal-shock problem can be classified simply in terms of analyses for describing environment, loading, material response, and behavior as cited for other problems in structural design. The principal problem in evaluating the thermal-shock resistance of a material has been in relating the response of the material (deformation and fracture) to the loading (self-equilibrating forces) imposed by the environment. It is not logical to assume that the appropriate conditions of thermal loading and the materials response can be stated simply in a materials parameter. The force-generating mechanism is the temperature gradient through the thickness of the part that can be defined only in terms of the thermal histories of all points in the body. This temperature distribution must be determined in detail from experiment and/or analysis. Thermal analyses are available for three-dimensional shapes. The required thermophysical properties are thermal conductivity, specific heat, and density as functions of temperature. Other thermal properties and analyses may be required, depending on the boundary conditions of the heat-transfer problem for the application or test of interest. The problem of measuring the transient thermal history of a body is difficult under the most ideal conditions, and only a few experimenters have been successful at this task. Research and development is needed to perfect transient high-temperature measuring techniques.

Nonsteady-state thermal stresses result from the temperature gradient and the corresponding differential thermal expansion, which cannot be accommodated by purely geometrical compatible displacements in the body. If these stresses reach a critical value, usually at the coolest portion of the body, failure will occur. The two resulting problems are apparent: first, to measure or predict stresses and strains, and then to determine whether or not failure will occur. Experimentally, one may measure deformation by a variety of techniques at selected locations on the body. Deformation may be related simply to stress, provided the appropriate stress-strain relationships are known. For example, knowing the total strain and temperature at a point on the sample for a given time, one may obtain the mechanical strain by subtracting the thermal strain from the total strain. The mechanical strain may be converted to stress using the uniaxial stress-strain curve for the temperature corresponding to the time and location of interest. The alternate procedure is to perform a detailed stress analysis to determine the stresses and strains at all points in the body. Information required as input to the thermal-stress analysis is the complete thermal history of the body and the mechanical properties as a function of temperature. Solutions are obtained for selected time intervals of interest. In general, analyses based on numerical procedures are available for most geometries of interest. Unfortunately, most analyses capable of handling complicated shapes require restricting assumptions to describe material behavior. Most two-dimensional axisymmetric and three-dimensional analyses require the assumptions of elastic, isotropic, and homogeneous behavior. The following discussion is given for a one-dimensional axisymmetric case to illustrate the special features and requirements for property data needed in accounting for the effects of plasticity and anisotropy.[2]

In general, the analysis can be applied either to long hollow cylinders or to thin annular discs subjected to an arbitrary radial temperature distribution. Axial symmetry is assumed, with no axial-temperature variations. Both plasticity and anisotropy are taken into account, and the material properties are treated as functions of temperature. The assumptions and basic equations used in this analysis follow.

Stress-strain relations. By symmetry, the r, θ, z directions are the principal stress directions for both the long cylinder and the thin disc, and thus the shear stresses and shear strains in the r, θ, z coordinate system are zero. In addition, the normal stresses and strains are only functions of the radial distance, r. Each of the three normal strain components can be expressed as the sum of four terms: (a) an elastic strain, (b) a plastic strain, (c) a residual strain, and (d) a thermal expansion. Thus,

$$\epsilon_r = \epsilon_r^{e\ell} + \epsilon_r^{P} + \epsilon_r^{R} + \epsilon_r^{T} \tag{1}$$

$$\epsilon_\theta = \epsilon_\theta^{e\ell} + \epsilon_\theta^{P} + \epsilon_\theta^{R} + \epsilon_\theta^{T} \tag{2}$$

$$\epsilon_z = \epsilon_z^{e\ell} + \epsilon_z^{P} + \epsilon_z^{R} + \epsilon_z^{T} . \tag{3}$$

The elastic-strain terms are defined in the usual way:

$$\epsilon_r^{e\ell} = \frac{1}{E_r} \sigma_r - \frac{\nu_{\theta r}}{E_\theta} \sigma_\theta - \frac{\nu_{zr}}{E_z} \sigma_z \tag{4}$$

$$\epsilon_\theta^{e\ell} = -\frac{\nu_{r\theta}}{E_r} \sigma_r + \frac{1}{E_\theta} \sigma_\theta - \frac{\nu_{z\theta}}{E_z} \sigma_z \tag{5}$$

$$\epsilon_z^{e\ell} = -\frac{\nu_{rz}}{E_r} \sigma_r - \frac{\nu_{\theta z}}{E_\theta} \sigma_\theta + \frac{1}{E_z} \sigma_z , \tag{6}$$

where the first subscript in each of the Poisson ratios refers to the direction in which the stress is applied. It can be shown by means of Rayleigh's reciprocal theorem that

$$\frac{\nu_{r\theta}}{E_r} = \frac{\nu_{\theta r}}{E_\theta} , \quad \frac{\nu_{rz}}{E_r} = \frac{\nu_{zr}}{E_z} , \quad \text{and} \quad \frac{\nu_{\theta z}}{E_\theta} = \frac{\nu_{z\theta}}{E_z} .$$

The elastic constants in the above equations can be determined from uniaxial tensile or compressive tests. The measurements required to accomplish such a determination are as follows:

1. Required whether isotropic or anisotropic: <u>stress vs longitudinal strain</u> and <u>one transverse strain</u> for loading in any direction (r, θ, or z)

2. Additional data required if anisotropic if 2 directions same, 1 different: <u>stress vs longitudinal strain</u> and <u>one transverse strain</u> for loading in a direction not the same as in (1)

3. If all 3 directions are different: <u>stress vs longitudinal strain</u> and <u>one transverse strain</u> for loading in each of the other two directions.

If the material is anisotropic, care must be taken to choose directions for the transverse-strain measurements that will give independent Poisson's ratio data.

The problem of obtaining an analytical formulation that will properly describe the plastic behavior of a material, particularly an anisotropic material, is a difficult one because the behavior to be described is usually extremely complicated and only partially understood. However, the symmetry and basic simplicity of this particular type of thermal-stress problem allows an especially simple analytical formulation, which avoids many of the complicating factors besetting similar problems. One simplifying factor, which results from the symmetry of the problem, is that the r, θ, z axes are the principal axes not only of stress, but of strain and strain increment, as well. In addition, the three components of stress, σ_r, σ_θ, and σ_z, at a given radial position will tend to increase more or less in constant ratio to each other (proportional loading), so that a deformation theory of plasticity, expressed in terms of total strains, can be used instead of an incremental theory that must deal with strain increments. The use of a deformation theory has been shown to be valid even though some deviation from strict proportional loading is encountered.[3]

The equations chosen to represent the plastic-material behavior, then, are:

$$\epsilon_r^p = \frac{3}{2(F+G+1)} \frac{\bar{\epsilon}^p}{\bar{\sigma}} \left[(G+1)\,\sigma_r - \sigma_\theta - G\sigma_z \right] \tag{7}$$

$$\epsilon_\theta^P = \frac{3}{2(F+G+1)} \frac{\bar{\epsilon}^p}{\bar{\sigma}} \left[-\sigma_r + (F+1)\,\sigma_\theta - F\sigma_z \right] \tag{8}$$

$$\epsilon_z^p = \frac{3}{2(F+G+1)} \frac{\bar{\epsilon}^p}{\bar{\sigma}} \left[-G\sigma_r - F\sigma_\theta + (F+G)\,\sigma_z \right] , \tag{9}$$

where the effective stress, $\bar{\sigma}$, and the effective plastic strain $\bar{\epsilon}^p$, are defined as

$$\bar{\sigma} = \sqrt{ \frac{3}{2(F+G+1)} \left[F\left(\sigma_\theta - \sigma_z\right)^2 + G\left(\sigma_z - \sigma_r\right)^2 + \left(\sigma_r - \sigma_\theta\right)^2 \right] } ,$$

and

$$\bar{\epsilon}^p = \sqrt{ \frac{2(F+G+1)}{3(FG+G+F)^2} \left[F\left(G\epsilon_\theta^P - \epsilon_z^P\right)^2 + G\left(\epsilon_z^P - F\epsilon_r^P\right)^2 + \left(F\epsilon_r^P - G\epsilon_\theta^P\right)^2 \right] } ,$$

and F and G are parameters characteristic of the state of anisotropy of the material. If the material is isotropic, F = G = 1. If the material properties happen to be the same in the r and θ directions, G = F. If the θ- and z-direction properties are the same, G = 1.

The plastic-strain components given above satisfy identically the constant volume condition, $\epsilon_r^P + \epsilon_\theta^P + \epsilon_z^P = 0$, and, for isotropic materials, they also satisfy the von Mises condition. The extension to cover the anisotropic case is based on a work-hardening theory by Hill,[4] where it is assumed that the anisotropy is already present in the material and that it remains effectively the same.

In other words, it is assumed that the flow stresses increase in strict proportion as the material work-hardens and that the relations between the strain ratios
and the stress ratios remain invariant. This, too, is probably a very good assumption in this particular case, because the strains, being induced by differential thermal expansions, remain relatively small—of the order of a few percent
at the most. Another similarity between the anisotropic equations and the corresponding equations for isotropic materials is the fact that, in both cases, the
area under the effective stress - effective plastic-strain curve is equal to the
work per unit volume.

The relationship between $\bar{\sigma}$ and $\bar{\epsilon}^p$ can be determined experimentally, along
with values for the anisotropic parameters, F and G, and by means of uniaxial
tensile or compressive tests. The measurements required for this purpose are
described briefly as follows:

1. Required whether isotropic or anisotropic: stress vs longitudinal plastic
strain for loading in any direction (r, θ, or z)

2. Additional data required if anisotropic if 2 directions same, 1 different:
yield stresses for loading in the "different" direction and one of the "same"
directions [one of these will come from (1)]; or both transverse strains for
loading in one of the "same" directions

3. If all 3 directions different: yield stresses for loading in all 3 directions
[one will come from (1)]; or both transverse strains for loading any 2 directions.

These represent the minimum property-data requirements for the purposes
of this analysis. In practice, some redundancy in measurement is desirable in
order to achieve a "best fit" to the behavior of the real material.

The residual-strain terms, ϵ_r^R, ϵ_θ^R, and ϵ_z^R, in equations 1, 2, and 3 represent strain-history effects that could arise from several sources, stress reduc-
tion or reversal being the most common. The means for determining the value
of these terms will depend upon the nature of the particular problem.

The thermal-expansion terms represent the total thermal expansion that
takes place when the temperature at any radial position is changed from the
starting temperature T_s to the temperature T. Thus,

$$\epsilon_r^T = \alpha_r T - \alpha_{rs} T_s \tag{11}$$

$$\epsilon_\theta^T = \alpha_\theta T - \alpha_{\theta s} T_s \tag{12}$$

$$\epsilon_z^T = \alpha_z T - \alpha_{zs} T_s, \tag{13}$$

where α_r, α_θ, and α_z are defined as the average thermal expansion in the r, θ,
and z directions, measured from 0 degrees to T (total expansion per unit length
divided by T), and α_{rs}, $\alpha_{\theta s}$, and α_{zs} are the corresponding values measured from
0 degrees to T_s. The starting temperature is the reference temperature at
which the total thermal expansion through the body is defined to be zero.

Equilibrium and compatibility equations. Equations 1, 2, and 3, with the terms
on the right-hand side as defined by equations 4 through 13, represent three
stress - strain equations containing six unknowns: $\epsilon_r, \epsilon_\theta, \epsilon_z, \sigma_r, \sigma_\theta$, and σ_z. All
the material properties, including $\bar{\epsilon}^p (\bar{\sigma}, T)$, and the temperature distribution,
T(r), are assumed to be known. Geometrical restrictions, expressed in terms
of two compatibility equations, plus a requirement based on the equilibrium of
forces, provide three additional equations containing one additional unknown (the
radial displacement, u). The compatibility equations are

$$\epsilon_\theta = \frac{u}{r}, \tag{14}$$

and

$$\epsilon_r = \frac{du}{dr}, \tag{15}$$

and the equilibrium equation is

$$\frac{d\sigma_r}{dr} = \frac{\sigma_\theta - \sigma_r}{r}. \tag{16}$$

<u>Axial-boundary condition</u>. One more equation is needed to determine the stresses and strains in the body. This equation is provided by the axial-boundary condition. For a long cylinder, planes normal to the cylinder axis must remain flat and parallel (plane strain). This condition can be written:

$$\epsilon_z = \text{constant}. \tag{17a}$$

The value of this constant can be specified directly or it can be made to adjust itself so that the net axial force transmitted by the cylinder, $\int \sigma_z (2\pi r) \, dr$, is equal to some specified value, normally zero. For the case of the thin disk, the additional equation is provided by specifying the axial-stress distribution on the face of the disk. If the face is free and unrestrained, the axial stress is zero (plane stress),

$$\sigma_z = 0. \tag{17b}$$

This stress analysis is basically a time-independent plasticity analysis. Such behavioral effects as strain-rate dependence, stress relaxation, and creep are included only to the extent that they can be accounted for in the incorporation of the material-property data. Strain-history effects can be included by the proper use of the material-property data and of the residual-strain terms in Equations 1, 2, and 3.

From the preceding discussion, it is apparent that the features of analysis influence greatly the requirements for property measurements. At the present time, uncertainties in the analytical solutions are due mainly to the lack of adequate property data rather than to limiting assumptions or conditions inherent to the analytical procedures. Future high-performance structures will most certainly make greater use of advanced analytical techniques for optimum design. The crude empirical approach for evaluating environmental behavior will, hopefully, lose its prominence.

The argument for empirical thermal-shock tests is still made on behalf of comparing new or improved materials in screening tests for specific applications when practically no property data are available. In this case it would seem advisable to rationalize and interpret the results of such tests in terms of analytical solutions based on assumed data. Valid comparisons could be made from parametric considerations with very meager data and in the absence of absolute predictions.

Failure from thermal shock can be defined by excessive irrecoverable deformation, by cracking, or by fracture and complete separation. Failure from excess deformation can be established from both experiment and analysis, since stresses and strains are calculated and strains are measured. Failure by fracture can be established from experiment but not from the results of the stress analysis alone. A criterion of failure such as maximum normal tensile stress, maximum shear stress, maximum principal strain, or maximum distortional energy must be verified for the material of interest under the appropriate environmental conditions before analytical predictions of failure can be justified.

A detailed discussion on the fracture of brittle ceramics was presented in a preceding section. An additional source of information on this subject is given in "Mechanical Properties of Ceramics: An Introductory Survey," by J. B. Wachtman, Jr., presented at the Symposium on Ceramic Materials and Their Properties, Gaithersburg, Maryland, October 1966.

REFERENCES

1. P. Boland and J. D. Walton, "Aerospace Ceramics - Characteristics and Design Principles," AFML-TR-65-171, June 1965.

2. J. Bohn and K. King, "An Investigation of the Thermal Shock Behavior of Refractory Materials," AFML-TR-65-393, December 1965.

3. B. Budiansky, "A Reassessment of Deformation Theories of Plasticity," Journal of Applied Mechanics, Vol. 26, Trans. ASME, Vol. 81, 295-264, 1959.

4. R. Hill, "The Mathematical Theory of Plasticity," Oxford, 1950, p. 332.

APPENDIX 3 TO CHAPTER 5

QUALITY CONTROL AND PROOF TESTS

Introduction

Regardless of the function of a ceramic component it is essential that it perform satisfactorily in service. The basic design and material selection is generally verified during development testing under simulated or actual service conditions. Once the design is considered acceptable it is then necessary to insure that each particular component of that design will perform satisfactorily in service. To meet this objective requires verification of dimensional accuracy, freedom from defects, and material properties that are within specification limits, that is, equal to or better than the properties used to design the component.* Therefore, quality control is concerned with the techniques and standards necessary to establish that these three requirements are met.

Because of the present lack of knowledge, it is essential that the control of ceramic-component quality begin at the earliest stage of component production, namely the raw materials, and continue throughout the process and finishing cycles—inspection of the finished component is not sufficient. Because of current shortcomings with respect to inspection procedures, it is considered necessary to subject each component to a proof test, which involves the application of an external load system in order to establish a minimum level of confidence when high reliability is required.

Discussion

Before discussing quality-control considerations of ceramic materials it is appropriate to consider briefly the type of quality control normally associated with components fabricated from ductile materials.

Dimensional accuracy is important from two points of view: proper fit of components into assemblies, and structural integrity (which is a function of physical dimensions). Surface finish may be considered from both dimensional and defect points of view. Standard gages, comparators, wave plates, and profilometers, for example, can be employed to insure dimensional accuracy. With available techniques, component dimensions can be measured with ease to the nearest 0.001 in. Special techniques, such as air gages, can be used to measure dimensions to an accuracy of 1×10^{-5} in. Surface finishes as fine as 2 to 5 microinch rms can also be measured.

Freedom from defects that might impair operational performance is also essential. Years of experience with numerous ductile alloys have permitted a general appreciation for the types of defects that may degrade structural performance. Cracks, scratches, chips, inclusions, porosity, voids, and laminations are among the more common types of defects that may be cause for rework or rejection. Visual, radiographic, dye-penetrant, magnetic-particle, and ultra-

---

*It should be noted that "better than" depends upon the particular property and specific application. For example, a higher value of thermal conductivity would be "better than" the design value when thermal stresses are of prime importance, while a lower value would be "better than" when insulation is of prime concern.

sonic techniques are commonly employed to detect such defects. In most instances, reliable, or at least conservative, standards can be established with relative ease for ductile materials because of extensive past experience and the general similarity in the response behavior of ductile materials to induced stresses.

For ductile materials a number of approaches may be followed in establishing confidence that the construction material actually contained within the component is the same as that used for the design of that component, including: certification of chemical analysis, procurement to government or industry specifications, or procurement to user specifications. For materials that have been commercially available for a long period of time and for which service experience has been accumulated, the first two procedures are usually adequate to assure confidence in the performance of the components produced from these materials. When greater assurance is necessary, determination of mechanical properties or property-related parameters is often employed. The extent of these determinations will vary depending upon the level of confidence deemed necessary. Microhardness measurements, room-temperature tensile tests, and microstructrual examination are employed most frequently. In some instances, the testing of mill products may include impact tests, elevated-temperature tensile tests, creep tests, or fatigue tests.

Quality control for ductile materials, then, is based on three primary considerations: (a) variability of material properties is small; (b) the structural performance can be predicted within reasonable limits by means of parameters, such as mechanical properties or characteristics that relate to properties that can be easily measured; and (c) a wealth of experience with similar materials enables establishment of meaningful standards of judgment.

When ceramic materials are considered, however, the present state of the art indicates a rather different state of affairs: First, a variability of material-strength properties is expected to be large; second, there is little assurance that general structural behavior can be predicted by means of parameters that are easily measured; and third, experience with respect to efficient structural application is very limited and few meaningful standards exist. Therefore, the development of quality-control procedures can be expected to be an evolutionary process. Continuing improvement can be expected as experience is gained. This evolutionary process can be accelerated by relating material character to properties, since such relationships should aid in reducing variability.

All aspects involved in the structural utilization of ceramics, of which quality control is only one, are intimately related to brittleness and variability of properties. Elimination of brittleness in ceramic materials, while certainly a desirable long-range objective, is not likely to be accomplished in the near future.

The reduction of strength variability* is one of the most effective ways of promoting usage of ceramics. Hence, a major goal of quality control should be the reduction of variability of strength properties. However, reproducibility of properties can hardly be expected if the character of the material is not reproducible. Chemical composition, impurities, and processing variables all influence the properties of ductile materials. No less can be expected of ceramics.

The sensitivity of properties and character features to variations of raw-material characteristics and process parameters will depend upon a particular ceramic material and the basic process used to produce it. One part of the quality-control problem is undoubtedly due to ignorance of the relationships among raw-material and process variations and the resultant character and properties of the ceramic. The determination of character features of the

*It has already been shown that the character features that influence strength properties also influence other properties. Thus, techniques that reduce the variability of strength should also reduce the variability of other properties. The converse is not necessarily true, however.

finished ceramic-body product appears to be a most promising and necessary link for the establishment of the necessary relationships. However, even if the relationships were known, it is not very clear whether or not presently available technology could meet the challenge of providing the degree of control required within the framework of practical economics.

The most expensive point at which to reject material is when it is in the completely finished state. Therefore, in-process quality control of ceramic products is highly desirable. The first step should involve the characterization of raw materials with respect to chemistry (including elemental composition, impurities, trace elements, compound identification, and stoichiometry), particle-size distribution, and particle shape. If liquids are used in early stages of processing (such as compaction), their characteristics should also be evaluated, including the residue left by evaporation, thermal degradation, or oxidation.

The second step should involve evaluations that can be conducted prior to production of the finished product. These will depend upon the particular process used. If any type of preform or green shape is available prior to final firing, it might be evaluated nondestructively with respect to density, density variations (by radiographic or ultrasonic techniques), and gross defects (by visual, radiographic, penetrant-dye, or ultrasonic-techniques). Care must be taken that the nondestructive in-process evaluations do not adversely affect the preform. The evaluations made after final firing but before machining might include the nondestructive types mentioned above as well as destructive tests conducted on samples cut from the fired body. With proper product design it should be possible to obtain a rather good description of the material within the fired item. Metallographic, chemical, and property-measurement techniques might be applied to the extent considered to be economically practical. The specific character features and properties that are of particular importance have already been discussed. Techniques that may be employed to determine the desired data have also been previously discussed. Special attention should be given to the adoption of techniques that have long been considered as tools for laboratory investigations to in-process evaluation of ceramic products.

The third area of quality control for ceramics involves inspection of finished components. There are requirements for dimensional inspection, defect identification, and assurance of reproducible properties among components of a given design and between the component and the test bars used for determining design properties. Faced with the incompleteness of present knowledge with respect to quality control, including nondestructive testing techniques, it may be desirable to conduct performance proof tests of ceramic components. Mechanical, thermal, electrical, or combined conditions may be used, depending upon the requirements for the particular component. In all cases, the purpose of such proof tests is to provide greater confidence of satisfactory performance. In the case of structural applications, mechanical and thermal loadings will be of most importance. One approach might be to select a limited number of the finished components and load them to destruction using the critical combination of loads. Another approach might be to apply a nominal loading to all components produced. With the latter approach the loading must not induce significant damage to the components. The degree to which performance proof-testing must be applied will, of course, depend upon the intended use of the ceramic component.

The dimensional accuracy and tolerances of ceramic components generally will be more exacting than those of ductile material components. Particular attention must be given to such dimensional aspects as flatness, parallelism, perpendicularity, concentricity, and surface finish. Dimensional mismatch, particularly in regions of attachments or of load transfer, which would be insignificant for ductile components, can induce very high local loads and stresses in ceramic components. While greater care must be taken in the specification and production of more exact dimensional requirements, the quality-control techniques available to insure compliance are adequate except in the case of surface finish. Since ceramic materials are expected to be more sensitive to variations than ductile materials, a more accurate definition of surface finish than can be obtained from the standard rms approach is necessary. Furthermore, the wide range of characters displayed by ceramic materials (the soft nature of the graphites, the porous nature of sintered products, in addition to the very hard nature of most ceramics) makes the rms approach meaningless in many cases. The difficulty of achieving identical surface finishes on the complex configurations typical of components and on the simple test bars used to determine properties should be obvious. Therefore, not only must an improved method be found for defining surface finish but meaningful standards must be established to define the tolerance range on surface finish that will not adversely influence the structural performance of the component.

The need for standards is even greater with respect to defect identification. Nondestructive techniques that can be used for the identification of defects include visual, radiographic, ultrasonic, liquid penetrant, thermal, electromagnetic, and other inspection procedures, as listed in Table 1. All the techniques provided data regarding the nature of the material being examined, either at the surface or within the total volume, but only on a relatively gross or macroscopic scale.

Visual examination provides information with respect to the surface condition of the product—cracks, scratches, voids, chips, and color variations, for example. Unaided observation detects only the larger defects, while various techniques such as magnifying glasses, surface comparators, and a wide variety of profilometer instruments permit higher resolution. With available instruments, it is possible to describe the nature of the surface to within 1 to 2 microinches.

The internal features of ceramic products can be investigated by radiographic and ultrasonic techniques. X-ray, gamma-ray, and neutron sources can be used in conjunction with radiation counters, fluorescent screens, or film. Without much difficulty, it is possible to obtain indications of voids as small as 1 to 2% of the product thickness. Density variations can also be detected. The identification of cracks by radiographic techniques is not expected to be significantly different from present procedures even when brittle materials are used. The tightness and orientation, with respect to the radiation, of the cracks are basic problems.

When ultrasonic inspection is employed, normal and angle-beam techniques can identify subsurface defects, while surface-wave techniques can identify surface defects. Pulse-echo, through transmission, and resonant modes of operation can be employed. Display of information is commonly obtained by means of cathode-ray oscilloscopes. The A-scan technique is used to determine flaw depth and the amplitude of the flaw signal, the B-scan technique to identify flaw depth and flaw distribution in a cross-sectional view, and the C-scan to identify flaw distribution in a plane view. Gated techniques can be employed to actuate audio or visual displays of defects in excess of a predetermined limit. Automatic recording is also possible with the gated-system and transograph techniques. Defects detected by surface-wave techniques are normally displayed visually.

Liquid penetrants provide another useful approach for identifying surface defects. Visual-dye, fluorescent-dye, and filtered-particle techniques can be employed. The first two techniques are preferable for high-density materials since the presence of porosity will generate a dye pattern that is almost impossible to interpret. The dye techniques essentially rely on the capillarity of surface defects, which draws the penetrant into the crevice and holds it there while the dye on the exterior surface is removed. The part is then coated with a developer which draws the dye from the crevices in much the same manner as a blotter. Ordinary or black light is used, depending upon the type of dye employed. The filtered-particle technique was developed primarily for materials of moderate porosity. Particles of a controlled size are suspended in the penetrant dye. The dye penetrates the surface porosity and leaves the large particles

Table 1. Nondestructive Inspection Techniques—Defect Identification

	Primary Applicability	
Technique	Surface	Volume
VISUAL		
Unaided	X	
Magnified	X	
RADIOGRAPHY		
X ray		X
Gamma ray		X
Neutron		X
ULTRASONIC		
Normal beam		X
Angle beam		X
Surface wave	X	
Sound velocity		X
LIQUID PENETRANT		
Visible dye	X	
Fluorescent dye	X	
Filtered particle	X	
THERMAL		
Coating		
Phase change		X
Color change		X
Infrared		X
ELECTROMAGNETIC		
Applied current	X	X
Eddy current	X	X
OTHER		
Electrified particle	X	
Magnetic particle	X	
Density		X

on the surface. Where surface defects are more severe than normal porosity there is sharper coloring because of the higher concentration of the suspended particles deposited by the greater degree of infiltration of the liquid into the part. The liquid-penetrant techniques accurately identify locations of defects but define the size of the defects in an approximate manner, since indications are larger than the actual defect.

Thermal techniques can also be utilized to identify defects, but because ceramic materials are generally used in relatively thick sections and have low thermal conductivity, thermal techniques for defect identification do not appear promising for general usage. However, they may be applicable in specific instances. The thermal-inspection techniques rely on the conduction of heat within the part. The presence of a void or crack will alter the flow of heat and produce a slight variation in local temperature. The temperature variations may be detected by phase or color changes in a previously applied coating or by measurement of infrared radiation. The sensitivity of the technique will depend upon the factors that influence heat flow by conduction, namely the thermal conductivity of the material, the dimensions of the part, and the nature of the defect. Thermal-inspection techniques are used on a production basis for the inspection of brazed-core to face-sheet joints in metallic honeycomb panels. One face of the panel is heated, and the heat flows to the other face primarily by conduction through the honeycomb core. Voids in the braze retard the flow of heat and produce a local temperature variation. In such an application the direction of heat flow is well defined and the type of defect to be detected is oriented in such a way as to simplify detection. When the component shape is complex, the thickness of the part is large, or the size of the defect is small, it is more difficult to obtain indications of defects.

Electromagnetic techniques for the detection of defects include applied-current and eddy-current approaches. With suitable variations these techniques can be used to observe surface defects and defects somewhat below the surface. These techniques are applicable only to electromagnetic materials and electrical conductors and are based on the fact that a discontinuity will disturb the electrical profile of a conductor. With the first method, current flows between two electrodes in contact with the sample and is measured by probes between the electrodes. The surface of the product is surveyed and points of electrical disturbance are noted. The significance of the disturbances must be determined by means of suitable calibrations. With the eddy-current technique, the part is surveyed by means of a coil that induces current flow in the product, and this in turn generates its own magnetic field. Disturbances in the induced magnetic field may be determined from measurements of impedance magnitude, reactance magnitude, losses, or vector orientation. While quite useful for metallic products, application of electromagnetic techniques to ceramics will certainly be limited because of the requirement that the product being inspected be an electrical conductor.

The electrified-particle technique is an approach employed for inspecting nonconducting materials. Positively charged particles are deposited on the surface of the ceramic material and are attracted to locations where electrons are available. To counterbalance the positively charged particles it is necessary to provide an electron source. A metallic substrate is one way of providing such a source, and this technique is widely used for the inspection of porcelainized steel products. When the ceramic is not integrally attached to a metallic substrate it is necessary to soak the ceramic product in a electrolyte, normally water with wetting agents and electrolytic salt, to wipe off the excess electrolyte, and to rely on the electrolyte trapped in surface defects to provide a source of electrons. The sensitivity of the technique depends upon the ability of the electrolyte to penetrate crevices. A high degree of magnification of the visible display is obtained. Fine cracks which are totally invisible to the unaided eye can be detected.

For those few ceramic materials in which a magnetic field may be induced, magnetic-particle inspection of surface defects is possible. This technique, however, is not generally applicable to many of the ceramic products.

The various techniques that have been reviewed briefly are capable of identifying a variety of "defects" in a ceramic component, such as scratches, porosity, voids, chips, cracks, laminations, and density variations. But, the significance of such indications on product performance is not always clear. In fact, without definitive standards only the most gross defects can be interpreted by exercising engineering judgment. For example, cracks and large voids, which can be detected by the various techniques listed in Table 1, could be considered cause for rejection without much fear of having scrapped material unnecessarily. But should a part with a few small internal voids be rejected? Are localized regions of porosity or density variations causes for rejection?

The limited experience with ceramics and the uncertainty of their strength-behavior patterns limit the accuracy of generalized judgments. Density measurement is one of the frequently used techniques for assessing general quality of a ceramic material. Yet, there are instances in the literature where strength is not related to density over as large a density range as 5% of theoretical. Even more disturbing are those cases where higher densities yield lower strengths. Pores that are detectable by the techniques of Table 1 are often considered indicative of poor strength, but the literature contains data where such a conclusion was unwarranted. Although the foregoing examples are exceptions rather than the rule, they occur frequently enough to necessitate caution when establishing standards based on limited experience. Where such exceptions occur, they are generally caused by factors other than the one observed. In many instances the factors that are really controlling strength are not detectable directly by means of conventional nondestructive techniques but may be identified indirectly.

For one particular material where there was no correlation of strength with density or macrovoids, 0.015 to 0.050 in. in diameter, there seemed to be a correlation between strength and the presence or absence of density variations as determined radiographically. Ultrasonic-inspection records indicated that the degree of sound attenuation varied with location. Further examination suggested that strength correlated with the extent of microcracking, which was probably influenced by the presence or absence of density variations and which was probably the reason for the variation of sound attenuation.

The identification of defects presents two basic problems. First, available nondestructive techniques yield data whose meaning is not always clear; second, there is no assurance that the techniques, as applied to a specific material, are sensitive enough to detect all significant defects. Associated with more sensitive techniques is the increased difficulty of interpretation.

Regardless of the technique employed to locate and identify defects, the significance of the defects cannot be assessed without adequate calibration of the observation. It is essential that the observations be related to service performance of the product. Within the scope of present experience, it would seem necessary to establish such standards for each ceramic material and each particular application. As standards are established and applied for more ceramic materials, patterns may emerge that will simplify the establishment of future standards.

A point of caution should be noted with respect to future efforts on defect identification. It is usually more glamorous to investigate new techniques than to improve upon the older ones. A variety of nondestructive techniques have been developed for ductile materials and applied to the control of the quality of components made therefrom. The applicability of these established techniques to ceramic materials should be investigated with at least as much vigor as that devoted to the study of new techniques.

Even after a component has been inspected to insure its dimensional accuracy and freedom from defects, the quality control effort must provide assurance that the material from which the component is made has properties which are the same as, or better than, those used for the design of the component and those possessed by the components used for design verification testing. The present lack of meaningful specifications with minimum guaranteed property requirements precludes the approach used for conventional ductile materials. While careful control of raw materials and processing tends to promote similarity, it does not provide adequate insurance of similarity. More positive checks are required. The assurance of similarity of material performance appears to be the most challenging aspect of quality control of ceramic components.

Similarity of material performance can only be attained through similarity of material properties that determine performance. Similarity of properties can be investigated either directly or indirectly. With the direct approach, the component, or a portion thereof, must be cut into test specimens, whose properties are then measured. The indirect approach utilizes nondestructive measurements that are related to properties in a well-defined manner. In general, both approaches have limitations. If the component is cut into test specimens, it is no longer useful as a component, while if only portions are cut from the component there is little positive assurance that the actual component has the same properties. The indirect approach is even more limited, because definitive relationships between easily observed material features and properties are ill defined for any particular material and are likely to be different for each material.

Because of these problems it is considered desirable to employ a combined approach to insure similarity of material properties. Indirect, nondestructive methods should be used to examine the component, while both indirect and direct methods should be used to examine samples cut from the blanks from which the components are fabricated. However, care must be taken to insure that the samples cut from the component are as representative of the component material as possible. To illustrate this point, consider a component having local mass discontinuities where differential shrinkage or similar effects may be suspected of occurring. In such a case, it would be desirable to have a similar discontinuity present in the sample which would be cut from the component and used for the evaluations of material similarity. In other words, the blank from which the component is made should be designed with the inspection function, as well as the operational function, in mind.

The similarity checks, among components of a group, that can be made on the actual components include all the nondestructive test techniques employed for detection of defects as well as speed of sound measurements and dynamic response characteristics. It should be recognized that when the nondestructive techniques are used to assess material-property similarity indirectly, the specifics of operation are apt to be different than when they are used to detect defects. Regardless of the indirect method used, there is a need to establish the relationship, or calibration curve, between the observed material feature and the material property of interest. In addition, for each application it will be necessary to define the range of variation that would not significantly detract from component performance. Once established, these same techniques can be used to assess the similarity of the component material and the material present in the test bars used to evaluate the properties used for design.

When samples cut from components are used to assess similarity, a much wider variety of techniques becomes available. Applicable techniques include all those mentioned in the preceding paragraph as well as microstructural and chemical features of the material samples and property measurements. Thus the results of the nondestructive observations from the components and samples cut therefrom can be compared with destructively obtained observations and property measurements from the samples. In addition, this information can be used to check for similarity with the test specimens employed for design-data generation.

As discussed previously, there are about 50 microstructural and chemical-composition features that may be examined and compared to assess similarity of material among components and between component material and test bar material. Conclusions reached as the result of such comparisons are based on the assumption that if the microstructural and chemical features are the same, the properties are the same. While such an assumption is most likely true, it would be necessary to compare all possible features—an expensive procedure. The accuracy of the techniques used for the comparisons would be in question, and it would be difficult, if not impossible, to make a logical disposition of a component whose material features compared in most but not all ways with the material features of the test bars.

A realistic solution to the problems just mentioned is to relate the microstructural and chemical features of the material to properties. With such an approach it should be possible to identify the features of prime importance and to define ranges of property variations that are related to variations in material features. In addition, the question of accuracy in determining the material features becomes less critical. If a useful relationship between a material feature and a property is found, then the method used to define the material is of sufficient accuracy. Even with this approach the large number of properties to be considered suggests a sizable effort.

Material properties are related to microstructural and chemical features of a material as discussed before. Most influence mechanical properties. Of the easily measured mechanical properties, short-time strength is known to be most variable. This is also one of the properties of primary interest for most structural applications. Hence, it would seem logical to attempt to relate observable features with strength. If strength variability can be controlled within reasonable limits, it is expected that the variation in most other properties will be within acceptable limits.

Destructive techniques that can be used to assess similarity of material properties indirectly were already discussed. It is interesting to note that both the features of importance in assessing material similarity and the techniques employed are those normally of interest during material-development efforts. Therefore, it seems logical that the foundation for the destructive-inspection procedures should be laid during the data-generation program for any particular material. Measured properties should be related to the microstructural and chemical characteristics of the material so that the latter characteristics can be used as the basis for destructive-inspection techniques.

In adopting any set of quality-control procedures, questions will arise regarding the adequacy of each particular technique and the interpretation of the resultant observations. Unfortunately, such questions are not easily answered. Conclusions can be reached only after a reasonable amount of data has been accumulated, analyzed, and correlated with product performance. References 2, 3, 4, and 5 are typical of recent attempts to apply nondestructive and destructive inspection and characterization techniques to ceramic materials and to correlate the results with variability of properties.

The boride composite ceramic shapes produced for the work of Reference 2 utilized single lots of raw materials. Each of the three types of starting powders were characterized by wet chemical analysis, spectrographic analysis, particle-size distribution, absolute surface-area measurements, and particle shape. A processing specification was prepared and strictly followed. The material was produced as a cold-pressed and sintered body, thereby providing a green preform. Preform densities were determined and the preforms were inspected for cracks both visually and with penetrant-dye techniques. After firing, density determinations and visual and penetrant-dye inspections for crack detection were repeated. After final machining, the nondestructive inspections of all parts included visual and penetrant-dye techniques for detection of cracks and surface flaws, density determination, x-radiography and physical-dimension measurements. Modulus-of-elasticity determinations were conducted on bend-test bars that were used during the program, plus ultrasonic inspection of a limited number of bend-test bars and of all typical components. In addition, control tabs were cut from the bend-test bars prior to the application of load and a limited number were subjected to metallographic examination and x-ray diffraction studies in attempts to correlate character features with structural performance.

Since only a single lot of each type of powder was used, variations due to differences in raw materials could not be assessed. It was found that variations of up to 10% in green densities resulted in variations of only 1% in as-fired densities. The penetrant-dye inspection identified several cracked preforms that would not have been detected by visual examination alone. The money saved by eliminating subsequent green-machining and sintering of the cracked preforms compensated for the cost of inspecting the total quantity of preforms.

After room-temperature bend tests were conducted, the strength values obtained were correlated with characterization and inspection results. No correlation was found between strength and x-ray-diffraction patterns, or between strength and fracture-surface features determined by examinations at 30 x. Surprisingly, no correlation was found between strength and density, though the density among the bars varied by as much as 5% [Figure 1(a)]. Strength appeared to be related to modulus of elasticity, although there was a significant amount of scatter [Figure 1(b)]. The best correlations were obtained between strength and radiographic inspection results when the radiographs were examined with respect to density variations [Figure 2(b)], strength and ultrasonic inspection results [Figure 2(a)], and strength and microcrack severity (Figure 3). The correlations obtained suggested that the strength of this particular material was controlled by the extent of internal microcracking. The severity of microcracking was associated with local density variations, which could be observed on the radiographs. The presence of the microcracks tended to scatter ultrasonic energy, thereby providing meaningful ultrasonic-inspection records.

Although only 30 bend-test bars were evaluated, analysis of the results indicated that the application of the material-selectivity techniques based on the correlations established would provide more than a 100% increase in design-allowable strength at the low probabilities of failures associated with the design of aerospace hardware. In other words, the application of inspection techniques that would tend to reject less than 10% of the material produced would double the design-allowable strength of an existing material. The cost involved in the

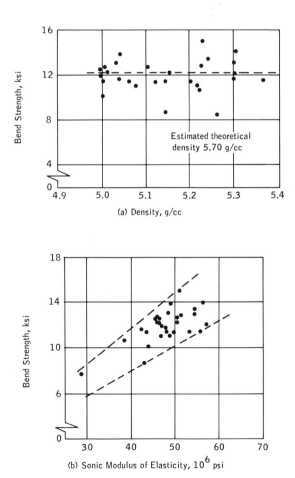

FIGURE 1. Strength correlation with density and modulus of elasticity
(Source: Anthony et al., "Selection Techniques for Brittle Materials,"
Vol. I and II, AFML-TR-65-209, 1959).

290

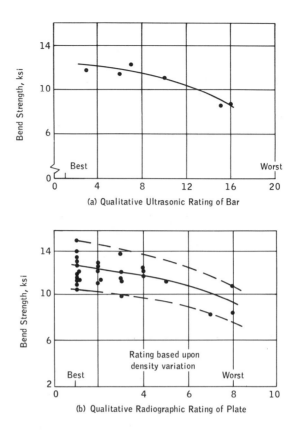

(a) Qualitative Ultrasonic Rating of Bar

(b) Qualitative Radiographic Rating of Plate

FIGURE 2. Strength correlation with ultrasonic inspection and with radiographic inspection (Source: Anthony et al., "Selection Techniques for Brittle Materials," Vols. I and II, AFML-TR-65-209, 1959).

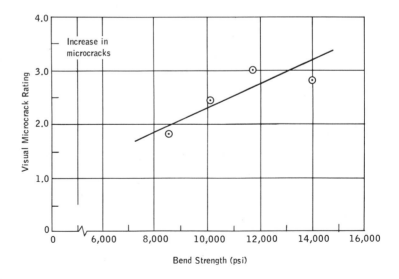

Bend Strength (psi)

FIGURE 3. Microcrack rating vs bend strength of ZrB_2 - $MoSi_2$ composite bars (Source: Anthony et al., "Selection Techniques for Brittle Materials," Vols. I and II, AFML-TR-65-209).

development and application of the techniques was perhaps orders of magnitude less than the cost of developing a new material having twice the usable design strength of the material investigated, while retaining its excellent oxidation-resistance characteristics.

The inspection, characterization, and correlation studies of Reference 3 closely parallel those of Reference 2, although here the material was a graphite-based particulate composite. The correlation of strength with character features was much less pronounced in this case, however. The material was transversely isotropic, and results of the correlations differed in the two primary material directions. There appeared to be a correlation between density and strength in each of the two directions, but the amount of scatter obtained precluded the use of density as a true measure of structural performance. Modulus of elasticity also appeared to have a weak relationship with strength, although here too the amount of scatter precluded the use of modulus-of-elasticity measurements to predict strength characteristics reliably. The only definite character feature that appeared to correlate well with strength was the silicon content of the material. Two billets had been produced from the same lots of starting powder but were found after hot-pressing to have silicon contents of 6 and 9% as compared to the nominal silicon content of 9%. The billet having a lower silicon content exhibited significantly lower strength in the with-grain direction, but in the across-grain direction, material from the two billets exhibited essentially the same strength.

In the work of Reference 4, three grades of graphite (ATJ, RVA, and CFW) were inspected by measuring longitudinal-wave velocity, electrical resistivity, and density variations (by means of Cobalt 60 radiometry). Modulus-of-elasticity and strength measurements were then made and correlated with the nondestructive inspection observations. Good correlations with relatively little data scatter were obtained between: modulus of elasticity and longitudinal wave velocity, bulk density and modulus of elasticity, electrical resistivity and bulk density, electrical resistivity and modulus of elasticity, longitudinal-wave velocity and ultimate tensile strength, longitudinal-wave velocity and total strain at failure, and bulk density and ultimate tensile strength. By plotting longitudinal-wave velocity versus the parameter modulus of elasticity divided by density and the parameter ultimate tensile strength divided by the product of total density and strain at failure, composite plots were obtained encompassing data from with- and across-grain samples of the grades of graphite inspected. Relatively little scatter was obtained, as shown in Figures 4 and 5.

The work of Reference 4 was extended in Reference 5 to additional grades of graphite, and the parametric relationships were modified somewhat with the resultant decrease in the amount of apparent scatter (Figures 6, 7, 8, and 9).

The studies reported in References 2, 3, 4, and 5 all employed state-of-the-art nondestructive and destructive inspection techniques. None is particularly expensive to employ and most tend to observe rather gross character features. While the scope of the investigations was limited with respect to the number of materials studied and the number of samples inspected and used for correlation purposes, very positive correlations were obtained in most cases, the exception being the work of Reference 3, which employed a particularly complex material. These extremely encouraging results suggest that increased emphasis in the area of nondestructive and destructive inspection techniques, including correlations with material properties, may permit significant increases in the usable design strengths of existing ceramic materials. Increased emphasis on inspection techniques that relate character features and properties may in fact be a more economical method of achieving higher design strengths than the development of newer materials whose major development criterion is strength alone.

The shortcomings with respect to defect identification and assessment of material-property similarity necessitate a final check of components. Simulated

292

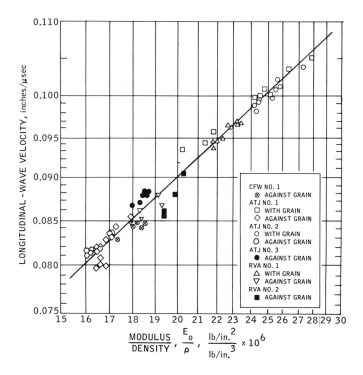

FIGURE 4. Longitudinal velocity vs ratio of modulus and density for CFW, ATJ, and RVA specimen blanks (Source: Lockyer, "Investigation of Nondestructive Methods for the Evaluation of Graphite Materials," AFML-TR-65-113, 1965).

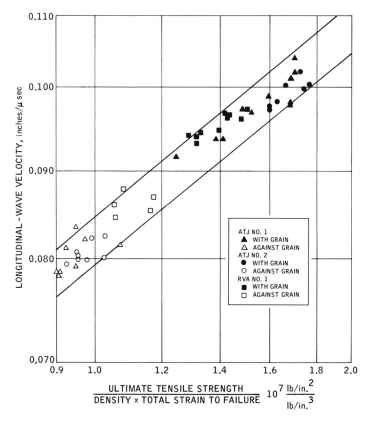

FIGURE 5. Longitudinal-wave velocity vs a tensile test parameter for ATJ and RVA specimens (Source: Lockyer, "Investigation of Nondestructive Methods for the Evaluation of Graphite Materials," AFML-TR-65-113, 1965).

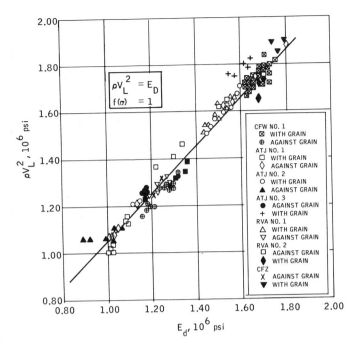

FIGURE 6. Product (ρV_L^2) vs dynamic modulus (E_d) for ATJ, RVA, CFW, and CFZ (Source: Lockyer et al., "Investigation of Nondestructive Methods for the Evaluation of Graphite Materials," AFML-TR-66-101, 1966).

service proof-testing of components that pass the other quality-control procedures offers such a final check before parts are placed into service.

Two approaches can be followed. The components being produced can be sampled, and the selected items can be loaded to destruction under simulated-service conditions; or, each component can be subjected to a simulated service

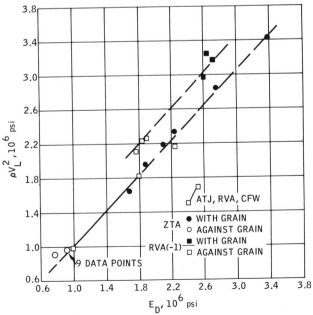

FIGURE 7. Product (ρV_L^2) vs dynamic modulus (E_d) extended to include grades ATA and RVA (-1) (Source: Lockyer et al., "Investigation of Nondestructive Methods for the Evaluation of Graphite Materials," AFML-TR-66-101, 1966).

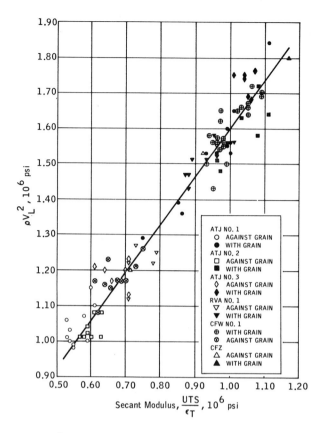

FIGURE 8. Product (ρV_L^2) vs secant modulus (E_s) for grades ATJ, RVA, CFW, and CFZ (Source: Lockyer et al., "Investigation of Nondestructive Methods for the Evaluation of Graphite Materials," AFML-TR-66-101, 1966).

loading of modest severity to insure a minimum level of performance capability. There is little experience to serve as a guide in choosing the approach to be followed. If sampling is used, there are the problems of selecting an appropriate sampling rate and the expense of the samples that are destroyed. If all components are subjected to a modest loading there are questions of test costs and of the test severity to be employed.

The type of simulated service proof-testing to be conducted will depend upon the particular component and its expected environment. Therefore, procedures that would generally be applicable cannot be formulated. However, factors of importance can be indicated.

Few aerospace components are designed for a single loading condition. Those applications where ceramics might be used to advantage will generally involve operation at high temperature. Hence, simulated service proof-testing will tend to be rather complex, so that all critical regions can be evaluated. In addition, the intent is to guarantee a minimum level of performance. If this is to be accomplished by the sampling approach, the sample must be large enough to cover the range of performance to be expected, or the sampling must be done in a nonrandom manner so that the components tested to destruction tend to be those of more questionable performance. When every component is to be tested, the application of actually expected loads may induce damage within the component without causing complete failure. This is more likely to happen when the design reliability objective is low, as it might be for a component that is used for only a single mission.

It might be argued that the use of a simulated service proof-testing approach would eliminate the need for prior inspections such as those associated with defect identification and similarity assessment. This is not expected to be the

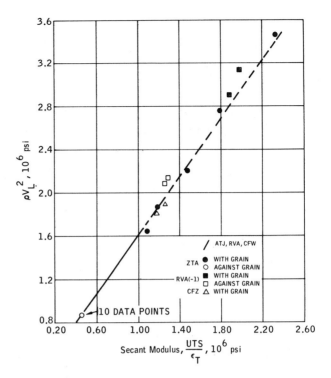

FIGURE 9. Product (ρV_L^2) versus secant modulus (E_s) extended to include grades ZTA, RVA (-1), and CFZ (Source: Lockyer et al., "Investigation of Nondestructive Methods for the Evaluation of Graphite Materials," AFML-TR-66-101, 1966).

case except in rare instances. If the sampling approach is adopted, prior inspections should aid in the choice of the components to be tested. Test results might then be compared with inspection results as a means of refining standards and revising sampling requirements. When each component is to be tested, the cost of testing will tend to be high because the test conditions are likely to be complex. Elimination of marginal components by means of defect identification and similarity assessment, as compared with proof-testing, would be justified in many cases on the basis of economics.

Summary

The control of quality of ceramic components provides the mechanism for defining the interfaces between processing, properties, and applications. These interfaces can be understood more clearly by considering the over-all design and production cycles. In the design cycle the particular application dictates component configuration and material-property requirements. These, in turn, define processing requirements. The production cycle, consisting of fabrication and quality control, proceeds in the reverse direction, beginning with primary fabrication of a useful component of the desired configuration and material. The function of quality control is to provide assurance that the resultant configuration and material meets the requirements of the application. If these requirements are not met, processing parameters or component configuration must be changed so as to decrease the economic penalties involved.

Quality control of ceramic components parallels that for ductile materials in that the user must have assurance that each part meets dimensional requirements, is free from defects that would adversely affect performance, and is made from a material with properties equal to or better than those used in the design of the part. Of these, assurance of similarity of material properties is the most difficult. Available techniques are adequate for assuring dimensional compliance except in the area of surface finish. Many nondestructive techniques are available for the detection of defects. Material similarity can also be assessed by nondestructive techniques, but destructive techniques which utilize samples cut from the material blank used for the component are also considered necessary. Available techniques can provide a wealth of information, but the significance of the data is not always clear. Therefore, it is difficult to determine if available techniques are adequate or if new techniques are required. In either case, a major problem with respect to defect identification and similarity assessment is the lack of meaningful standards. The most logical starting point for establishing meaningful standards is in the area of destructive inspection techniques. Material-design data-generation programs, if slightly expanded in scope, could provide much of the necessary basic data. Until such standards are firmly established, proof tests of finished components will be necessary for critical applications.

Conclusions and Recommendations

The following conclusions were reached with respect to quality control of ceramic components:

1. The raw materials used to produce the ceramic components must be well characterized and controlled.

2. Every step of the process employed to produce the ceramic component must be standardized and controlled to the highest degree possible. In-process quality control is advantageous.

3. Control of raw materials and processing procedures is not sufficient to provide components of consistent performance when high structural efficiency and reliability are the design objective.

4. Quality control of finished components must provide assurance of: dimensional accuracy, freedom from defects that would adversely influence performance, and material properties equal to or better than those used for design.

5. Assurance of adequate material properties is the most important and difficult aspect of quality control.

6. Available techniques are adequate for insuring compliance to dimensional requirements except with respect to surface finish, where meaningful standards are lacking.

7. A variety of nondestructive inspection techniques are available for the identification of defects, but meaningful standards are lacking.

8. Both nondestructive and destructive techniques should be used to assess material similarity and hopefully, thereby, similarity of properties. Nondestructive techniques should be applied to components and to pieces of extra material cut from components. Destructive techniques can be applied only to the latter on a regular basis and should include actual measurement of properties.

9. Meaningful standards for assessing similarity of material performance, without actual property measurements, are lacking.

10. The most logical place to begin developing meaningful standards for assessing similarity of material properties is during material-design data-generation programs.

11. Until adequate standards are available to assure freedom from defects and adequate material properties, simulated service proof-tests will be required prior to putting components into service.

Based on these conclusions, the following recommendations are made with respect to quality control of ceramic components:

1. Intensive efforts should be devoted to the establishment of meaningful standards for assessing the adequacy of surface finish, the criticality of abnormalities that might be identified as possible defects by nondestructive inspection techniques, and the similarity of properties among components of a

given type and between components and test bars used to generate design data.

2. While new inspection techniques should continue to be investigated, major emphasis should be placed on the evaluation of available techniques to determine their applicability to ceramic materials.

3. All future material-design data-generation efforts should include studies to define the effects of surface finish.

4. All future material-design data-generation efforts should be expanded from their normal scope to include characterization of the material used and correlation of observable material characteristics with properties, particularly strength. Such efforts would then provide a foundation for establishing meaningful standards for destructive and possible nondestructive inspection techniques.

5. The relative advantages of sampling and proof-testing as final inspection techniques should be investigated.

BIBLIOGRAPHY

1. R. C. McMasters, "Nondestructive Testing Handbook," Vols. 1 and 2, Roland Press, New York, N.Y., 1959.
2. F. M. Anthony, L. Marcus, and A. L. Mistretta, "Selection Techniques for Brittle Materials," Vol. I, Wise, Washington, D.C., Vol. II, AFML-TR-65-209, September 1959.
3. F. M. Anthony, A. L. Mistretta, J. Y. L. Ho, and L. Marcus, "Selection Techniques for Brittle Materials (The Evaluation of JTA Graphite Composite as a Structural Refractory Ceramic Body)," AFML-TR-67-78, May 1967.
4. G. E. Lockyer, "Investigation of Nondestructive Methods for the Evaluation of Graphite Materials," AFML-TR-65-113, 1965.
5. G. E. Lockyer, E. M. Lenoe, and A. W. Schultz, "Investigation of Nondestructive Methods for the Evaluation of Graphite Materials," AFML-TR-66-101, July 1966.
6. E. Kubiak, R. Hosek, and W. Lichodziejewski, "Development of Nondestructive Testing Methods for the Evaulation of Thin and Ultrathin Sheet Materials," AFML-TR-66-304, Feburary 1967.
7. W. E. Lawrie et al., "Nondestructive Methods for the Evaluation of Ceramic Coatings," WADD TR-61-91, Parts I - VI, 1961 - 1966.
8. R. W. Walloch, "Integrity of ATJ-Base Graphite for Critical Applications: X-Ray Inspection," Investigation of Feasibility of Utilizing Available Heat-Resistant Materials for Hypersonic Leading Edge Applications, WADC TR-59-744, Vol. VI, Appendix IV, 1960.
9. R. W. Walloch, "Adaptation of Radiographic Principles to the Quality Control of Graphite," WADD TR 61-72, Vol. IV, 1961.

PANEL ON EVALUATION

JESSE D. WALTON, JR., <u>Chairman</u>
Chief, High Temperature Materials Division
Engineering Experiment Station
Georgia Institute of Technology

Members

FRANK M. ANTHONY
Assistant Chief Engineer for
  Structural Development
Structural Systems Department
Bell Aerosystems Company

RALPH L. BARNETT
Senior Research Engineer
Structures Research
Illinois Institute of Technology
  Research Institute

J. T. BOHN
TRW, Inc./Systems

FRANK A. HALDEN
Director, Ceramics and Metallurgy Division
Stanford Research Institute

COULTAS D. PEARS
Head, Mechanical Engineering Division
Southern Research Institute

LIAISON MEMBER FROM THE MAB <u>AD HOC</u> COMMITTEE ON CERAMIC PROCESSING

KARL SCHWARTZWALDER
Director of Research
AC Spark Plug Division
General Motors Corporation

LIAISON REPRESENTATIVES

CHARLES F. BERSCH
Materials Engineer
Naval Air Systems Command
U.S. Department of the Navy

LT. E. H. BEARDSLE
U.S. Department of the Air Force
Wright-Patterson Air Force Base

DANIEL W. GATES
National Aeronautics and Space
  Administration

PHILIP A. ORMSBY
Structures and Mechanics Laboratory
U.S. Army Missile Command

J. B. WACHTMAN, JR.
Chief, Physical Properties Section
Inorganic Materials Division
National Bureau of Standards

MATERIALS ADVISORY BOARD STAFF

DONALD G. GROVES
Staff Engineer
National Academy of Sciences
National Research Council